KU-038-845

PREFACE

Essential Mathematics Books *7*, *8* and *9* are written for more able pupils in years *7*, *8* and *9*. Most classrooms contain children with a range of abilities in mathematics. These books are written to cater for this situation.

The author is an enthusiastic supporter of the National Numeracy Strategy. The books have been prepared with the cooperation of teachers and pupils in NNS pilot schools. It is encouraging that most teachers are confident that this more structured approach will help to raise standards of understanding and attainment. There is a comprehensive NNS guide at the start of the book with references to all topics.

There is no set path through the books but topics appear in the order suggested in the NNS planning charts. Broadly speaking, parts 1 and 2 can be studied in the Autumn Term, parts 3 and 4 in the Spring Term and parts 5 and 6 in the Summer Term.

The author believes that children learn mathematics most effectively by *doing* mathematics. Many youngsters who find mathematics difficult derive much more pleasure and enjoyment from the subject when they are doing questions which help them build up their confidence. Pupils feel a greater sense of satisfaction when they work in a systematic way and when they can appreciate the purpose and the power of the mathematics they are studying.

No text book will have the 'right' amount of material for every class and the author believes that it is better to have too much material rather than too little. Consequently teachers should judge for themselves which sections or exercises can be studied later. On a practical note, the author recommends the use of exercise books consisting of 7 mm squares.

Opportunities for work towards the 'Using and Applying Mathematics' strand appears throughout the book. Many activities, investigations, games and puzzles are included to provide a healthy variety of learning experiences. The author is aware of the difficulties of teaching on 'Friday afternoons' or on the last few days of term, when both pupils and teachers are tired, and suitable activities are included.

The author is indebted to his co-authors David Allman and Laurence Campbell whose work from the first edition of Essential Mathematics has been included where appropriate. The author would also like to thank his colleagues at school, in particular Christine Godfrey who has written material for this book.

David Rayner

CONTENTS

Teaching programme: Year 8

Using and applying mathematics and solve problems

Applying mathematics and solving problems

2.6 • Solve more demanding problems and investigate in a range of contexts: number, algebra, shape, space and measures, and handling data; compare and evaluate solutions.
4.3 • **Identify the necessary information to solve a problem; represent problems and interpret solutions in algebraic, geometric or graphical form,** using correct notation and appropriate diagrams.
2.6 • Solve more complex problems by breaking
3.7 them into smaller steps or tasks, choosing and using efficient techniques for calculation, algebraic manipulation and graphical representation, and resources, including ICT.
5.7 • **Use logical argument to establish the truth of a statement;** give solutions to an appropriate degree of accuracy in the context of the problem.
5.7 • Suggest extensions to problems, conjecture and generalise; identify exceptional cases or counter-examples.

Numbers and the number system

Place value, ordering and rounding

3.1 • Read and write positive integer powers of 10; multiply and divide integers and decimals by 0.1, 0.01.
3.1 • Order decimals.
2.1 • Round positive numbers to any given power of 10; round decimals to the nearest whole number or to one or two decimal places.

Integers, powers and roots

3.1 • Add, subtract, multiply and divide integers.
1.5 • Recognise and use multiples, factors (divisors), common factor, highest common factor, lowest common multiple and primes; find the prime factor decomposition of a number (e.g. $8000 = 2^6 \times 5^3$).
1.5 • Use squares, positive and negative square roots, cubes and cube roots, and index notation for small positive integer powers.

Fractions, decimals, percentages, ratio and proportion

4.5 • Know that a recurring decimal is a fraction; use division to convert a fraction to a decimal; order fractions by writing them with a common denominator or by converting them to decimals.
1.2 • Add and subtract fractions by writing them with a common denominator; calculate fractions of quantities (fraction answers); multiply and divide an integer by a fraction.
4.5 • Interpret percentage as the operator 'so many
6.2 hundredths of' and express one given number as a percentage of another; **use the equivalence of fractions, decimals and percentages to compare proportions; calculate percentages and find the outcome of a given percentage increase or decrease.**
5.1 Consolidate understanding of the relationship between ratio and proportion; reduce a ratio to its simplest form, including a ratio expressed in different units, recognising links with fraction notation; **divide a quantity into two or more parts in a given ratio; use the unitary method to solve simple word problems involving ratio and direct proportion.**

Calculations

Number operations and the relationships between them

3.1 • Understand addition and subtraction of fractions and integers, and multiplication and division of integers; use the laws of arithmetic and inverse operations.
3.4 • Use the order of operations, including brackets, with more complex calculations.

Mental methods and rapid recall of number facts

3.3 • Recall known facts, including fraction to decimal conversions; use known facts to derive unknown facts, including products involving numbers such as 0.7 and 6, and 0.03 and 8.
3.3 • Consolidate and extend mental methods of calculation, working with decimals, fractions and percentages, squares and square roots, cubes and cube roots; solve word problems mentally.
2.1 • Make and justify estimates and approximations of calculations.

Written methods

3.1 • Consolidate standard column procedures for addition and subtraction of integers and decimals with up to two places.
3.1 • **Use standard column procedures for multiplication and division of integers and decimals, including by decimals such as 0.6 or 0.06; understand where to position the decimal point by considering equivalent calculations.**
For calculations with fractions and percentages, see above.

Calculator methods

3.4 • Carry out more difficult calculations effectively and efficiently using the function keys for sign change, powers, roots and fractions; use brackets and the memory.
3.4 • Enter numbers and interpret the display in different contexts (negative numbers, fractions, decimals, percentages, money, metric measures, time).

Checking results

2.1 • Check a result by considering whether it is of the right order of magnitude and by working the problem backwards.

Algebra

Equations, formulae and identities

2.2 • Begin to distinguish the different roles played by letter symbols in equations, formulae and functions; know the meanings of the words *formula* and *function*.

2.2 • Know that algebraic operations follow the same conventions and order as arithmetic operations; use index notation for small positive integer powers.

4.3 • **Simplify or transform linear expressions by collecting like terms; multiply a single term over a bracket.**

4.3 • Construct and solve linear equations with integer coefficients (unknown on either or both sides, without and with brackets) using appropriate methods (e.g. inverse operations, transforming both sides in same way).

4.2 • Begin to use graphs and set up equations to solve simple problems involving direct proportion.

3.6 • Use formulae from mathematics and other subjects; **substitute integers into simple formulae**, including examples that lead to an equation to solve, and positive integers into expressions involving small powers (e.g. $3x^2 + 4$ or $2x^3$); derive simple formulae.

Sequences, functions and graphs

1.1 • Generate and describe integer sequences.

1.1 • Generate terms of a linear sequence using term-to-term and position-to-term definitions of the sequence, on paper and using a spreadsheet or graphical calculator.

5.3 • Begin to use linear expressions to describe the *n*th term of an arithmetic sequence, justifying its form by referring to the activity or practical context from which it was generated.

5.4 • Express simple functions in symbols; represent mappings expressed algebraically.

5.4 • Generate points in all four quadrants and **plot the graphs of linear functions, where y is given explicitly in terms of x**, on paper and using ICT; **recognise that equations of the form $y = mx + c$ correspond to straight-line graphs.**

4.2 • Construct linear functions arising from real-life problems and plot their corresponding graphs; discuss and interpret graphs arising from real situations.

Shape, space and measures

Geometrical reasoning: lines, angles and shapes

2.3 • **Identify alternate angles and corresponding angles; understand a proof that:**
- **the sum of the angles of a triangle is 180° and of a quadrilateral is 360°;**
- the exterior angle of a triangle is equal to the sum of the two interior opposite angles.

2.3 • Solve geometrical problems using side and angle properties of equilateral, isosceles and right-angled triangles and special quadrilaterals, explaining reasoning with diagrams and text; classify quadrilaterals by their geometric properties.

5.5 • Know that if two 2-D shapes are congruent, corresponding sides and angles are equal.

6.4 • Know and use geometric properties of cuboids and shapes made from cuboids; begin to use plans and elevations.

Transformations

4.1 • Transform 2-D shapes by simple combinations of rotations, reflections and translations, on paper and using ICT; identify all the symmetries of 2-D shapes.

• Recognise and visualise the transformation and symmetry of a 2-D shape:

5.2 • Understand and use the language and notation associated with enlargement; **enlarge 2-D shapes, given a centre of enlargement and a positive whole-number scale factor;** explore enlargement using ICT.

6.5 • Make simple scale drawings.

Coordinates

5.4 • Given the coordinates of points A and B, find the mid-point of the line segment AB.

Construction

2.4 • **Use straight edge and compasses to construct:**
- **the mid-point and perpendicular bisector of a line segment;**
- the perpendicular from a point to a line;
- **the perpendicular from a point on a line;**

construct a triangle, given three sides (SSS); use ICT to explore these constructions.

2.4 • Find simple loci, both by reasoning and by using ICT, to produce shapes and paths, e.g. an equilateral triangle.

Measures and mensuration

2.6 • Use units of measurement to estimate, calculate and solve problems in everyday contexts involving length, area, volume, capacity, mass, time, angle and bearings; know rough metric equivalents of imperial measures in daily use (feet, miles, pounds, pints, gallons).

6.5 • Use bearings to specify direction.
1.3 • **Deduce and use formulae for the area of a triangle, parallelogram** and trapezium; calculate areas of compound shapes made from rectangles and triangles.
6.6 • **Know and use the formula for the volume of a cuboid; calculate volumes and surface areas of cuboids** and shapes made from cuboids.

Handling data

Specifying a problem, planning and collecting data

6.3 • Discuss a problem that can be addressed by statistical methods and identify related questions to explore.
6.3 • Decide which data to collect to answer a question, and the degree of accuracy needed; identify possible sources.
6.3 • Plan how to collect the data, including sample size; construct frequency tables with given equal class intervals for sets of continuous data; design and use two-way tables for discrete data.
6.3 • Collect data using a suitable method, such as observation, controlled experiment, including data logging using ICT, or questionnaire.

Processing and representing data, using ICT as appropriate

3.2 • Calculate statistics, including with a calculator; recognise when it is appropriate to use the range, mean, median and mode and, for grouped data, the modal class; calculate a mean using an assumed mean; construct and use stem-and-leaf diagrams.
4.4 • **Construct, on paper and using ICT:**
- **pie charts for categorical data;**
- **bar charts and frequency diagrams for discrete and continuous data;**
- **simple line graphs for time series;**
- **simple scatter graphs;**

identify which are most useful in the context of the problem.

Interpreting and discussing results

4.4 • Interpret tables, graphs and diagrams for both discrete and continuous data, and draw inferences that relate to the problem being discussed; relate summarised data to the questions being explored.
3.2 • Compare two distributions using the range and one or more of the mode, median and mean.
6.3 • Communicate orally and on paper the results of a statistical enquiry and the methods used, using ICT as appropriate; justify the choice of what is presented.

Probability

6.1 • Use the vocabulary of probability when interpreting the results of an experiment; appreciate that random processes are unpredictable.
6.1 • Know that if the probability of an event occurring is p, then the probability of it not occurring is $1 - p$; **find and record all possible mutually exclusive outcomes for single events and two successive events in a systematic way**, using diagrams and tables.
6.1 • Estimate probabilities from experimental data; understand that:
- if an experiment is repeated there may be, and usually will be, different outcomes;
- increasing the number of times an experiment is repeated generally leads to better estimates of probability.

6.1 • Compare experimental and theoretical probabilities in different contexts.

Part 1

1.1 Sequences

Exercise 1

Find the next number in each sequence

1. 10, 12, 14, 16,
2. 9, 8, 7, 6,
3. 4, 8, 12, 16,
4. 2, 5, 8, 11,
5. 14, 12, 10, 8,
6. 2, 4, 8, 16,
7. 5, 8, 11, 14,
8. 1, 3, 5, 7,
9. 2, 3, 5, 8, 12,
10. 3, 5, 9, 17,
11. 5, 10, 20, 40
12. 8, 9, 11, 14, 18,
13. 1, 6, 11, 16,
14. 1, 4, 8, 13,
15. 2, 20, 200, 2000,
16. 54, 52, 49, 45,
17. 100, 10, 1, 01,
18. 1, 3, 9, 27,
19. 45, 36, 28, 21,
20. 4, 7, 13, 25, 49,
21. Find the missing numbers

(a) 1

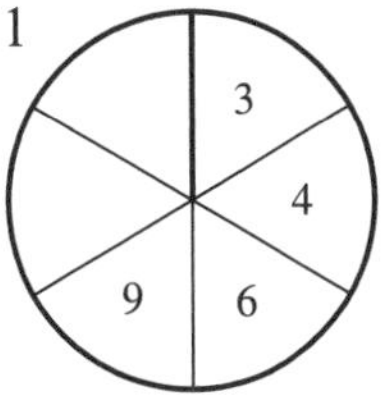

(b) 1

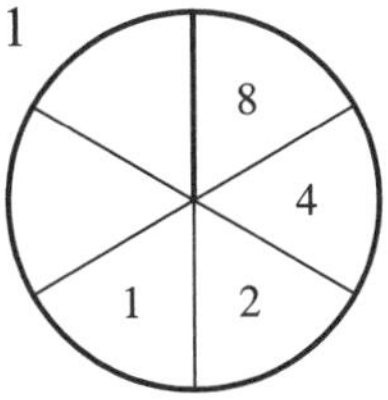

(c)

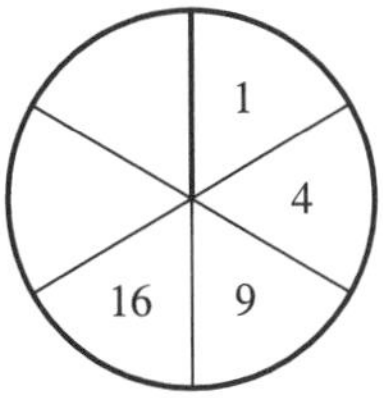

22. Square numbers can be written using consecutive odd numbers.

$$2^2 = 1 + 3$$
$$3^2 = 1 + 3 + 5$$
$$4^2 = 1 + 3 + 5 + 7$$
$$5^2 = 1 + 3 + 5 + 7 + 9$$

(a) Complete the line: $10^2 = 1 + 3 + 5 + \ldots\ldots$

(b) Find the value of n below

$$100^2 = 1 + 3 + 5 + \ldots\ldots + n.$$

Sequence rules

For the sequence 3, 7, 11, 15, 19, ... the first term is 3 and the term-to-term rule is 'add 4'.

For the sequence 30, 27, 24, 21, ... the term-to-term rule is 'subtract 3'.

For the sequence 2, 5, 11, 23, ... the term-to-term rule is 'double and add 1'.

Exercise 2

1. Here is a sequence 7, 12, 17, 22, 27, ... Write down
(a) The first term
(b) The term-to-term rule.

2. Copy and complete the table

Sequence	First-term	Rule
(a) 5, 7, 9, 11, 13 ...		
(b) 80, 77, 74, 71, ...		
(c) 3, 6, 12, 24, ...		

3. The first term of a sequence is 4 and the term-to-term rule is 'add 7'. Write down the first five terms of the sequence.

4. You are given the first term and the rule of several sequences. Write down the first five terms of each sequence.

	First term	Rule
(a)	6	add 3
(b)	32	subtract 2
(c)	5	double
(d)	6000	divide by 10

5. The rule for the number sequences below is

'double and add 1'

Find the missing numbers
(a) 3 → 7 → 15 → 31 → □
(b) □ → 9 → 19 → 39
(c) □ → 7 → □ → □

6. The rule for the sequences below is

'multiply by 3 and take away 1'

Find the missing numbers.

(a) $1 \to 2 \to 5 \to \square$

(b) $\square \to 8 \to 23 \to \square$

(c) $4 \to \square \to \square \to \square$

7. Write down the rule for each of these sequences
(a) $2\frac{1}{4}, 2\frac{1}{2}, 2\frac{3}{4}, 3, \ldots$
(b) 7, 14, 28, 56, ...
(c) 2, 1·9, 1·8, 1·7, ...
(d) $180, 90, 45, 22\frac{1}{2}, \ldots$

8. Find the rule for each sequence and then find the missing numbers.
(a) $1 \to \square \to 4 \to 8 \to 16$

(b) $\square \to 11 \to 19 \to 27 \to 35$

(c) $0.5 \to 5 \to \square \to 500$

(d) $\square \to 2{\cdot}2 \to 2{\cdot}1 \to 2 \to \square$

9. Look at this sequence

$$3^2 = 9$$
$$33^2 = 1089$$
$$333^2 = 110\,889$$
$$3333^2 = 11\,108\,889$$

Write down the value of $33\,333^2$ and the value of $33\,333\,333^2$.

10. Copy and complete the following sequence.

$2 \times 99 = 198$

$3 \times 99 = 297$

$4 \times 99 = 396$

$5 \times 99 = \square$

$\square \times 99 = \square$

11. (a) What is the next term in the sequence 1, 2, 3, ...?
There is more than one possible answer.
The sequence may continue 1, 2, 3, 4, 5, ... (add 1)
or it may continue 1, 2, 3, 5, 8, 13, ... (add the last 2 terms)

(b) Look at the sequence which starts 2, 4, 8, ...
Write down the next three terms in *two different* ways so that a consistent rule applies.

Differences in sequences

Different numbers of lines are drawn below and the maximum number of crossovers for each is shown.

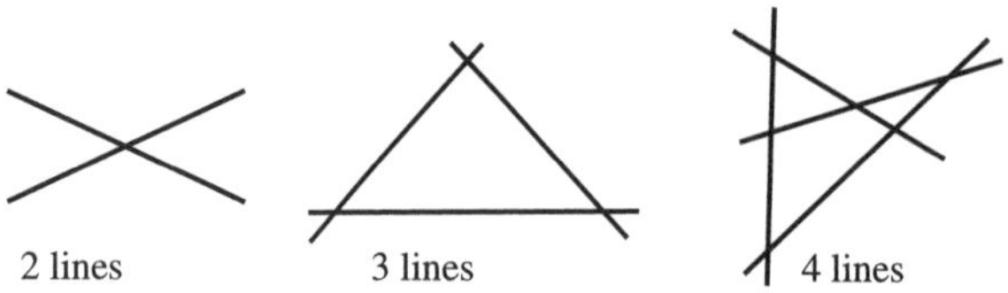

2 lines
1 crossover

3 lines
3 crossovers

4 lines
6 crossovers

lines	crossovers
2	1
3	3
4	6
5	10

One method for predicting further results is to look at the *differences* between the numbers in the 'crossovers' column.

The differences form an easy pattern so that we can predict that there will be 15 crossovers when 6 lines are drawn.

lines	crossovers	differences
2	1	
3	3	2
4	6	3
5	10	4
6	15	5

predictions

- In some sequences in the next exercise you may need to find the 'differences of the differences', called the second differences.

[In the table above the second differences are all 1.]

- Consider the sequence below.

2
10
30
68
130

- The first, second and third differences are shown below.

	First difference	Second difference	Third difference
2			
10	8		
30	20	12	
68	38	18	6
130	62	24	6
222	92	30	6

An obvious pattern is seen so that the numbers circled can be predicted.

Exercise 3

1. Here is a sequence of matchstick squares

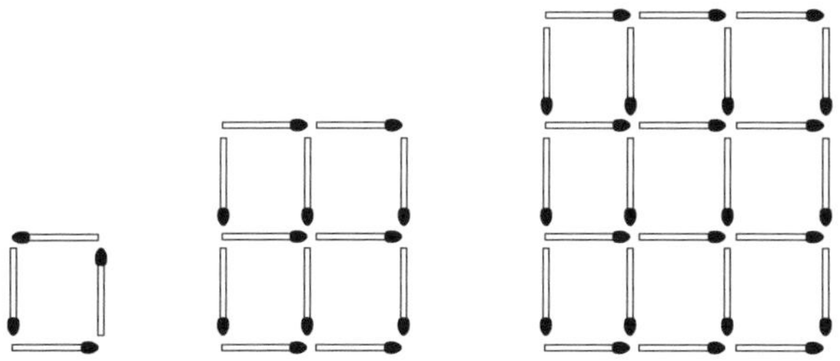

n = 1 n = 2 n = 3

Shape number, *n*	No. of matches	Difference
1	4	
2	12	8
3	24	12
4	40	16
5	?	

Use the differences to predict the number of matches in shape number 5.

2. Below is a sequence of rectangles where each new diagram is obtained by drawing around the outside of the previous diagram, leaving a space of 1 unit.

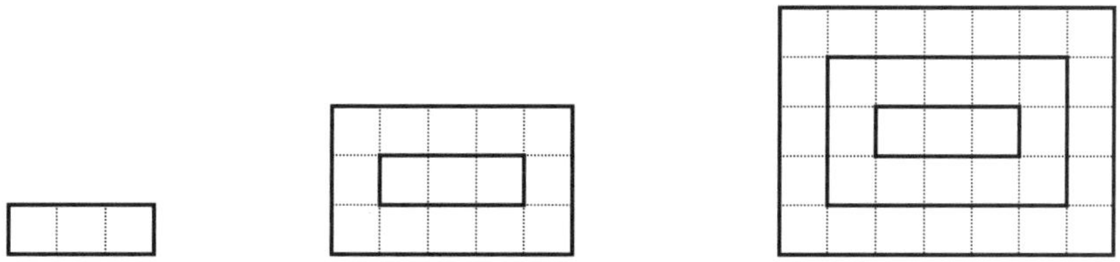

diagram 1 3 squares

diagram 2 15 squares

diagram 3 35 squares

(a) Draw diagram 4 and count the number of squares it contains. Enter the number in a table and use differences to *predict* the number of squares in diagram 5.

(b) Now draw diagram 5 to check if your prediction was correct.

diagram	squares	differences
1	3	
2	15	12
3	35	20
4		

3. Below are the first three members of a sequence of patterns of hexagons made with sticks.

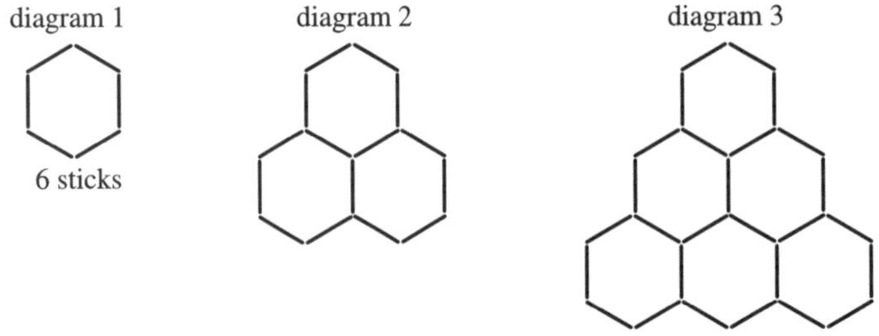

Draw diagram 4 and count the number of sticks it contains. Write your results in a table and then predict the number of sticks needed to make diagram 6.

4. Below are three sequences. Use differences to predict the next two numbers in each sequence.

(a)	(b)	(c)
1	3	11
6	6	14
13	13	22
22	24	35
33	39	53
?	?	?
?	?	?

5. The numbers 1, 2, 3, . . . 96 are written in a spiral which starts in the centre.

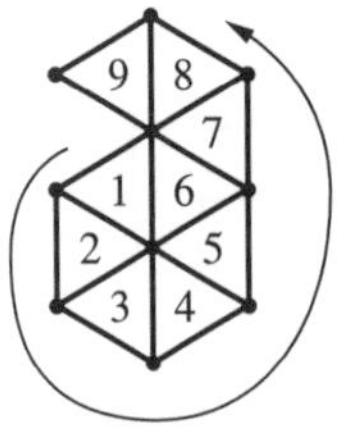

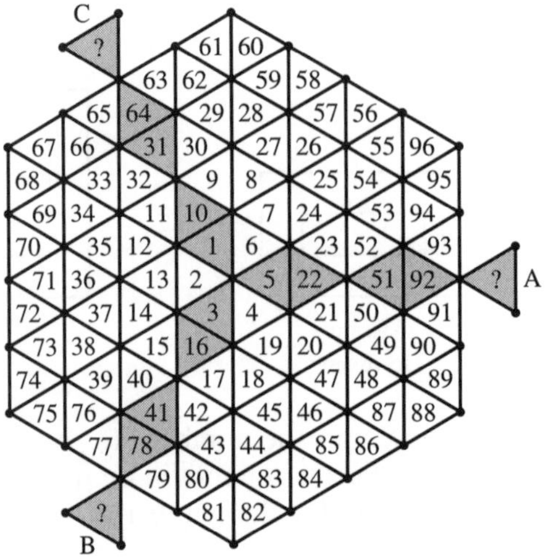

There are, in fact, many sequences in the pattern.

(a) In the row marked A, the numbers are

5 22 51 92.

Predict the next number in this sequence.

(b) Predict the next number in the rows marked B and C.

6. (a) This sequence is more difficult

number	difference
2	2
4	4
8	7
15	11
26	

(b) The first differences make no obvious pattern. Work out the second differences and find the missing numbers.

number	difference	second difference
2		
	2	
4		2
	4	
8		3
	7	
15		4
	11	
26		?
	?	
?		

7. Use first, second and third differences to predict the next number in each of the sequences below.

(a)	(b)	(c)
2	3	1
5	11	4
13	31	13
28	69	34
52	131	73
87	?	?
?		

8. Playing cards can be used to build (rather unstable!) 'houses'. Houses with 1 storey, 2 storeys and 3 storeys are shown below, together with the number of cards required to make each one.

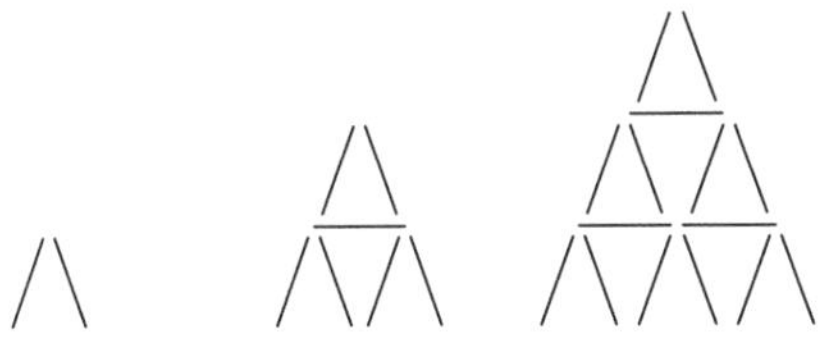

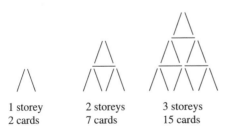

1 storey 2 cards | 2 storeys 7 cards | 3 storeys 15 cards

(a) Draw a house with 4 storeys and count the number of cards required.
Write down the sequence of the numbers of cards needed for 1, 2, 3 and 4 storeys.

(b) Ceri has a very steady hand and decides to build a house with as many storeys as possible. How many storeys will it be possible to build if she has 5 packs of 52 cards?

1.2 Fractions

Adding and taking away

- Fractions can be added when they have the same denominator (bottom number).
- Here are some easy ones.
  $\frac{1}{5} + \frac{2}{5} = \frac{3}{5}$, $\frac{2}{7} + \frac{3}{7} = \frac{5}{7}$, $\frac{1}{10} + \frac{5}{10} = \frac{6}{10}$
- In these questions one of the fractions has to be changed to an equivalent fraction

(a) $\frac{1}{2} + \frac{1}{4}$
$= \frac{2}{4} + \frac{1}{4}$
$= \frac{3}{4}$

(b) $\frac{1}{6} + \frac{1}{3}$
$= \frac{1}{6} + \frac{2}{6}$
$= \frac{3}{6}$

(c) $\frac{5}{8} - \frac{1}{4}$
$= \frac{5}{8} - \frac{2}{8}$
$= \frac{3}{8}$

Exercise 1

Work out

1. $\frac{1}{7} + \frac{2}{7}$ **2.** $\frac{1}{6} + \frac{4}{6}$ **3.** $\frac{5}{8} + \frac{1}{8}$

4. $\frac{2}{9} + \frac{3}{9}$ **5.** $\frac{3}{10} + \frac{4}{10}$ **6.** $\frac{3}{11} + \frac{2}{11}$

Draw fraction charts, using squared paper, and use them with the remaining questions

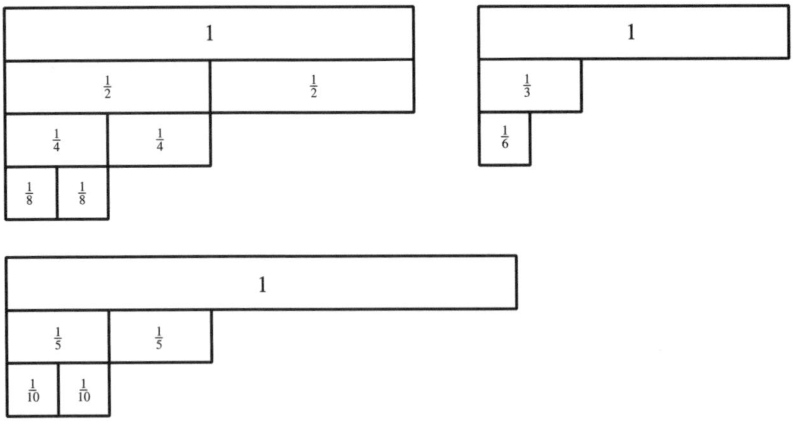

In Questions **7 to 15** fill in the missing numbers.

7. $\frac{1}{2} = \frac{}{8}$ **8.** $\frac{2}{3} = \frac{}{6}$ **9.** $\frac{3}{5} = \frac{}{10}$

10. $\frac{3}{4} = \frac{}{8}$ **11.** $\frac{4}{5} = \frac{}{10}$ **12.** $\frac{1}{3} = \frac{}{6}$

13. $\frac{1}{2} = \frac{}{10}$ **14.** $\frac{1}{4} = \frac{2}{}$ **15.** $\frac{8}{10} = \frac{}{5}$

Work out

16. $\frac{1}{4}+\frac{1}{2}$ **17.** $\frac{1}{6}+\frac{2}{3}$ **18.** $\frac{3}{8}+\frac{1}{2}$

19. $\frac{3}{8}+\frac{1}{4}$ **20.** $\frac{4}{5}+\frac{1}{10}$ **21.** $\frac{2}{5}+\frac{3}{10}$

22. $\frac{7}{8}-\frac{1}{2}$ **23.** $\frac{2}{3}-\frac{1}{6}$ **24.** $\frac{1}{2}-\frac{1}{8}$

25. $\frac{3}{5}-\frac{1}{10}$ **26.** $\frac{3}{4}-\frac{3}{8}$ **27.** $\frac{5}{6}-\frac{1}{3}$

28. $\frac{1}{5}+\frac{1}{10}$ **29.** $\frac{1}{8}+\frac{1}{16}$ **30.** $\frac{1}{10}+\frac{1}{20}$

31. Joe gave $\frac{1}{8}$ of his sweets to his brother and $\frac{1}{4}$ of his sweets to his sister. What fraction did he give away altogether?

32. Kate gave $\frac{1}{10}$ of her toys to a friend and $\frac{1}{5}$ of her toys to her sister. What fraction of her toys does she still have?

33. In her will a woman leaves $\frac{1}{2}$ of her money to her son, $\frac{1}{4}$ to her daughter, $\frac{1}{8}$ to her dog and the rest to her goldfish.
What fraction does the goldfish receive?

34. In an election, everyone voted for either A, B or C. If A got $\frac{1}{4}$ of the votes and B got $\frac{3}{8}$ of the votes, what fraction of the votes did C get?

Harder questions

- To work out $\frac{1}{2}+\frac{1}{5}$ we have to change *both* fractions so that they have the same denominator (bottom number).
  So $\frac{1}{2}+\frac{1}{5}$
  $=\frac{5}{10}+\frac{2}{10}$ (Think: 'What number do 2 and 5 go into?')
  $=\frac{7}{10}$
- To work out $\frac{3}{4}-\frac{1}{6}$ we have to change *both* fractions
  So $\frac{3}{4}-\frac{1}{6}$
  $=\frac{9}{12}-\frac{2}{12}$ (Think: 'What number do 4 and 6 go into?')
  $=\frac{7}{12}$

Exercise 2

1. Copy and complete these calculations

(a) $\frac{1}{2}+\frac{2}{5}$
$=\frac{5}{10}+\frac{4}{10}$
$=$

(b) $\frac{3}{5}-\frac{1}{2}$
$=\frac{\square}{10}-\frac{\square}{10}$
$=$

(c) $\frac{1}{2}-\frac{1}{5}$
$=\frac{\square}{10}-\frac{\square}{10}$
$=$

2. Copy and complete these calculations

(a) $\dfrac{1}{3} + \dfrac{2}{5}$

$= \dfrac{\square}{15} + \dfrac{6}{15}$

$=$

(b) $\dfrac{1}{2} + \dfrac{1}{7}$

$= \dfrac{\square}{14} + \dfrac{\square}{14}$

$=$

(c) $\dfrac{2}{5} + \dfrac{1}{4}$

$= \dfrac{8}{20} + \dfrac{\square}{20}$

$=$

3. Work out

(a) $\frac{1}{3} + \frac{1}{7}$

Think: What do 3 and 7 go into?

(b) $\frac{1}{5} + \frac{1}{6}$

Think: What do 5 and 6 go into?

4. These diagrams illustrate the addition $\frac{1}{4} + \frac{1}{3}$.

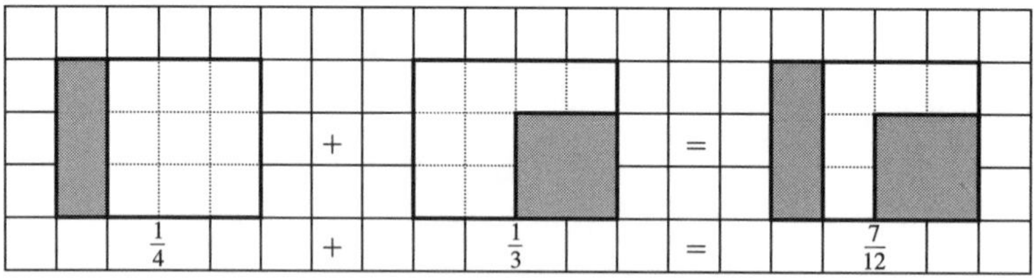

Copy the diagrams below, one for each part.

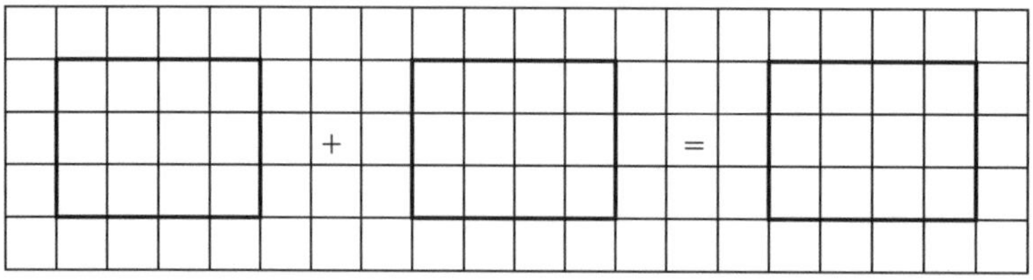

Shade in the diagrams to show the additions

(a) $\frac{1}{12} + \frac{1}{4}$ (b) $\frac{1}{6} + \frac{2}{3}$ (c) $\frac{1}{3} + \frac{1}{12}$

5. Work out

(a) $\frac{1}{2} + \frac{1}{3}$ (b) $\frac{2}{3} - \frac{1}{2}$ (c) $\frac{2}{3} + \frac{1}{4}$

(d) $\frac{1}{6} + \frac{1}{4}$ (e) $\frac{1}{3} + \frac{1}{4}$ (f) $\frac{3}{4} - \frac{1}{3}$

6. Work out

(a) $\frac{1}{3} + \frac{1}{5}$ (b) $\frac{2}{5} + \frac{2}{3}$ (c) $\frac{1}{4} + \frac{1}{5}$

(d) $\frac{4}{5} - \frac{1}{2}$ (e) $\frac{2}{3} - \frac{1}{4}$ (f) $\frac{2}{3} - \frac{1}{5}$

7. Copy and complete.

(a) $\frac{1}{4} + \square = \frac{5}{12}$ (b) $\square - \frac{3}{7} = \frac{5}{21}$ (c) $\square - \frac{2}{5} = \frac{4}{15}$

(d) $\square - \frac{2}{3} = \frac{1}{6}$ (e) $\frac{4}{9} + \square = \frac{25}{36}$ (f) $\square + \square = \frac{11}{15}$

(ask a friend to check)

8. (a) To work out $2\frac{1}{4}+\frac{1}{3}$, we write $2\frac{1}{4}$ as $\frac{9}{4}$

Then $\frac{9}{4}+\frac{1}{3}=\frac{27}{12}+\frac{4}{12}=\frac{31}{12}=2\frac{7}{12}$

(b) Work out $1\frac{3}{4}+\frac{2}{3}$, by writing $1\frac{3}{4}$ as a top-heavy fraction.

9. Work out

(a) $3\frac{2}{5}+\frac{1}{4}$ (b) $2\frac{2}{3}+\frac{3}{4}$ (c) $1\frac{1}{2}+2\frac{2}{3}$

(d) $3\frac{1}{6}-2\frac{1}{2}$ (e) $5\frac{1}{4}-3\frac{2}{3}$ (f) $4\frac{3}{5}+1\frac{1}{2}$

Questions **10** to **13** are more difficult.

10. A cylinder is $\frac{1}{2}$ full of water

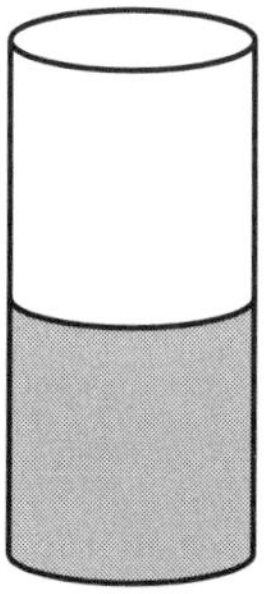

After 60 ml of water is added the cylinder is $\frac{4}{5}$ full.

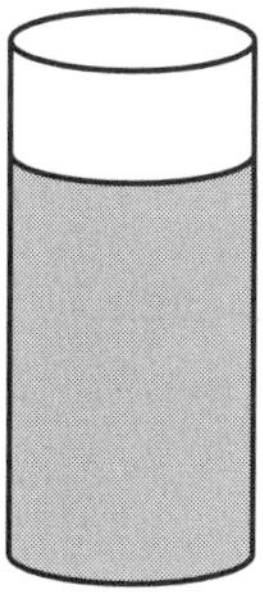

Calculate the total volume of the cylinder.

11. A swimming pool is $\frac{1}{4}$ full. After a further 6000 gallons of water are pumped in, the pool is $\frac{2}{5}$ full.
(a) What is the total volume of the pool?
(b) How many more gallons are required to fill the pool?

12. By noon one day, $\frac{1}{4}$ of the eggs in a crocodile's nest have hatched. By midnight a further 5 baby crocodiles are walking around, leaving only $\frac{1}{3}$ of the eggs still to hatch.
How many eggs were in the nest originally?

13. Copy and complete the addition square.

+		$\frac{1}{6}$		$\frac{2}{3}$
	$\frac{7}{12}$			1
$\frac{3}{8}$				
			$\frac{7}{10}$	
	$\frac{3}{4}$		1	

Fractions of fractions

- The grey shaded strip is $\frac{1}{5}$ of the rectangle

  The black section is $\frac{1}{4}$ of $\frac{1}{5}$ of the rectangle.

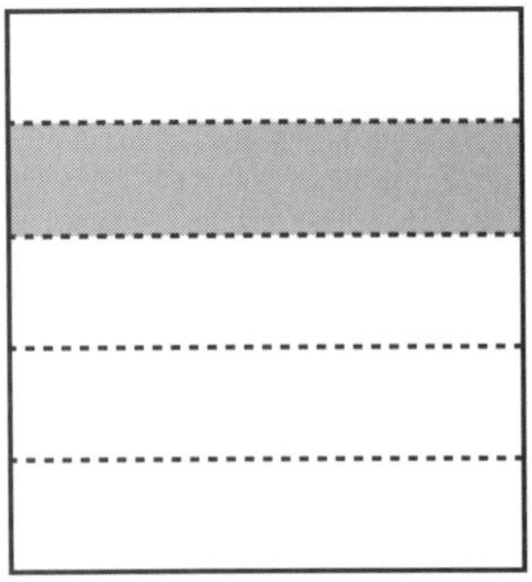

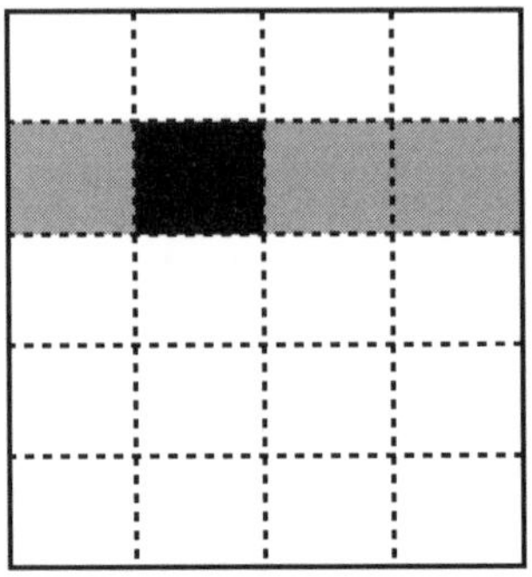

The rectangle on the right is divided into 20 equal parts so the black section is $\frac{1}{20}$ of the rectangle.
So $\frac{1}{4}$ of $\frac{1}{5}$ of the rectangle $= \frac{1}{20}$ of the rectangle
Notice that $\frac{1}{4} \times \frac{1}{5} = \frac{1}{20}$.
The word 'of' can be replaced by a multiplication.

- Look at these multiplications

(a) $\frac{2}{3} \times \frac{1}{5} = \frac{2}{15}$ (b) $\frac{3}{7} \times \frac{1}{4} = \frac{3}{28}$

(c) $\frac{3}{4} \times \frac{1}{6} = \frac{\cancel{3}^{1}}{\cancel{24}_{8}} = \frac{1}{8}$ (d) $\frac{6}{7} \times \frac{2}{3} = \frac{\cancel{12}^{4}}{\cancel{21}_{7}} = \frac{4}{7}$

Multiply the numerators, multiply the denominators and then cancel down.

- Some people prefer to cancel earlier. For example

(a) $\frac{5}{\cancel{6}_3} \times \frac{\cancel{2}^1}{3} = \frac{5}{9}$ (b) $\frac{3}{\cancel{8}_4} \times \frac{\cancel{6}^3}{7} = \frac{9}{28}$ (c) $\frac{\cancel{5}^1}{\cancel{12}_4} \times \frac{\cancel{9}^3}{\cancel{10}_2} = \frac{3}{8}$

Exercise 3

All fractions should be given in their simplest form.

1. What fractions are these?

(a) $\frac{1}{4}$ of $\frac{1}{3}$ (b) $\frac{1}{5}$ of $\frac{3}{5}$ (c) $\frac{2}{3}$ of $\frac{3}{4}$ (d) $\frac{3}{5}$ of $\frac{1}{4}$

2. Work out

(a) $\frac{2}{5} \times \frac{3}{5}$ (b) $\frac{3}{7} \times \frac{1}{4}$ (c) $\frac{3}{8} \times \frac{2}{5}$ (d) $\frac{3}{4} \times \frac{1}{6}$

(e) $\frac{5}{8} \times \frac{1}{2}$ (f) $\frac{5}{6} \times \frac{3}{4}$ (g) $\frac{2}{7} \times \frac{3}{4}$ (h) $\frac{1}{8} \times \frac{3}{5}$

(i) $\frac{2}{9} \times \frac{3}{5}$ (j) $\frac{3}{11} \times \frac{1}{2}$ (k) $\frac{4}{9} \times \frac{3}{4}$ (l) $\frac{5}{12} \times \frac{8}{10}$

3. The diagram shows a square of side 1 m divided into four rectangles A, B, C and D.
Find the areas of A, B, C and D in m^2.

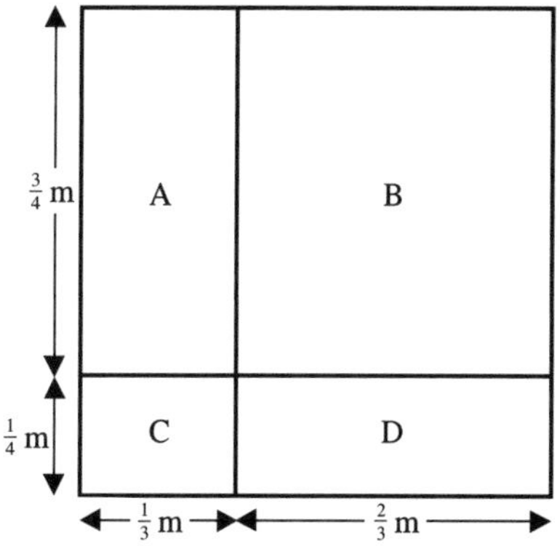

4. (a) To find $\frac{5}{9} \times 12$, we can write $\frac{5}{9} \times \frac{12}{1}$.

So $\frac{5}{\cancel{9}_3} \times \frac{\cancel{12}^4}{1} = \frac{20}{3} = 6\frac{2}{3}$

(b) Work out $\frac{3}{8} \times 12$

5. Work out

(a) $\frac{7}{8} \times 12$ (b) $\frac{5}{8} \times 10$ (c) $\frac{7}{12} \times 16$ (d) $\frac{5}{6}$ of 9

(e) $16 \times \frac{1}{24}$ (f) $11 \times \frac{7}{33}$ (g) $\frac{11}{36}$ of 9 (h) $\frac{2}{15} \times 20$

6. A centipede is born with 60 legs. It loses $\frac{1}{5}$ of its legs falling downstairs and a further $\frac{1}{3}$ of the remainder following an argument with a blackbird. How many legs has it left?

7. We can multiply mixed fractions by changing them to improper fractions ('top heavy fractions')
For example: $2\frac{1}{2} \times \frac{3}{4} = \frac{5}{2} \times \frac{3}{4} = \frac{15}{8} = 1\frac{7}{8}$

Work out (a) $3\frac{1}{2} \times \frac{2}{3}$ (b) $1\frac{3}{4} \times \frac{1}{5}$

8. Work out

(a) $2\frac{1}{2} \times \frac{1}{4}$ (b) $2\frac{1}{2} \times \frac{1}{6}$ (c) $3\frac{1}{2} \times \frac{3}{10}$ (d) $1\frac{1}{2} \times \frac{2}{3}$

(e) $3\frac{1}{4} \times \frac{1}{10}$ (f) $\frac{3}{5} \times 4\frac{1}{4}$ (g) $2\frac{1}{2} \times 1\frac{1}{2}$ (h) $3\frac{1}{2} \times 3\frac{1}{2}$

9. A photograph is $3\frac{1}{4}$ inches tall and $2\frac{1}{2}$ inches wide. Calculate the area of the photograph.

Dividing an integer by a fraction

- 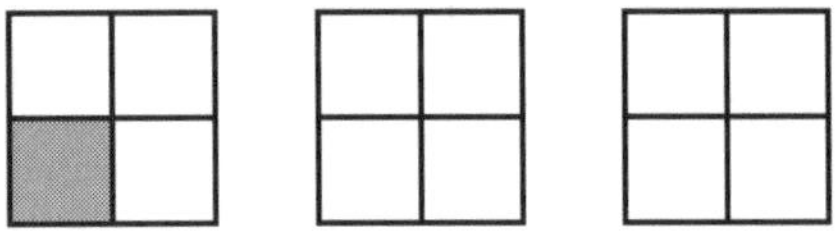

  How many quarters are there in 3?
  Answer: 12

- $2 \div \frac{1}{3}$ 'How many thirds are there in 2?' Answer: 6
- $5 \div \frac{1}{2}$ 'How many halves are there in 5?' Answer 10

Exercise 4

How many thirds are there in 33?

1. (a) How many thirds are there in 1?
(b) How many thirds are there in 2?
(c) How many thirds are there in 4?

2. (a) How many quarters are there in 1?
(b) How many quarters are there in 3?
(c) How many quarters are there in 6?

3. (a) How many tenths are there in 2?
(b) How many fifths are there in 3?
(c) How many sevenths are there in 2?

4. Work out

(a) $1 \div \frac{1}{5}$ (b) $3 \div \frac{1}{2}$ (c) $1 \div \frac{1}{10}$
(d) $2 \div \frac{1}{2}$ (e) $9 \div \frac{1}{3}$ (f) $12 \div \frac{1}{3}$

5. (a) Look at the pattern.

$60 \times \frac{1}{5} = 12$ $12 \div \frac{1}{5} = 60$
$30 \times \frac{2}{5} = 12$ $12 \div \frac{2}{5} = 30$
$20 \times \frac{3}{5} = 12$ $12 \div \frac{3}{5} = 20$
$15 \times \frac{4}{5} = 12$ $12 \div \frac{4}{5} = 15$

(b) Copy and complete this pattern

$60 \times \frac{1}{6} = 10$ $10 \div \frac{1}{6} = 60$
$30 \times \frac{2}{6} = 10$ $10 \div \frac{2}{6} = \square$
$20 \times \frac{3}{6} = 10$ $10 \div \frac{3}{6} = \square$
$15 \times \frac{4}{6} = \square$ $10 \div \frac{4}{6} = \square$
$12 \times \frac{5}{6} = \square$ $10 \div \frac{5}{6} = \square$

6. Copy and complete

(a) $10 = \square \times \frac{1}{2}$ (b) $\square \times \frac{1}{3} = 8$ (c) $\square \times \frac{1}{4} = 5$
(d) $\square \times \frac{1}{3} = 2$ (e) $11 = \square \times \frac{1}{2}$ (f) $\square \times \frac{1}{5} = 5$

Dividing a fraction by a fraction

- How many $\frac{1}{8}$s are there in $\frac{1}{2}$?
  The answer is 4.
  Notice that $\frac{1}{2} \div \frac{1}{8} = \frac{1}{2} \times \frac{8}{1} = 4$.

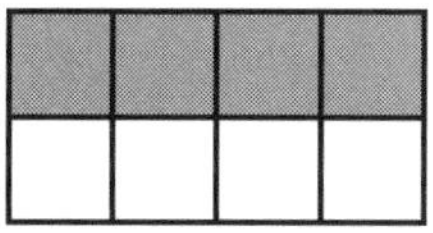

To divide by a fraction, turn the fraction you are dividing by upside down and then multiply.

Examples

(a) $\frac{3}{5} \div \frac{1}{4} = \frac{3}{5} \times \frac{4}{1}$
$= \frac{12}{5}$
$= 2\frac{2}{5}$

(b) $\frac{5}{6} \div \frac{3}{4} = \frac{5}{6} \times \frac{4}{3}$
$= \frac{20}{18} = \frac{10}{9}$
$= 1\frac{1}{9}$

Exercise 5

1. $\frac{1}{2} \div \frac{1}{4}$ **2.** $\frac{1}{3} \div \frac{1}{2}$ **3.** $\frac{3}{4} \div \frac{1}{3}$ **4.** $\frac{2}{3} \div \frac{1}{2}$

5. $\frac{1}{5} \div \frac{1}{2}$ **6.** $\frac{1}{2} \div \frac{1}{5}$ **7.** $\frac{3}{4} \div \frac{4}{5}$ **8.** $\frac{1}{2} \div \frac{1}{6}$

9. $\frac{5}{6} \div \frac{1}{3}$ **10.** $\frac{2}{5} \div \frac{2}{3}$ **11.** $\frac{5}{7} \div \frac{9}{10}$ **12.** $\frac{5}{12} \div \frac{1}{8}$

13. $\frac{3}{7} \div \frac{3}{5}$ **14.** $\frac{9}{14} \div \frac{6}{7}$ **15.** $\frac{11}{15} \div \frac{1}{10}$ **16.** $\frac{4}{3} \div \frac{8}{1}$

17. $\frac{2}{5} \div \frac{2}{1}$ **18.** $\frac{5}{7} \div \frac{6}{1}$ **19.** $\frac{4}{9} \div 6$ **20.** $\frac{5}{11} \div 3$

In Questions **21** to **26** you must decide whether to multiply or divide.

21. A wine glass holds $\frac{1}{7}$ of a litre of wine. How many times can the glass be filled from a bottle which contains 2 litres of wine?

22. How many pieces of wood, each $5\frac{1}{2}$ cm long, can be cut from a plank 132 cm long?

23. An unfortunate motorist has to fill a five litre petrol can using a mug which takes only $\frac{5}{8}$ of a litre each time. How many times does he have to use a mug?

24. A sum of £20 is divided between several people so that each receives $\frac{2}{5}$ of a pound.
How many people receive a share?

25. A sheet of paper is $\frac{1}{10}$ mm thick. How thick is a pad containing 360 sheets of paper?

26. Five people share a prize of £11·20. How much does each person receive?

1.3 Area

Exercise 1

Calculate the area of each shape. The lengths are in cm.
[Reminder: area of triangle $= \frac{1}{2}b \times h$]

1.

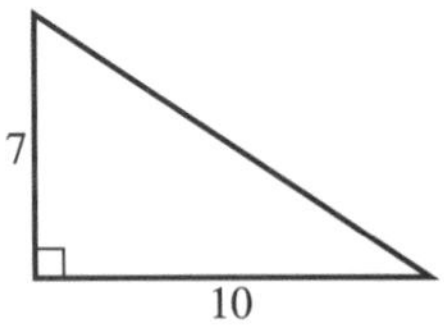

2.

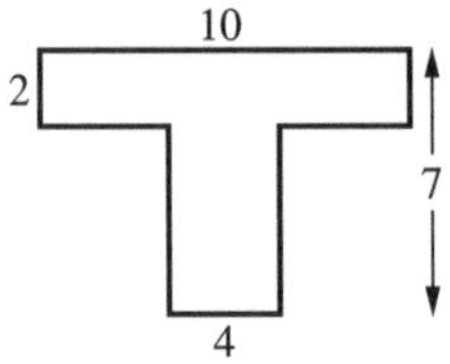

3.

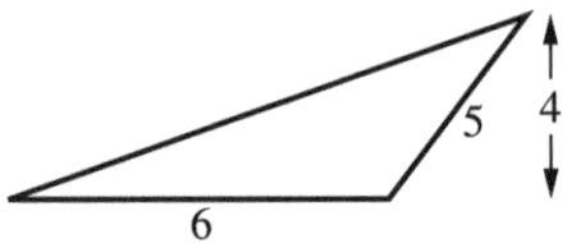

4.

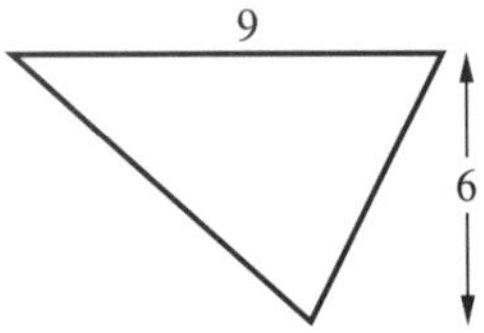

5.

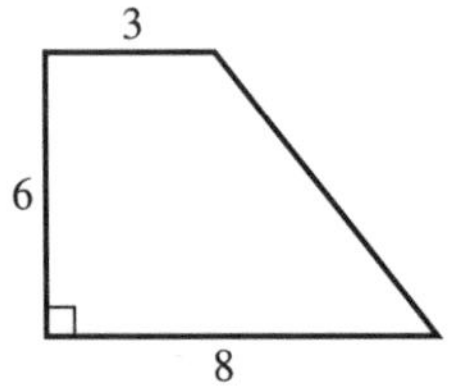

6.

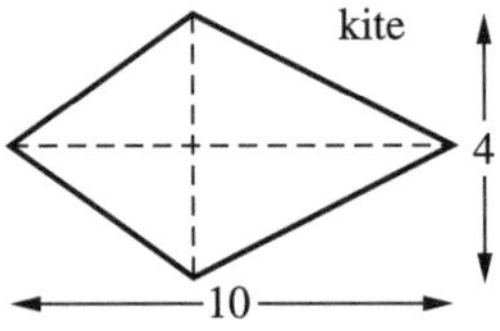

7. Here are some shapes made with centimetre squares.

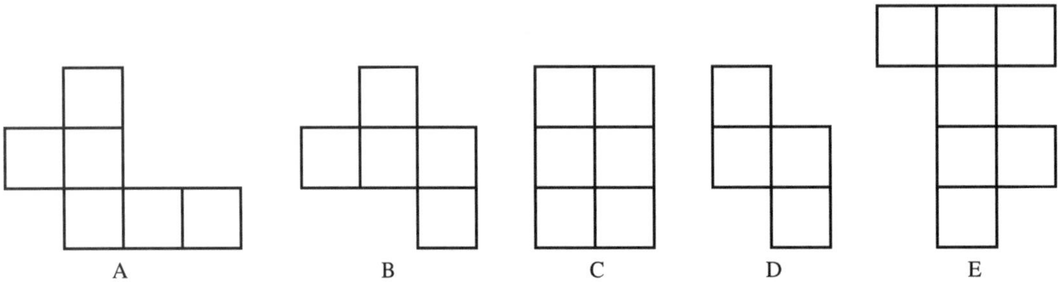

(a) Which shape has an area of $4\,cm^2$?
(b) Which shape has a perimeter of 12 cm?
(c) Which two shapes have the same perimeter?

8. (a) The pentagon is drawn on a 1 cm grid. Calculate its area.
(b) On a 1 cm grid draw an obtuse-angled triangle with an area of (i) $3\,cm^2$
(ii) $7{\cdot}5\,cm^2$

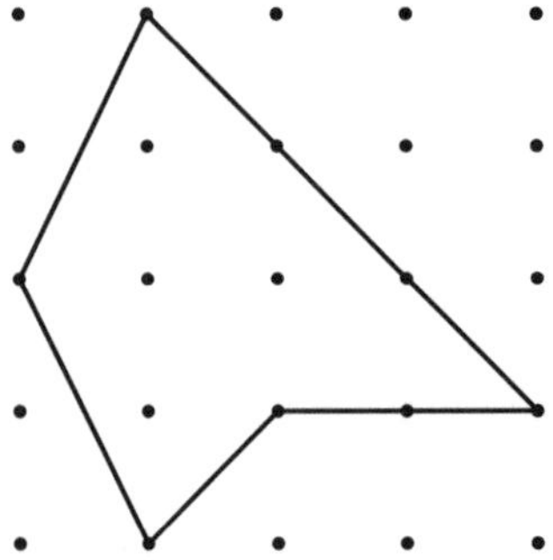

Parallelogram and trapezium

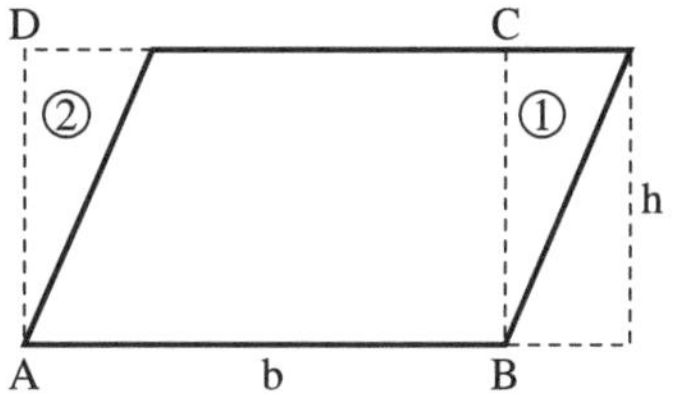

Area of parallelogram
= area of rectangle ABCD + area of △1–area of △2.
But area of △1 = area of △2

∴ area of parallelogram = b × h

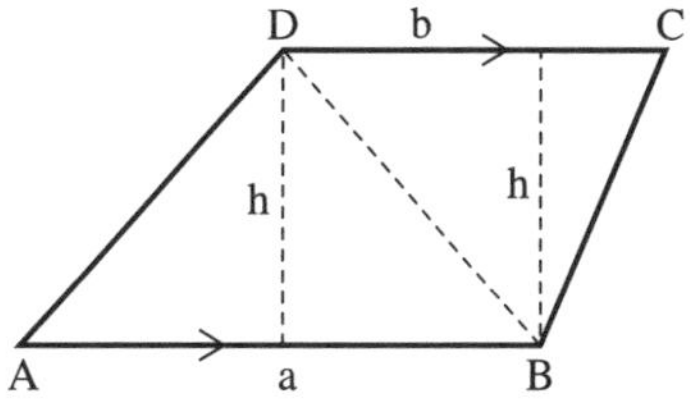

Area of trapezium = area of △ ABD + area of △ DCB

$= \frac{1}{2}ah + \frac{1}{2}bh$

$= \frac{1}{2}(a + b)h$

area of trapezium = $\frac{1}{2}$ (sum of parallel sides) × height

Exercise 2

Calculate the area of each shape. The lengths are in cm.

1. 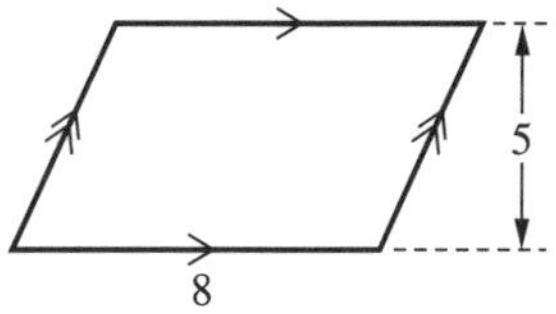

2. 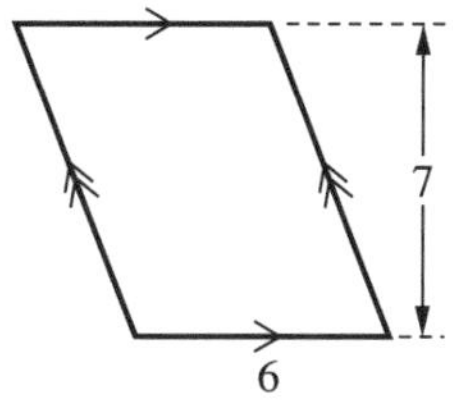

3. 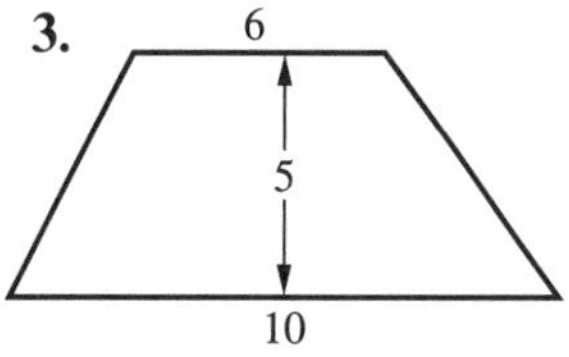

4. 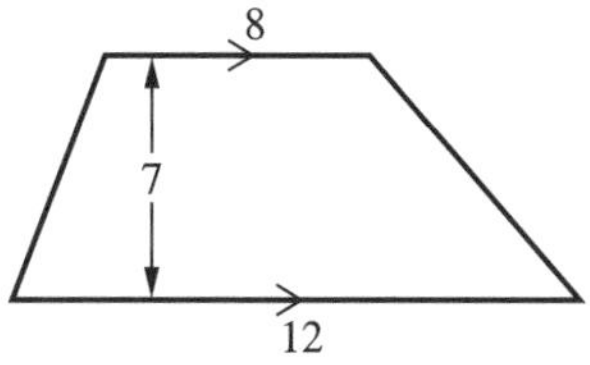

5. 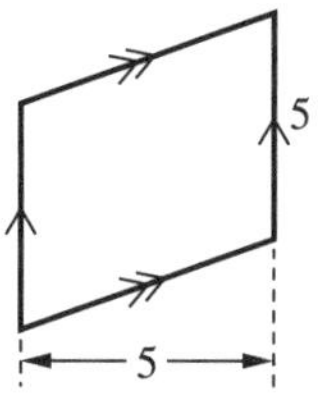

6. Find the shaded area

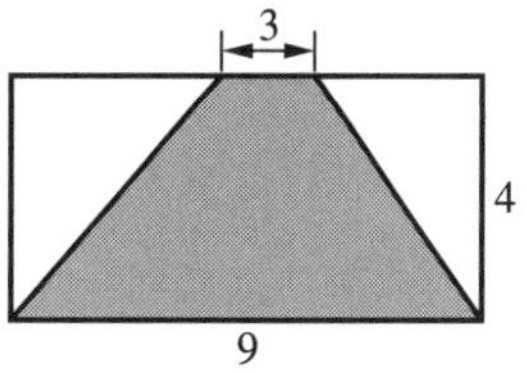

7. Sketch a trapezium with parallel sides of length 5 cm and 7 cm. The distance between the parallel sides is 4 cm. Calculate the area of the trapezium.

8. A parallelogram has a base of length 10 cm and an area of 60 cm^2. Calculate the height of the parallelogram.

9. 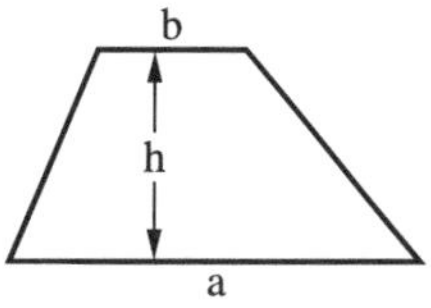

The area of the trapezium shown is 12 cm^2. Find a possible set of values for a, b and h.

The remaining questions involve area and perimeter.

10. Here are two shapes *both* with a perimeter of 32 cm. Calculate the *area* of each shape.

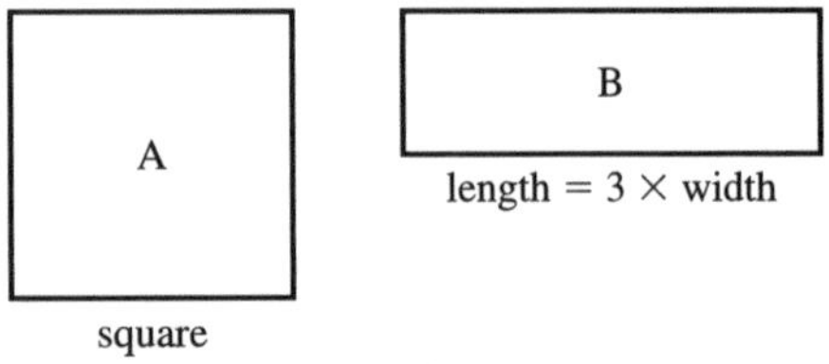

11.* A gardener is spreading fertilizer on his lawn (but not the pond in the middle!). The instructions only say that 2 measures of the fertilizer will treat $10\,\text{m}^2$ of lawn. Each measure of fertilizer costs 60 p. Find the cost of the fertilizer required.

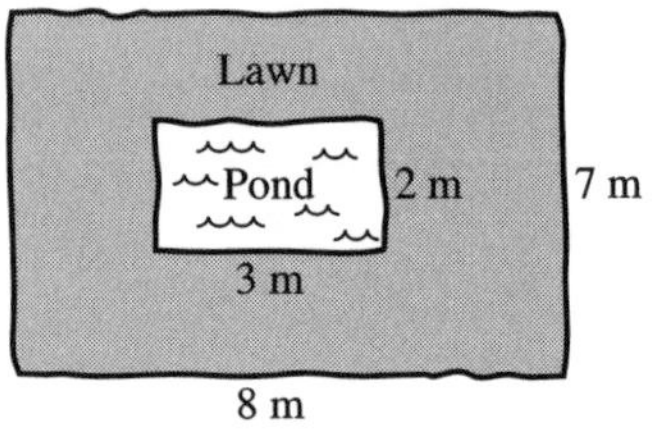

12.

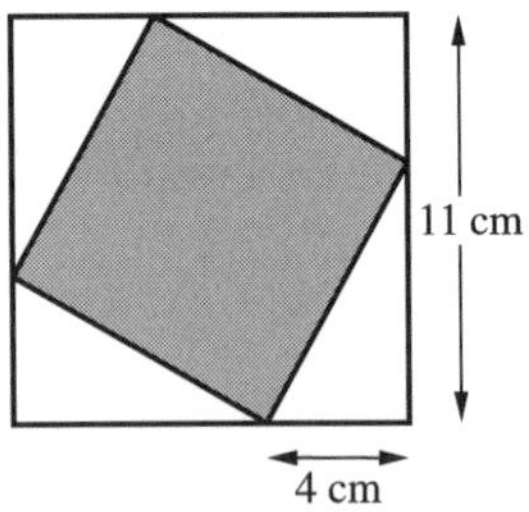

The diagram shows a shaded square inside a larger square. Calculate the area of the shaded square.

13. A square field has an area of 4 hectares. Calculate the perimeter of the field. [1 hectare = $10\,000\,\text{m}^2$]

In questions **14** to **19** the area is written inside the shape. Calculate the length of the side x, correct to 1 decimal place where necessary.

14.

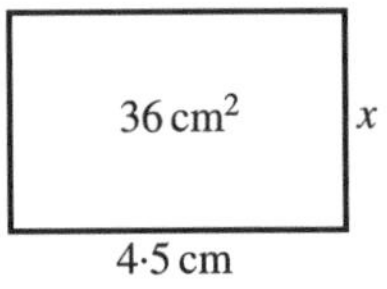

15.

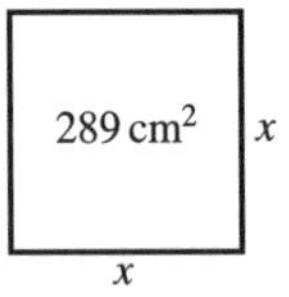

16.

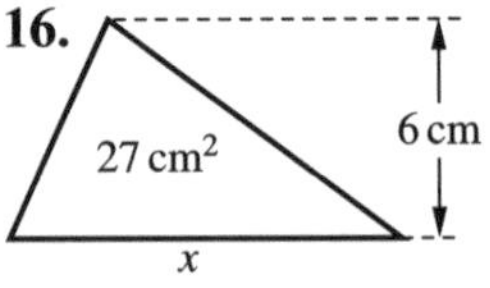

17.

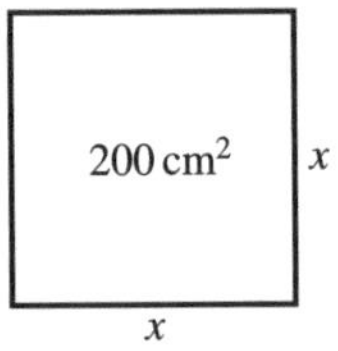

18.

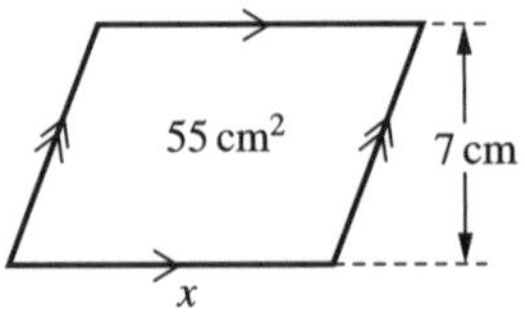

19.

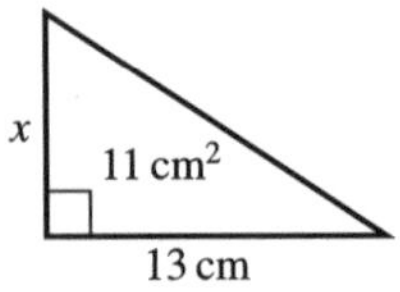

20.

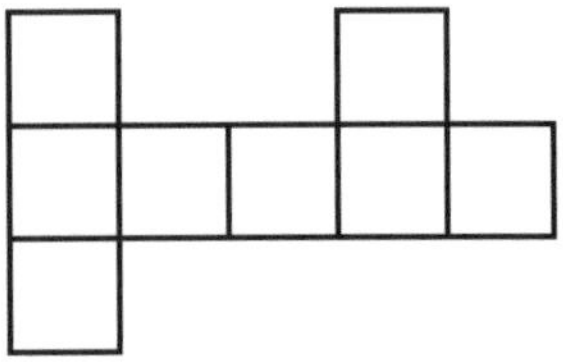

This shape has an area of $175\,\text{cm}^2$. Calculate its perimeter.

21. Calculate the area of each shaded triangle. Give your answers in square units.

(a)

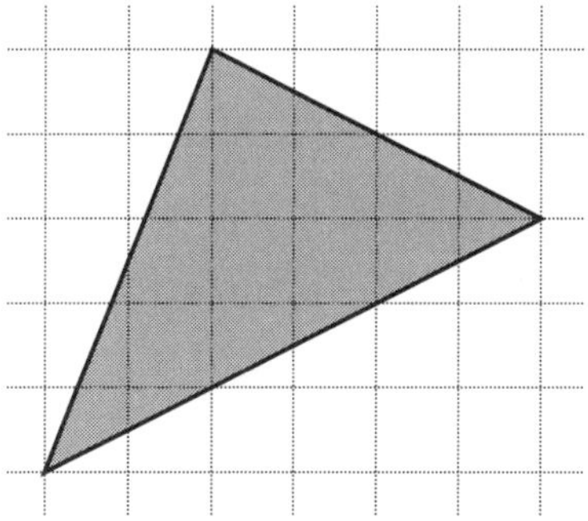

(b)

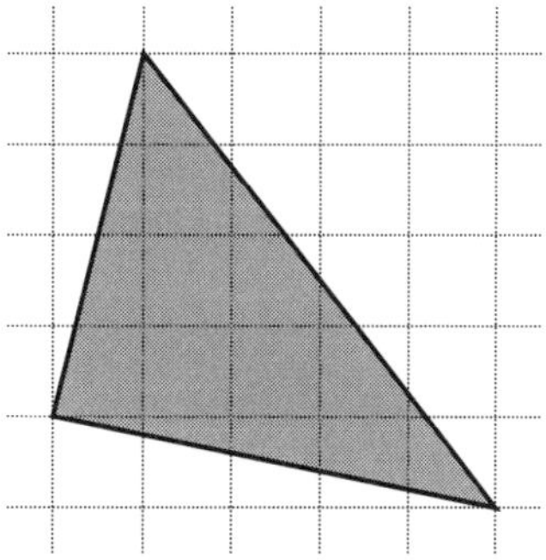

(c)

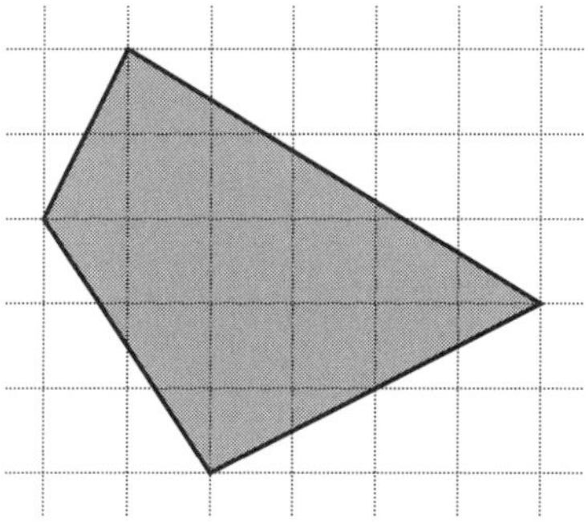

(d)

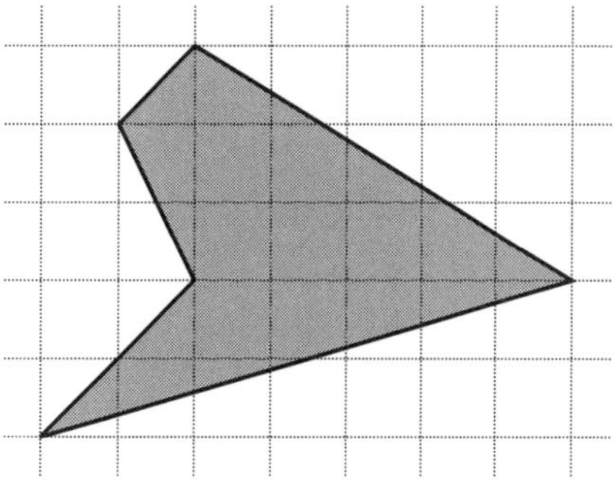

Find the connection

You need square 'dotty' paper or ordinary squared paper.

(a) Draw *any* triangle ABC and shade it.
(b) Draw a square on each of the sides of the triangle.
(c) Join PQ to form $\triangle$ PQC (marked ①).
Join RS to form $\triangle$ RSB (marked ②).
Join UT to form $\triangle$ UTA (marked ③).
(d) Find the areas of triangles ABC, PQC, RSB, UTA. you may be able to use the formula $\left(\frac{\text{base} \times \text{height}}{2}\right)$ or you may need to draw construction lines as in the questions above.
(e) What do you notice? Draw another triangle and repeat the procedure. Do you get the same result?

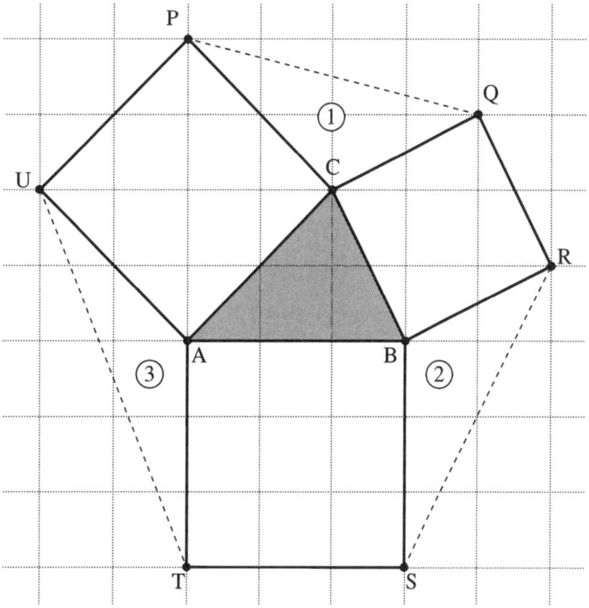

1.4 Negative numbers

Adding and subtracting

For adding and subtracting with negative numbers a number line is very useful.

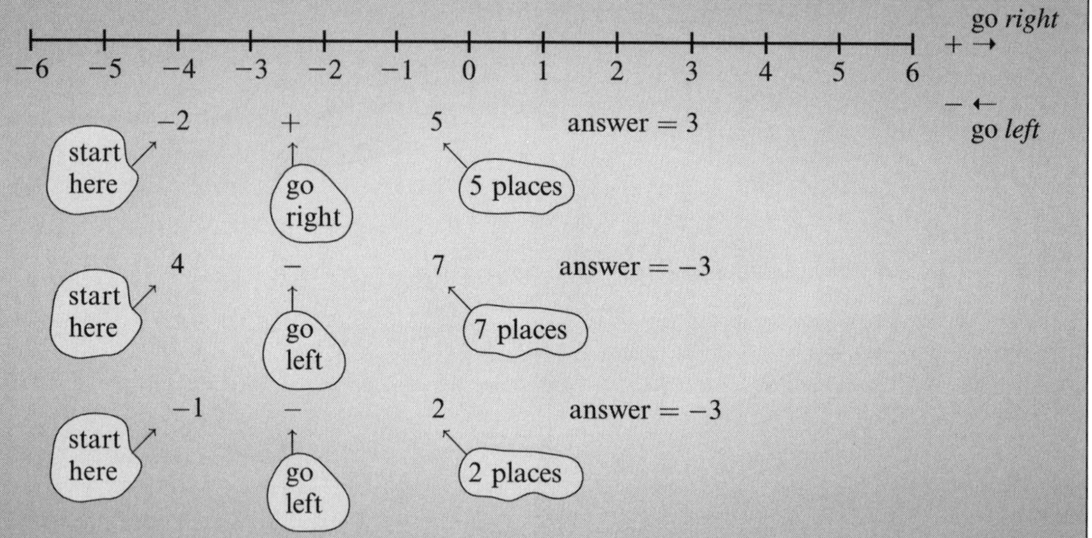

Exercise 1

1. Use a number line to work out
   (a) $4 - 5$ (b) $-2 + 4$ (c) $-3 + 6$ (d) $-2 - 1$
   (e) $3 - 7$ (f) $-2 + 5$ (g) $4 - 9$ (h) $-3 + 2$
   (i) $-5 - 1$ (j) $7 - 8$ (k) $4 - 7$ (l) $-3 + 8$

2. Work out
   (a) $6 - 11$ (b) $-3 - 3$ (c) $-5 + 4$ (d) $-3 + 3$
   (e) $8 - 12$ (f) $11 - 13$ (g) $-4 - 4$ (h) $10 - 20$
   (i) $-5 - 15$ (j) $-3 - 13$ (k) $8 - 5$ (l) $-6 + 20$

3. Copy each sentence and fill in the missing numbers.
   (a) 9, 6, 3, □, □ (b) □, −1, 3, 7, 11 (c) □, □, −10, −5, 0

4. Copy and complete the addition squares

(a)

+	7	−1		
		0		−1
−3			1	
2	9			
				3

(b)

+	−5	3		
−1		2		0
			10	
4				
			6	−1

Two signs together

The calculation $8-(+3)$ can be read as '8 take away positive 3'.

Similarly $6-(-4)$ can be read as '6 take away negative 4'

It is possible to replace *two* signs next to each other by *one* sign as follows:

$+\ + = +$
$-\ - = +$
$-\ + = -$
$+\ - = -$

Remember: 'same signs: +'
'different signs: −'

When two adjacent signs have been replaced by one sign in this way, the calculation is completed using the number line as before.

Work out the following

(a) $-7+(-4)$
$=-7-4$
$=-11$

(b) $8+(-14)$
$=8-14$
$=-6$

(c) $5-(+9)$
$=5-9$
$=-4$

(d) $6-(-2)$
$=6+2$
$=8$

Exercise 2

1. Work out
(a) $5+(-2)$ (b) $4+(-5)$ (c) $6+(-6)$ (d) $4+(-8)$
(e) $8-(+2)$ (f) $7-(+8)$ (g) $3-(-1)$ (h) $4-(-2)$
(i) $6-(-3)$ (j) $4-(-4)$ (k) $9-(+1)$ (l) $10-(+5)$

2. Work out
(a) $4-(-2)$ (b) $6-(-6)$ (c) $8+(-10)$ (d) $3+(-2)$
(e) $8+(+2)$ (f) $7-(+4)$ (g) $6-(-5)$ (h) $4-(-2)$
(i) $10+(-20)$ (j) $15+(-16)$ (k) $9+(-12)$ (l) $-3-(-4)$

3. Copy and complete the tables

a	9	3	8	3	2	5	4	7		
b	5	5	3	7	−2	−2			4	2
a–b	4	−2					−2	−3	−3	−1

a	−3	4	3	5	7	4	6			
b			−3	−1				5	−1	2
a–b	−3	−5			8	10	6	2	3	−2

Multiplying and dividing

- In the sequence of multiplications shown, the numbers in column A go down by one each time.
  The numbers in column B go down by five each time

$$\begin{array}{rcrcr} & & A & & B \\ & & \downarrow & & \downarrow \\ 5 & \times & 3 & = & 15 \\ 5 & \times & 2 & = & 10 \\ 5 & \times & 1 & = & 5 \\ 5 & \times & 0 & = & 0 \end{array}$$

  Continuing the sequence:

$$\begin{array}{rcrcr} 5 & \times & -1 & = & -5 \\ 5 & \times & -2 & = & -10 \\ 5 & \times & -3 & = & -15 \end{array}$$

  We see that:

  'When a positive number is multiplied by a negative number the answer is negative'.

- In this sequence the numbers in column C go down by one each time.
  The numbers in column D *increase* by 3 each time.

$$\begin{array}{rcrcr} & & C & & D \\ & & \downarrow & & \downarrow \\ -3 & \times & 3 & = & -9 \\ -3 & \times & 2 & = & -6 \\ -3 & \times & 1 & = & -3 \\ -3 & \times & 0 & = & 0 \end{array}$$

  Continuing the sequence:

$$\begin{array}{rcrcr} -3 & \times & -1 & = & 3 \\ -3 & \times & -2 & = & 6 \\ -3 & \times & -3 & = & 9 \end{array}$$

  We see that:

  'When two negative numbers are multiplied together the answer is positive.'

Summary of rules.

(a) When two numbers with the *same sign are multiplied together, the answer is positive.*

(b) When two numbers with *different signs are multiplied together, the answer is negative.*

(c) For division the rules are the same as for multiplication.

Examples: $-3 \times (-7) = 21$ $\quad 5 \times (-3) = -15$ $\quad -12 \div 3 = -4$

$20 \div (-2) = -10$ $\quad -10 \div (-20) = \frac{1}{2}$ $\quad -1 \times (-2) \times (-3) = -6$

Exercise 3

Copy and complete the multiplication square below. Some numbers inside the square are shown as an explanation.

×	−5	−4	−3	−2	−1	○	+1	+2	+3	+4	+5
+5						○					
+4						○					
+3		−12				○					
+2						○				8	
+1						○					
○	○	○	○	○	○	○	○	○	○	○	○
−1						○					
−2						○		−4			
−3				6		○					
−4						○					
−5						○					

Exercise 4

Work out

1. $5 \times (-2)$
2. -2×4
3. $7 \times (-2)$
4. $-3 \times (-2)$
5. $-3 \times (-1)$
6. $-4 \times (-1)$
7. -5×2
8. $5 \times (-1)$
9. -4×2
10. $-3 \times (-3)$
11. $6 \times (-3)$
12. $-8 \times (-1)$
13. $12 \div (-2)$
14. $-8 \div (-1)$
15. $6 \div (-2)$
16. $-10 \div (-2)$
17. $-20 \div (-1)$
18. $12 \div (-3)$
19. $-3 \div (-1)$
20. $9 \div (-3)$

21. Work out
(a) $-7 \times (-2)$
(b) -3×6
(c) $8 \div (-8)$
(d) $10 \times (-3)$
(e) $-2 \times (-2)$
(f) $-12 \div 3$
(g) $-5 \times (-4)$
(h) -1×23
(i) $-2 \times (-2)^2$
(j) $0 \times (-7)$
(k) $(-3)^2$
(l) $-3 \times (-2) \times (-3)$

22. Find the missing numbers
(a) $-4 \times \square = 12$
(b) $3 \times \square = -12$
(c) $-8 \div -4 = \square$
(d) $5 \times \square = -5$
(e) $\square \times (-3) = 9$
(f) $12 \div \square = -6$
(g) $\square \div (-3) = 2$
(h) $\square \div 5 = -4$
(i) $-2 \times \square = 20$
(j) $-3 \times \square = 6$
(k) $-2 \times \square = 4$
(l) $(-1)^2 = \square$

Review exercise

This exercise has questions involving addition, subtraction, multiplication and division.

1. Work out

(a) $-7+13$ (b) $-5-(-4)$ (c) -7×4
(d) $-12\div(-12)$ (e) $-6+(-3)$ (f) $-10+10$
(g) $-8-5$ (h) $12-60$ (i) $3\times(-3)$
(j) $(-2)^2$ (k) $5-(-5)$ (l) $6\div(-6)$

2. Find the missing numbers

(a) $5\times\square=-50$ (b) $-2\div\square=1$ (c) $\square-3=12$
(d) $\square+(-7)=-9$ (e) $10-\square=-3$ (f) $\square\div(-3)=-1$
(g) $-7-7=\square$ (h) $\square\times(-7)=14$ (i) $1-\square=-9$
(j) $-3\times\square=0$ (k) $8-\square=-8$ (l) $(-1)^3=\square$

3. Work out

(a) $-3+(-2)$ (b) $-8\div 8$ (c) $5+(-7)$
(d) $-2\times\left(-\frac{1}{2}\right)$ (e) $8\div(-8)$ (f) $-7-(-2)$
(g) $-12\div(-2)$ (h) $(-3)^3$ (i) $6+(-6{\cdot}5)$
(j) $(-8+2)^2$ (k) $(-2)^2\times(-3)$ (l) $(-3-(-2))^2$

4. Copy and complete the addition square shown. The numbers inside the square are found by adding together the numbers across the top and down the side.

Add	−2	4	−5	3	−1
−3	−5				
0					
1			−4		
5					
−2					

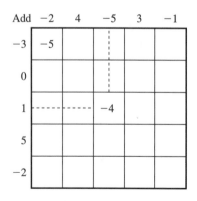

5. Copy and complete the *multiplication* square shown.

×	−2	5	3	−1	4
−4	−5				
6			18		
−3					
−1					
5					

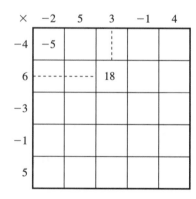

6. The sum of the numbers −3 and 4 is 1 and their product is −12. ('product' means multiplied together)

(a) Find two numbers whose sum is 3 and whose product is −10.
(b) Find two numbers whose sum is −1 and whose product is −12.
(c) Find two numbers whose sum is 4 and whose product is −12.

7. Copy and complete the table.

	Sum	Product	Two numbers
(a)	−7	10	
(b)	−13	30	
(c)	−5	6	
(d)	5	−6	
(e)	−8	12	
(f)	−2	−15	
(g)	−13	42	

Practice tests

Questions on negative numbers are more difficult when the different sorts are mixed together. Do one of these tests every two weeks or so.

Test 1

1. $-8 - 8$ **2.** $-8 \times (-8)$
3. -5×3 **4.** $-5 + 3$
5. $8 - (-7)$ **6.** $20 - 2$
7. $-18 \div (-6)$ **8.** $4 + (-10)$
9. $-2 + 13$ **10.** $+8 \times (-6)$
11. $-9 + (+2)$ **12.** $-2 - (-11)$
13. $-6 \times (-1)$ **14.** $2 - 20$
15. $-14 - (-4)$ **16.** $-40 \div (-5)$
17. $5 - 11$ **18.** -3×10
19. $9 + (-5)$ **20.** $7 \div (-7)$

Test 2

1. $-10 \times (-10)$ **2.** $-10 - 10$
3. $-8 \times (+1)$ **4.** $-8 + 1$
5. $5 + (-9)$ **6.** $15 - 5$
7. $-72 \div (-8)$ **8.** $-12 - (-2)$
9. $-1 + 8$ **10.** $-5 \times (-7)$
11. $-10 + (-10)$ **12.** $-6 \times (+4)$
13. $6 - 16$ **14.** $-42 \div (+6)$
15. $-13 + (-6)$ **16.** $-8 - (-7)$
17. $5 \times (-1)$ **18.** $2 - 15$
19. $21 + (-21)$ **20.** $-16 \div (-2)$

Test 3

1. $-2 \times (+8)$ **2.** $-2 + 8$
3. $-7 - 6$ **4.** $-7 \times (-6)$
5. $+36 \div (-9)$ **6.** $-8 - (-4)$
7. $-14 + 2$ **8.** $5 \times (-4)$
9. $11 + (-5)$ **10.** $11 - 11$
11. $-9 \times (-4)$ **12.** $-6 + (-4)$
13. $3 - 10$ **14.** $-20 \div (-2)$
15. $16 + (-10)$ **16.** $-4 - (+14)$
17. $-45 \div 5$ **18.** $18 - 3$
19. $-1 \times (-1)$ **20.** $-3 - (-3)$

Test 4

1. $-4 + 4$ **2.** $-4 \times (+4)$
3. $-2 - 12$ **4.** $-2 \times (-12)$
5. $3 + (-4)$ **6.** $4 - (-10)$
7. $-22 \div 11$ **8.** $-9 + 7$
9. $-6 - (-13)$ **10.** $-3 \times (-11)$
11. $4 - 5$ **12.** $-20 - (+10)$
13. $4 \times (-7)$ **14.** $7 - (-12)$
15. $9 - 18$ **16.** $56 \div (-7)$
17. $7 - 6$ **18.** $-11 + (+2)$
19. $-2 \times (+8)$ **20.** $-8 \div (-2)$

1.5 Properties of numbers

Prime numbers, factors, multiples

- A *prime* number is divisible by just two different numbers: by itself and by one. Notice that 1 is *not* a prime number.

  Here are some prime numbers: 7 23 11
- The *factors* of 15 divide into 15 exactly.

  1×15 3×5 The factors of 15 are 1, 3, 5 and 15.
- The first four *multiples* of 6 are 6, 12, 18, 24

  The first four multiples of 11 are 11, 22, 33, 44

Exercise 1

1. Find all the factors of
(a) 12 (b) 30 (c) 17 (d) 50

2. 7 is a factor of which numbers between 20 and 30?

3. (a) List the factors of 24.
(b) List the factors of 40.
(c) List the common factors of 24 and 40. [i.e. the numbers which are in list (a) and list (b).]

4. (a) List the factors of 28.
(b) List the factors of 36.
(c) List the common factors of 28 and 36.
(d) Write down the highest common factor of 28 and 36.

5. Find the highest common factor of
(a) 24 and 42 (b) 35 and 49

6. Factors occur in pairs. For example $48 = 1 \times 48$, 2×24, 3×16, 4×12, 6×8
Write down all the factor pairs for
(a) 28 (b) 30

7. The number in the square is the product of the two numbers on either side of it. Copy and complete:

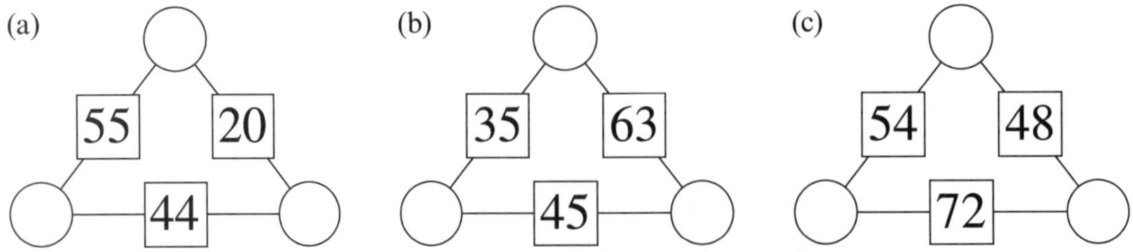

8. Write down the first four multiples of
(a) 3 (b) 7 (c) 10 (d) 15

9. Here are the first six multiples of 12 and 15

12 :	12	24	36	48	60	72
15 :	15	30	45	60	75	90

Write down the lowest common multiple of 12 and 15. [i.e. the lowest number which is in both lists.]

10. Copy and complete the first five multiples of 6 and 8.

6 : 6, 12, ☐, ☐, ☐

8 : 8, ☐, ☐, ☐, ☐

Write down the L.C.M. of 6 and 8

11. The number [n] is a multiple of 7 between 30 and 40.

The number [m] is a multiple of 9 between 40 and 50.

Work out $n + m$.

12. True or false:
(a) 'All multiples of 9 are multiples of 3.'
(b) 'All factors of 12 are factors of 6.'
(c) 'All numbers have an even number of different factors.'

13. Which of these are prime numbers: [13, 21, 27, 31, 49, 51, 63, 65, 67]

14. Add together all the prime numbers less than 16.

15. 60 is mid-way between 2 prime numbers. What are they?

16. (a) How many even prime numbers are there?
(b) How many prime numbers have 5 as their last digit?

17. The number 13 is prime. When the digits are reversed we get 31, and 31 is also prime.
Find two more numbers with this property.

18. Here are the first three triangle numbers.

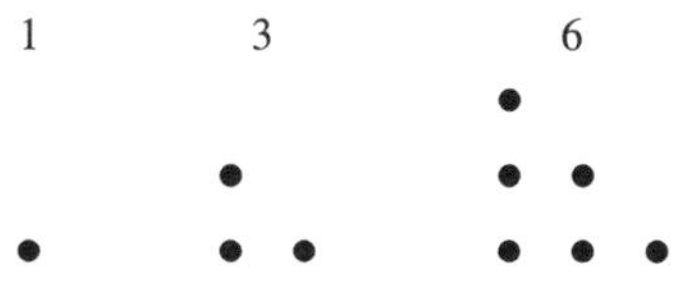

Draw similar diagrams to show the next two triangle numbers.
Show that consecutive pairs of triangle numbers add up to make square numbers.

Prime factor decomposition

Factors of a number which are also prime numbers are called prime factors. We can find these prime factors using a 'factor tree'. Here are two examples.

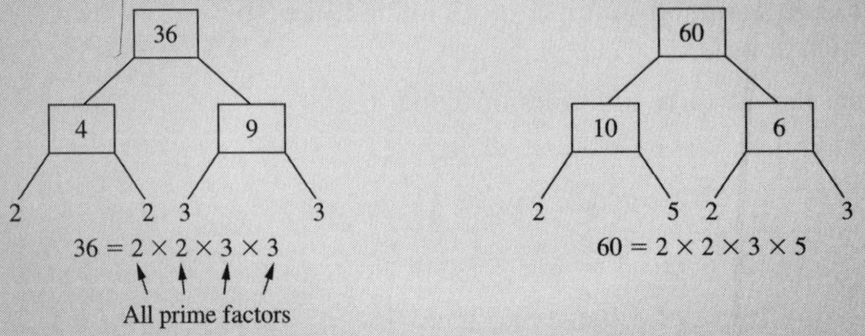

Exercise 2

1. Draw a factor tree for 108 and for 300. Remember that you only stop when you get to prime numbers.

2. Draw factor trees for the following numbers.
   (a) 24 (b) 81 (c) 84 (d) 200
   (e) 294 (f) 630 (g) 392 (h) 3960

3. $154 = 2 \times 7 \times 11$ and $1365 = 3 \times 5 \times 7 \times 13$. Find the highest common factor of 154 and 1365. [i.e. the highest number that goes into 154 and 1365.]

4. $105 = 3 \times 5 \times 7$ and $330 = 2 \times 3 \times 5 \times 11$. Find the highest common factor of 105 and 330. [i.e. the highest number that goes into 105 and 330.]

5. $975 = 3 \times 5 \times 5 \times 13$ and $550 = 2 \times 5 \times 5 \times 11$

   Find the highest common factor (H.C.F.) of 975 and 550.

6. (a) $625 = 5 \times 5 \times 5 \times 5$. The square root, $\sqrt{625} = 5 \times 5 = 25$
   (b) Given $36 = 2 \times 2 \times 3 \times 3$, find $\sqrt{36}$
   (c) Given $2401 = 7 \times 7 \times 7 \times 7$, find $\sqrt{2401}$

7. Write the following numbers as the product of prime factors and then find the square root of each number.

   (a) 100 (b) 324 (c) 441

8. Some prime numbers can be written as the sum of 2 square numbers e.g. $1^2 + 2^2 = 5$.
   Find 5 two-digit prime numbers that can be written as the sum of two square numbers. [Hint: start by listing the square numbers.]

Cubes and higher powers

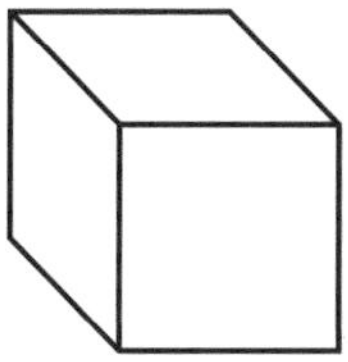

- The first three *cube numbers* are: $1^3 = 1 \times 1 \times 1 = 1$
  $2^3 = 2 \times 2 \times 2 = 8$
  $3^3 = 3 \times 3 \times 3 = 27$
- Finding the *cube root* of a number is the inverse function.
  e.g. $\sqrt[3]{27} = 3$ $\sqrt[3]{8} = 2$
- Higher powers are written in a similar way
  $3 \times 3 \times 3 \times 3 \times 3$ is written 3^5. 'Three to the power 5'
  $2 \times 2 \times 2 \times 2 \times 2 \times 2$ is written 2^6. 'Two to the power 6'

  To work out 7^4 on a calculator, press [7] [x^y] [4] [=]

Exercise 3

1. Work out
(a) 4^3 (b) 5^3 (c) 6^3 (d) 10^3

2. Write down a cube number which is also a square number.

3. Work out (a) $\sqrt[3]{27}$ (b) $\sqrt[3]{125}$ (c) $\sqrt[3]{64}$

4. Work out the following, without a calculator.

(a) 3^2 (b) 1^3 (c) 2^5 (d) 7^1 (e) 10^4
(f) 11^2 (g) 100^2 (h) $0{\cdot}1^2$ (i) $\left(\frac{1}{2}\right)^2$ (j) 10^6

5. Copy and complete with either <, = or > in the box.

(a) $3^2 \square 2^5$ (b) $2^4 \square 4^2$ (c) $5^2 \square 2^5$
(d) $10^2 \square 2^{10}$ (e) $0{\cdot}9^2 \square 0{\cdot}9$ (f) $8^7 \square 8^6$

6. Use the [x^y] key to work out
(a) 7^5 (b) 5^6 (c) $0{\cdot}5^3$ (d) $2{\cdot}1^4$

7. *Without* using the cube root key, use a calculator to estimate the following. Give your answers correct to the nearest whole number.
(a) $\sqrt[3]{20}$ (b) $\sqrt[3]{400}$ (c) $\sqrt[3]{111}$

8. Copy and complete the following

(a) If $a = 2^2$ and $b = 2^3$, then $ab = 2^{\square}$
(b) If $p = 3^3$ and $q = 3^4$, then $pq = 3^{\square}$
(c) If $c = 5^2$ and $d = 5^3$, then $cd = 5^{\square}$
(d) If $x = 4^2$, $y = 4^3$, $z = 4^5$, then $xyz = \square^{\square}$

Part 2

2.1 Estimating and checking answers

Rounding off

- Using a calculator, $\sqrt{11} = 3{\cdot}3166248$
  We can *round off* this number to either 1 or 2 decimal places.
- Rounding to one decimal place.
  If the figure in the 2nd decimal place is *5 or more*, round up.
  Otherwise do not

  2·761 = 2·8 to 1 d.p. (↑ under the 6)

  13·45 = 13·5 to 1 d.p. (↑ under the 5)

  0·337 = 0·3 to 1 d.p. (↑ under the second 3)
- Rounding to two decimal places.
  If the figure in the 3rd decimal place is *5 or more*, round up.
  Otherwise do not.

  1·4281 = 1·43 to 2 d.p. (↑ under the 8)

  0·0742 = 0·07 to 2 d.p. (↑ under the 4)

  8·555 = 8·56 to 2 d.p. (↑ under the last 5)

Exercise 1

1. Round off these numbers correct to one decimal place.

(a) 8·24 (b) 7·166 (c) 0·762 (d) 11·27
(e) 0·352 (f) 8·741 (g) 11·518 (h) 0·648

2. Round off these numbers correct to two decimal places.

(a) 1·246 (b) 8·043 (c) 11·222 (d) 3·084
(e) 0·1355 (f) 22·456 (g) 0·8592 (h) 6·097

3. Work out these answers on a calculator and then round off the answers correct to two decimal places.

(a) $11{\cdot}21 \div 7$ (b) $0{\cdot}54 \times 8{\cdot}1$ (c) $4216 \div 214$ (d) $12{\cdot}6 \times 0{\cdot}071$
(e) $\sqrt{13}$ (f) $\sqrt{8{\cdot}5}$ (g) $1{\cdot}36^2$ (h) $0{\cdot}97^2$
(i) $0{\cdot}77 \times 0{\cdot}78$ (j) $11{\cdot}82 \div 13$ (k) $2{\cdot}4 \times 0{\cdot}716$ (l) $\sqrt{(4{\cdot}2 \times 3{\cdot}5)}$

4. Round off these numbers to the nearest hundred.

(a) 1741 (b) 22 483 (c) 807·1 (d) 15 255
(e) 562·8 (f) 2222 (g) 3552 (h) 1027

Calculating with estimates

- Harry worked out 506·3 ÷ 9·5 and wrote down 5·3295.
  He can check his answer by working with estimates.
  Instead of 506·3 use 500, instead of 9·5 use 10.
  So $500 \div 10 = 50$.
  Clearly Harry's answer is wrong. He put the decimal point in the wrong place.

- Here are three more calculations with estimates.

(a) $31{\cdot}2 \times 9{\cdot}2$
$\approx 30 \times 10$
≈ 300

(b) $28{\cdot}4 \div 0{\cdot}971$
$\approx 30 \div 1$
≈ 30

(c) 11% of £78·99
$\approx \frac{1}{10}$ of £80
$\approx$ £8

Exercise 2

Do not use a calculator. Decide, by estimating, which of the three answers is closest to the exact answer. Write the calculation and the approximate answer for each question (use ≈).

	Calculation	A	B	C
1.	$97{\cdot}9 \times 11{\cdot}3$	90	500	1000
2.	$6{\cdot}73 \times 9{\cdot}65$	30	70	300
3.	$1{\cdot}03 \times 60{\cdot}6$	6	60	200
4.	$2{\cdot}3 \times 96$	200	90	20
5.	$18{\cdot}9 \times 21{\cdot}4$	200	400	4000
6.	$5{\cdot}14 \times 5{\cdot}99$	15	10	30
7.	$811 \times 11{\cdot}72$	8000	4000	800
8.	99×98	1 million	100 000	10 000
9.	$1{\cdot}09 \times 29{\cdot}6$	20	30	60
10.	$81\,413 \times 10{\cdot}96$	8 million	1 million	800 000
11.	$601 \div 3{\cdot}92$	50	100	150
12.	$402 \div 4{\cdot}97$	8	0·8	80
13.	$58{\cdot}4 \div 0{\cdot}98$	60	300	600
14.	$0{\cdot}2 \times 111{\cdot}3$	10	20	180
15.	$217 \div 201{\cdot}4$	0·2	1	10
16.	$88{\cdot}4 + 95 + 141$	300	100	3000
17.	9·83% of (2567·3 + 1·92)	250	400	2500
18.	$\frac{1}{5}$ of ($20{\cdot}27 \times 20{\cdot}11$)	16	80	160
19.	$\frac{9}{19}$ of 1% of 6060	30	60	300
20.	$\frac{2}{3}$ of 24·8% of $\frac{1}{2}$ of 2403·62	20	200	2000

Exercise 3

Do not use a calculator for these questions.

1. A do-it-yourself table and chairs kit cost £38·49. Estimate the total cost of 11 kits.
2. Daily disposable contact lenses cost 96p per pair. Find the approximate cost of 2 years supply of lenses.
3. A cut-price video was sold at £6.95 per copy. Estimate the total cost of 42 copies.
4. The rent for a flat is £95 per week. Estimate the total spent on rent in one year.
5. 2105 people share the cost of hiring a cruise boat. Roughly how much does each person pay, if the total cost was half a million pounds?
6. A boxer earned a fee of \$5 million for a fight which lasted 1 minute 35 seconds. Estimate the money he earned per second of the fight.

In Questions **7** and **8** there are six calculations and six answers. Write down each calculation and insert the correct answer from the list given. Use estimation.

7. (a) $5{\cdot}9 \times 6{\cdot}1$ (b) $19{\cdot}8 \div 5$ (c) $32 \times 9{\cdot}9$
   (d) $0{\cdot}89 + 14{\cdot}7$ (e) $4{\cdot}5 \times 44$ (f) $4141 \div 40$

Answers:	198, 35·99, 103·5, 15·59, 316·8, 3·96

8. (a) $102{\cdot}8 \div 5$ (b) $11{\cdot}2 \div 98{\cdot}6$ (c) $3 \times 0{\cdot}41$
   (d) $34 \times 2{\cdot}9$ (e) $51 \times 3{\cdot}9$ (f) $238{\cdot}6 \div 4{\cdot}7$

Answers:	50·76, 20·56, 1·23, 198·9, 98·6, 0·114

9. Write the decimal point in the correct place.

(a) length of a football pitch	9572 m
(b) weight of an 'average' new born baby	3124 kg
(c) width of this book	1831 mm
(d) area of the classroom floor	560 m^2
(e) weight of a packet of sugar	100 kg
(f) diameter of a football	3140 cm

10. At a fun fair, customers pay 95p for a ride on a giant spinning wheel. The operator sells 2483 tickets during the weekend and his costs for electricity and rent were £114. Estimate his profit over the weekend.

11. A quick way of adding lots of figures on a shopping bill is to round every number to the nearest pound.
So £2·43 becomes £2, £0·91 becomes £1, £0·24 becomes £0 and so on.

(a) Use this method to estimate the totals below:

(i)

WSKAS COCKTAIL	*	0.85
H/EATING MINCE		3.95
HAWAIIAN CRN		1.85
PAIN AU CHOC		0.54
PAIN AU CHOC		0.54
PAIN AU CHOC		0.54
BUTTER		0.89
BUTTER		0.89
EGGS		0.78
PORK/CHICK/PIE		2.03
MED.MAT.CHDR.		1.21
HOT PIES		1.47
POT. WAFFLES		1.39
WHOLE BRIE		1.01
MUFFINS		0.49
BACON RASHERS		0.65
BEETROOT		0.99
LOOSE CHEESE		0.99

(ii)

PLN BAGUETTE		0.49
FOIL	*	0.65
LETTUCE ROUND		0.24
JW TUNA MAYO		0.75
SOYA MILK		0.47
SOYA MILK		0.47
ORNGE MRMLDE		0.74
YOGHURT		0.99
SPGHTI/HOOPS		0.26
CHEESE		1.34
WHISKAS	*	0.45
WHISKAS	*	0.45
VINEGAR		0.68
KING EDWARDS.		0.99
UHT H/FAT MILK	*	0.26
APPLES		1.89
WHISKAS	*	0.45
PEACHES		0.24
FROM. FRAIS		0.72

(b) Use a calculator to work out the exact total for part (i).
Compare the answer with your estimate above.

12. Estimate:

(a) the number of times your heart beats in one day (24 h),

(b) the thickness of one page in this book.

13. (a) In 1989 thousands of people formed a human chain right across the U.S.A., a distance of about 4300 km.
Estimate the number of people in the chain.

(b) Estimate the number of people needed to form a chain right around the equator. (Assume you have enough people volunteering to float for a while in the sea.) The distance right around the equator is about 40 000 km.

14. Give an estimate for each of the following calculations

(a) $\dfrac{62{\cdot}4 \times 19{\cdot}3}{10{\cdot}7}$ (b) $\dfrac{3198 - 207}{93{\cdot}7}$ (c) 52% of £987·50

(d) $30{\cdot}23^2 - 112$ (e) $\frac{2}{3}$ of 589 m (f) $\dfrac{407{\cdot}5 + 2{\cdot}794}{15{\cdot}6 + 24{\cdot}7}$

Checking answers

Here are five calculations followed by appropriate checks, using inverse operations.

(a) $22{\cdot}5 \div 5 = 4{\cdot}5$ check $4{\cdot}5 \times 5 = 22{\cdot}5$

(b) $29{\cdot}5 - 1{\cdot}47 = 28{\cdot}03$ check $28{\cdot}03 + 1{\cdot}47$

(c) $78{\cdot}5 \times 20 = 1570$ check $1570 \div 20$

(d) $\sqrt{11} = 3{\cdot}31662$ check $3{\cdot}31662^2$

(e) $14{\cdot}7 + 28{\cdot}1 + 17{\cdot}4 + 9{\cdot}9$ check $9{\cdot}9 + 17{\cdot}4 + 28{\cdot}1 + 14{\cdot}7$ [add in reverse order]

Exercise 4

1. Work out the following and check using inverse operations

(a) $83{\cdot}5 \times 20 = \square$ check $\square \div 20$

(b) $104 - 13{\cdot}2 = \square$ check $\square + 13{\cdot}2$

(c) $228{\cdot}2 \div 7 = \square$ check $\square \times 7$

(d) $\sqrt{28} = \square$ check $\square^2$

(e) $11.5 + 2{\cdot}7 + 9{\cdot}8 + 20{\cdot}7$ check $20{\cdot}7 + 9{\cdot}8 + 2{\cdot}7 + 11{\cdot}5$

2. (a) Will the answer to $64 \times 0{\cdot}8$ be larger or smaller than 64?

(b) Will the answer to $210 \div 0{\cdot}7$ be larger or smaller than 210?

(c) Will the answer to $17{\cdot}4 \times 0{\cdot}9$ be larger or smaller than 17·4?

3. Here are the answers obtained by six children. Some are correct but some are clearly impossible or highly unlikely.
Decide which answers are 'OK' and which are 'impossible' or 'highly unlikely'.

(a) Top speed of winning snail = 10 m/sec

(b) Time taken to walk 1 mile to school = 21 minutes

(c) The height of Mrs Brown's washing machine = 315 cm

(d) Number of bricks needed to build a 2 bedroom house = 1 million

(e) The mean value of the numbers 32, 35, 31, 36, 32 = 37·8

(f) One per cent of the UK population = 60 000 people.

Estimating game

- This is a game for two players. On squared paper draw an answer grid with the numbers shown.

Answer grid

198	1089	99	100	360	18
180	450	22	440	155	1980
1240	200	45	62	100	550
40	620	495	279	800	55
2000	80	220	10	891	250
4950	1550	1000	3960	3069	341

- The players now take turns to choose two numbers from the question grid below and multiply them on a calculator.

Question grid

2	5	9
11	20	31
40	50	99

The number obtained is crossed out on the answer grid using the player's own colour.

- The game continues until all the numbers in the answer grid have been crossed out. The object is to get four answers in a line (horizontally, vertically or diagonally). The winner is the player with most lines of four.

- A line of *five* counts as *two* lines of four.
  A line of *six* counts as *three* lines of four.

2.2 Rules of algebra

- A algebraic *expression* is formed from letter symbols and numbers. For example $3n$, $4n + 5$ and $1 - 2x$ are all expressions. Notice that there is no equals sign in an expression.
- In an *equation*, like $2n - 1 = 15$, n is one particular unknown number.
- In the *formula* $A = LB$, A, L and B are variable quantities, related by the formula. If we know the values of L and B we can calculate the value of A.

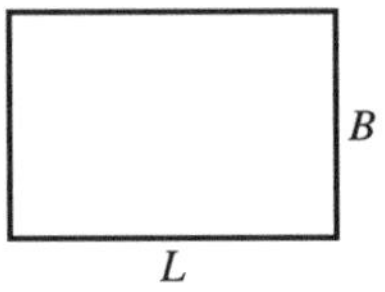

- In the *function* $y = 2x + 7$, the value of y can be found for any chosen value of x.

Basic algebra

- $3 \times n = 3n$
  $m \times n = mn$
  $n \times (a + b) = n(a + b)$
  $(c + d) \div x = \dfrac{c + d}{x}$
- Like terms can be added:
  $3a + b + 2a + 5b = 5a + 6b$
  $n^2 + 3n^2 = 4n^2$
  $4n + 5 - 2n - 8 = 2n - 3$
- Cancelling fractions:
  $\dfrac{\not{4} \times 3}{\not{4}} = 3$ $\quad \dfrac{2 \times \not{d}}{\not{d}} = 2$
  $\dfrac{\not{n} \times n \times n}{\not{n}} = n^2$ $\quad \dfrac{6x}{2} = 3x$
- A flow diagram can be used to show the correct order of operations. For the expression $3(4n - 1)$ we have:

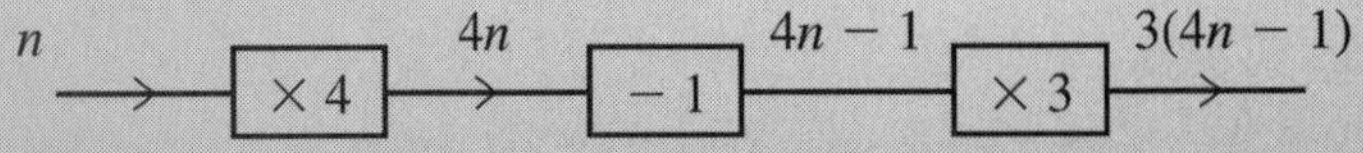

- Sometimes you are not sure that two expressions are the same. Check by putting in numbers.

(a) Is $2n^2$ equal to $(2n)^2$?
Try $n = 1$: $2n^2 = 2 \times 1^2 = 2$
$(2n)^2 = (2 \times 1)^2 = 4$
So $2n^2 \neq (2n)^2$

(b) Is $\dfrac{6n}{3}$ equal to $2n$?
Try $n = 1$: $\dfrac{6n}{3} = \dfrac{6 \times 1}{3} = 2$
$2n = 2 \times 1 = 2$
So $\dfrac{6n}{3} = 2n$

Exercise 1

In questions **1** to **15** answer 'true' or 'false'.

1. $5 \times n = 5 + n$ **2.** $a \times a = a^2$ **3.** $a + b = b + a$

4. $t \times t \times t = 3t$ **5.** $h \times 3 = 3h$ **6.** $p - q = q - p$

7. $a + A = 2a$ **8.** $a + a^2 = a^3$ **9.** $n \times n \times n = n^3$

10. $4n - n = 4$ **11.** $a \div 5 = \frac{a}{5}$ **12.** $(a + b) \div n = \frac{a+b}{n}$

13. $m \div 4 = 4 \div m$ **14.** $\frac{n+n}{n} = 2$ **15.** $a \times b \times a = a^2b$

16. Here are some cards.

$3n$	$n+2$	$n+n$	n
n^2	$2n \div 2$	n^3	
$n-2$	$3n-n$	$2 \div n$	$n \times n$

(a) Which cards will always be the same as $\boxed{2n}$?

(b) Which card will always be the same as $\boxed{n \times n \times n}$?

(c) Which card will always be the same as $\boxed{\frac{2}{n}}$?

(d) Draw a new card which will always be the same as $\boxed{2n + 2n}$.

17. In the expression $3(2n + 4)$, three operations are performed in the following order:

$$\rightarrow \boxed{\times 2} \rightarrow \boxed{+4} \rightarrow \boxed{\times 3} —$$

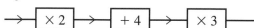

Draw similar diagrams to show the correct order of operations for the following expressions.

(a) $4n - 3$ (b) $7(6n + 3)$ (c) $\frac{5n-2}{3}$

(d) $x^2 + 5$ (e) $(x + 2)^2$ (f) $\frac{(3x^2 - 2)}{5}$

In Questions **18** to **32** simplify the expressions.

18. $\frac{n}{n}$ **19.** $\frac{5a}{a}$ **20.** $\frac{n^2}{n}$

21. $2n^2 - n^2$ **22.** $a + b + c + a$ **23.** $m - 3 + 3m$

24. $pq + pq$ **25.** $\frac{n \times n \times n}{n}$ **26.** $\frac{a + a + a}{a}$

27. $\frac{4x}{2}$ **28.** $\frac{a^2}{a^3}$ **29.** $\frac{n}{2} + \frac{n}{2}$

30. $3p - 1 - 3p + 2$ **31.** $8n \div 8$ **32.** $a^2 \times a$

Exercise 2

1. Draw your own addition square like the one shown here.

	1	2	3	4	5	6	7	8	9
1	2	3	4	5	6	7	8	9	10
2	3	4	5	6	7	8	9	10	11
3	4	5	6	7	8	9	10	11	12
4	5	6	7	8	9	10	11	12	13
5	6	7	8	9	10	11	12	13	14
6	7	8	9	10	11	12	13	14	15
7	8	9	10	11	12	13	14	15	16
8	9	10	11	12	13	14	15	16	17
9	10	11	12	13	14	15	16	17	18

2. In this 2 by 2 square, taken from the main square, the smallest number is 8. Draw the square and fill in the missing numbers.

8	?
?	?

3. (a) Here is a 2 by 2 square. The top left number is x.

x	

The other three main numbers are shown

x	$x+1$
$x+1$	$x+2$

(b) Draw the three squares shown and use x's to write down the other 3 numbers in each square.

	x

	x

x	

4. Draw the squares shown and use x's to fill in the other 8 numbers

x		

		x

	x	

5. Draw each of the shapes below and fill in the missing numbers using the letters given.

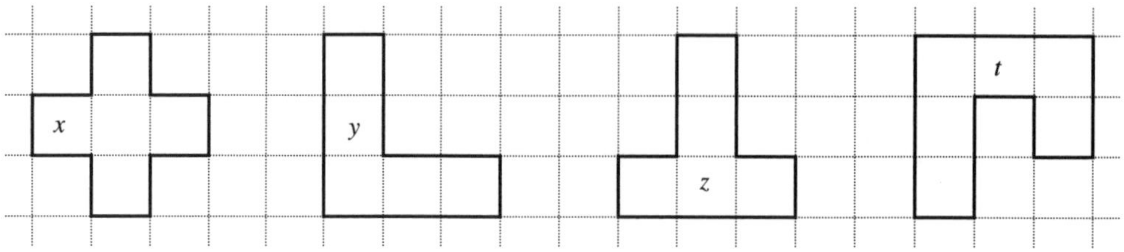

Using letters for numbers

Find the expressions you are left with.

(a) Start with n, multiply by 5 and then add 8. $n \longrightarrow 5n \longrightarrow 5n+8$

(b) Start with a, subtract b and then add 10. $a \longrightarrow a-b \longrightarrow a-b+10$

(c) Start with p, add 3 then multiply the result by 4. $p \longrightarrow p+3 \longrightarrow 4(p+3)$

(d) Start with m, subtract t and then square the result. $m \longrightarrow m-t \longrightarrow (m-t)^2$

Notice that *brackets* are needed in parts (c) and (d).

Exercise 3

Write down the expression you get. If any of your answers contain brackets, do not remove them.

1. Start with n, multiply by 5 then add x.
2. Start with n, add x and then multiply the result by 5.
3. Start with h, multiply by 6 and then subtract t.
4. Start with h, subtract t and then multiply the result by 6.
5. Start with b, add x and then multiply the result by 5.
6. Start with b, multiply by a and then add x.
7. Start with y, square it and then multiply the result by 3
8. Start with n, multiply by d and then subtract 3.
9. Start with a, double it and then add A.
10. Start with h, subtract H and then multiply the result by 5.
11. Start with x, subtract 8 and then multiply the result by 5.
12. Start with x, square it and then add 2
13. Start with y, double it and then subtract 3.
14. Start with a, add 10 and then square the result.
15. Here is a flow diagram for the expression $2(3n+7)$

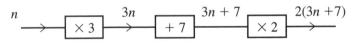

$n \rightarrow$ [× 3] $\rightarrow 3n \rightarrow$ [+ 7] $\rightarrow 3n+7 \rightarrow$ [× 2] $\rightarrow 2(3n+7)$

Find the expression for each of the following flow charts:

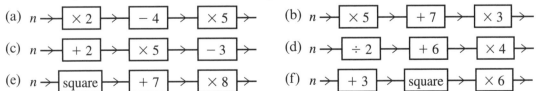

(a) $n \rightarrow$ [× 2] $\rightarrow$ [− 4] $\rightarrow$ [× 5] $\rightarrow$

(b) $n \rightarrow$ [× 5] $\rightarrow$ [+ 7] $\rightarrow$ [× 3] $\rightarrow$

(c) $n \rightarrow$ [+ 2] $\rightarrow$ [× 5] $\rightarrow$ [− 3] $\rightarrow$

(d) $n \rightarrow$ [÷ 2] $\rightarrow$ [+ 6] $\rightarrow$ [× 4] $\rightarrow$

(e) $n \rightarrow$ [square] $\rightarrow$ [+ 7] $\rightarrow$ [× 8] $\rightarrow$

(f) $n \rightarrow$ [+ 3] $\rightarrow$ [square] $\rightarrow$ [× 6] $\rightarrow$

16. Draw the flow diagram for the following expressions.

(a) $2n+7$ (b) $3(5n-3)$ (c) $\dfrac{6n+1}{5}$

(d) n^2-3 (e) $(n+5)^2$ (f) $3(n^2-1)$

17. Draw the flow diagram for the expression $2\left[\frac{3n^2 - 1}{5} + 7\right] + 100$

18. A machine makes x chocolates every minute. It runs for 5 minutes, after which 7 of the chocolates are rejected. How many good chocolates did the machine make in the 5 minutes?

19. A small bag of peanuts contains y nuts, and a large bag contains 5 times as many. If a boy buys a large bag and then eats 9 nuts, how many are left in his bag?

20. Bill used to earn £d per week. He then had a rise of £6 per week. How much will he now earn in 7 weeks?

21. A tile weighs t kg. How much do n tiles weigh?

22. In a butcher's shop: chicken weigh m kg each;
ducks weigh x kg each;
turkeys weigh z kg each.

Find the total weight of
(a) n chickens, y ducks and t turkeys.
(b) v ducks, 8 turkeys and p chickens.

23. The height of a balloon increases at a steady rate of x metres in t hours.
How far will the balloon rise in one hour?
How far will the balloon rise in t hours?

24. Unleaded petrol costs z pence per litre, which is x pence per litre less than 4 star.
How much do I pay for n litres of 4 star?

Exercise 4

1. Phil has 3 bags of coins.
Each bag has n coins inside.

Write an expression to show the total number of coins in Phil's 3 bags after the following.

(a) Phil took 4 coins out of *one* bag.
(b) Phil took 1 coin out of *each* bag.
(c) Phil took 3 coins out of each of *two* of the bags and *none* out of the other bag.
(d) Phil took 5 coins out of one bag and 2 coins out of each of the other two bags.

2. Write an expression for each of the missing lengths in these rectangles.

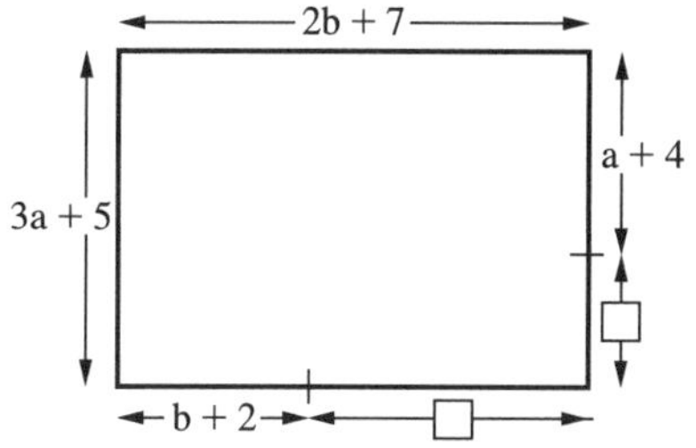

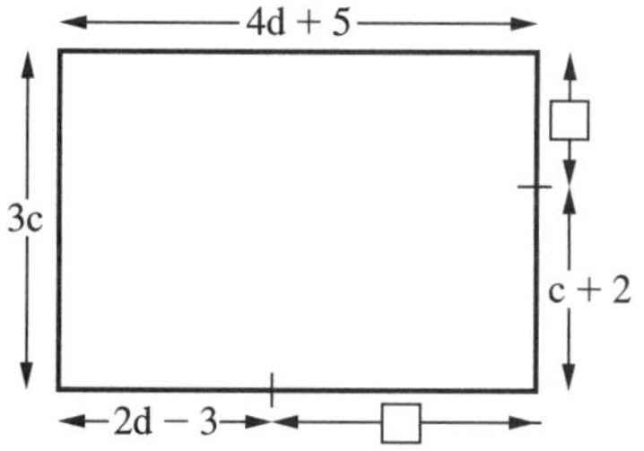

3. Selmin has found a sequence for square numbers:

$$2^2 = 1^2 + 1 + 2$$
$$3^2 = 2^2 + 2 + 3$$
$$4^2 = 3^2 + 3 + 4$$

(a) Write down the line that starts '$5^2 = \ldots\ldots$'
(b) Using ns, write down the line that starts '$n^2 = \ldots\ldots$'

4. Leila has a different sequence:

$$2^2 = 1 \times 3 + 1$$
$$3^2 = 2 \times 4 + 1$$
$$4^2 = 3 \times 5 + 1$$

(a) Write down the line that starts '$5^2 = \ldots\ldots$'
(b) Write down the line that starts '$n^2 = \ldots\ldots$'

5. Here is a sequence for square numbers using consecutive odd numbers.

$$2^2 = 1 + 3$$
$$3^2 = 1 + 3 + 5$$
$$4^2 = 1 + 3 + 5 + 7$$

Similarly, $n^2 = 1 + 3 + 5 + 7 + \ldots\ldots + k$.
Express k in terms of n. Write $k = \ldots\ldots.$

6. 'Think of a number'. Ask someone to follow these instructions:
(a) Think of a number.
(b) Add 3 to the number.
(c) Multiply the answer by 5.
(d) Subtract 7 from the new number.
(e) Double the answer.
(f) Subtract 6 from the last number.
(g) Read out the final answer.

You can now work out the original number as follows:
'Subtract 10 and divide by 10'
[E.g. if the final answer is 370, the original number was $(370 - 10) \div 10$. It was 36.]
Try this a few times and then explain why it works by using algebra. [Hint: Think of a number $x\ldots\ldots$].

2.3 Geometrical reasoning

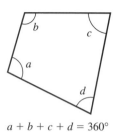

Reminders

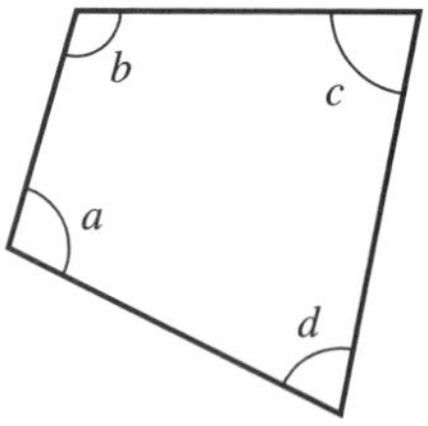

$a + b + c + d = 360°$

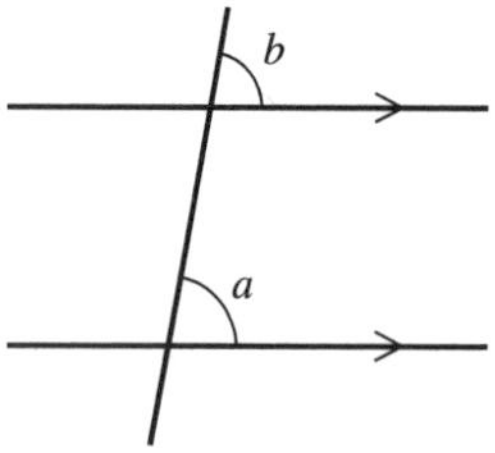

$a = b$ (corresponding angles)

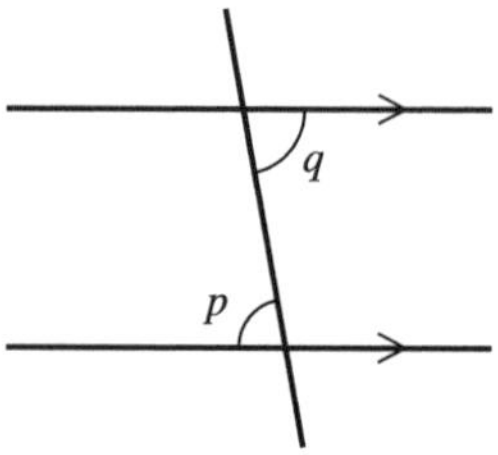

$p = q$ (alternate angles)

Exercise 1

This exercise contains a mixture of questions which require a knowledge of all parts of this section. Parts B and C are more difficult than part A.

Part A. Find the angles marked with letters.

1.

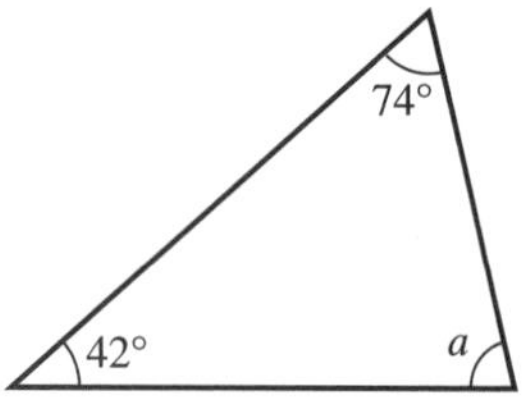

2.

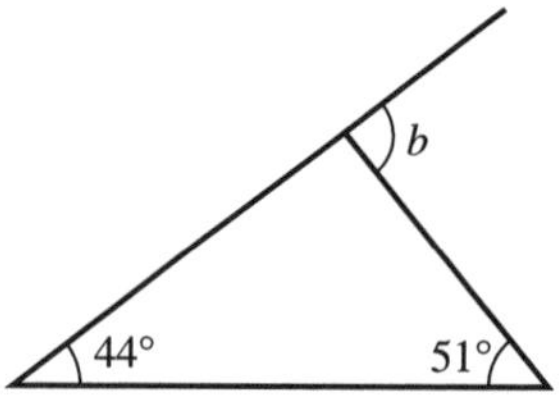

3.

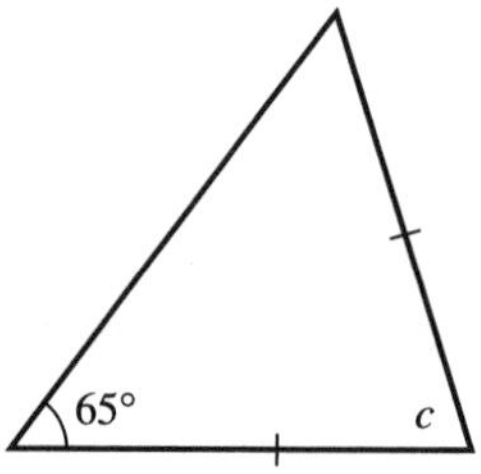

4.

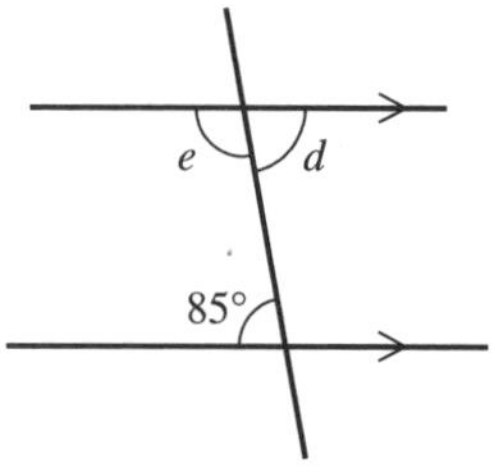

5.

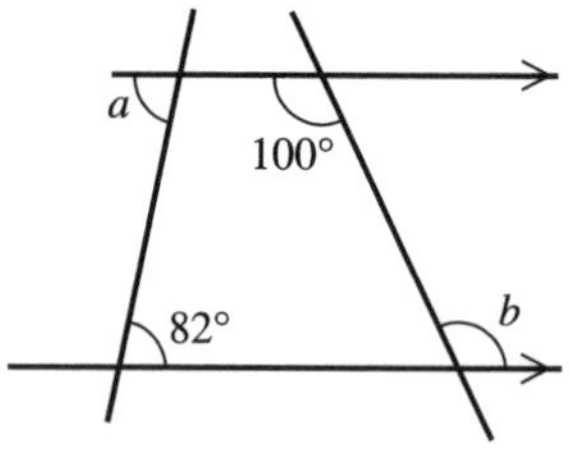

6.

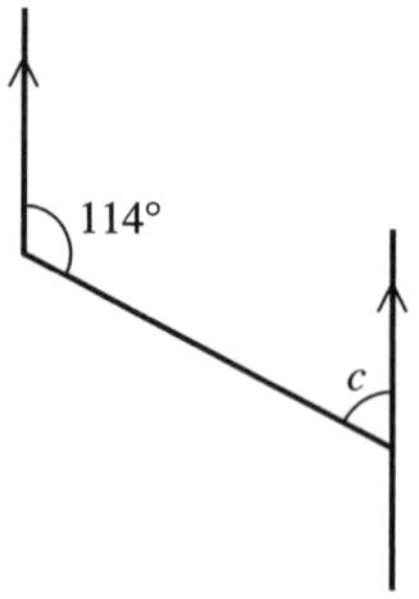

7.

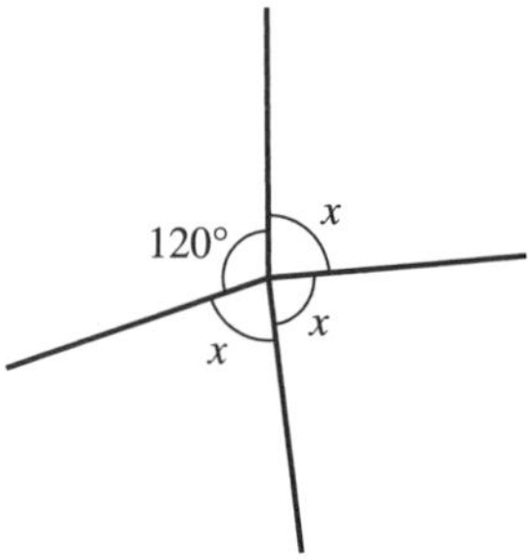

8.

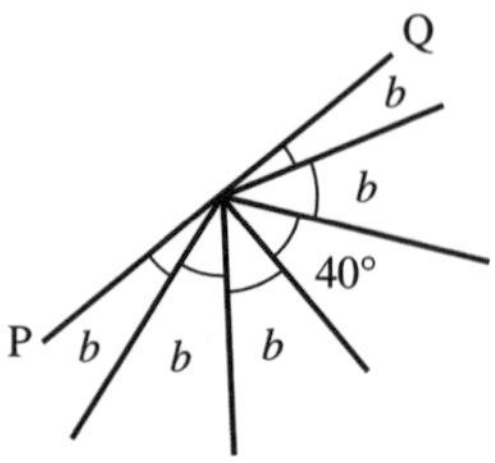

PQ is a straight line

9.

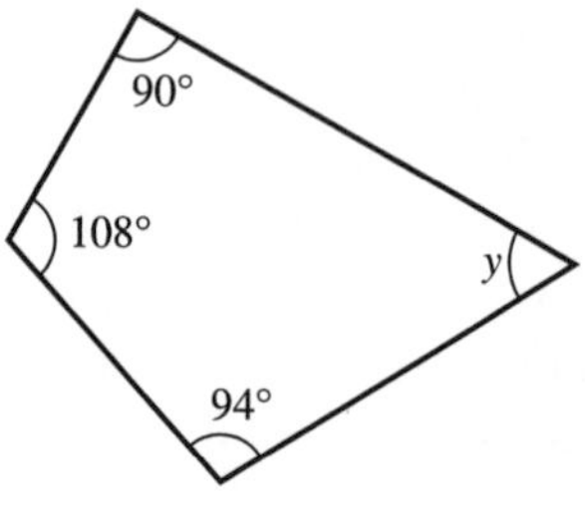

Part B

Find the angles marked with letters. Draw each diagram and show your working.

10.

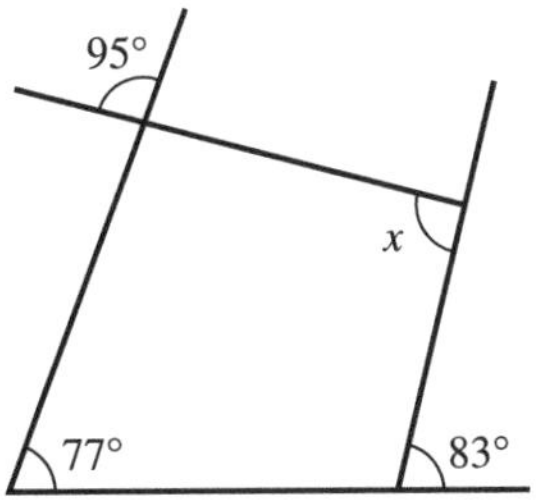

11.

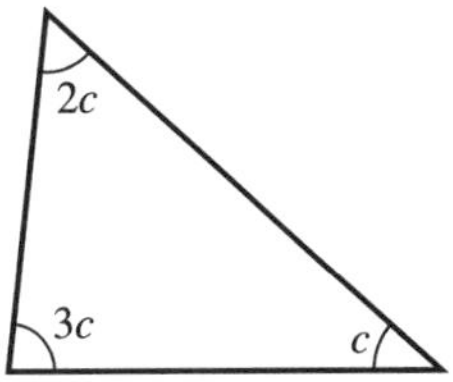

12.

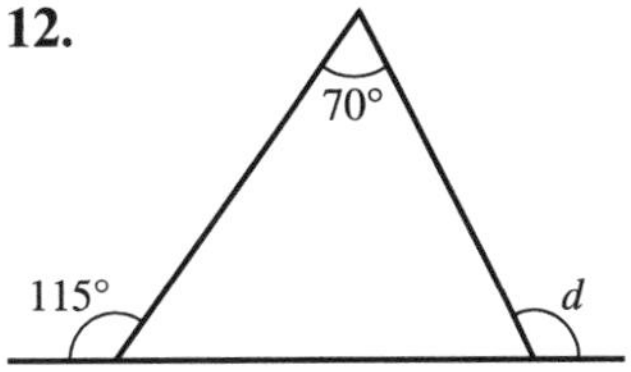

13.

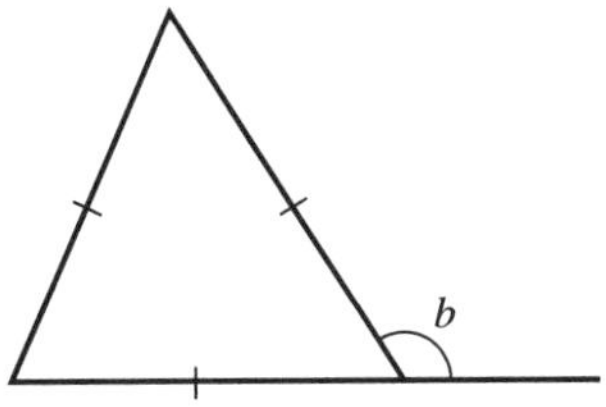

14.

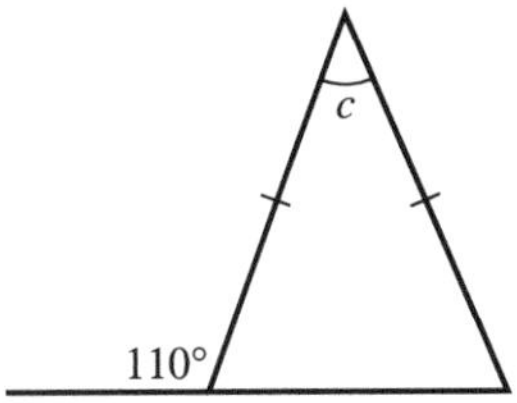

15.

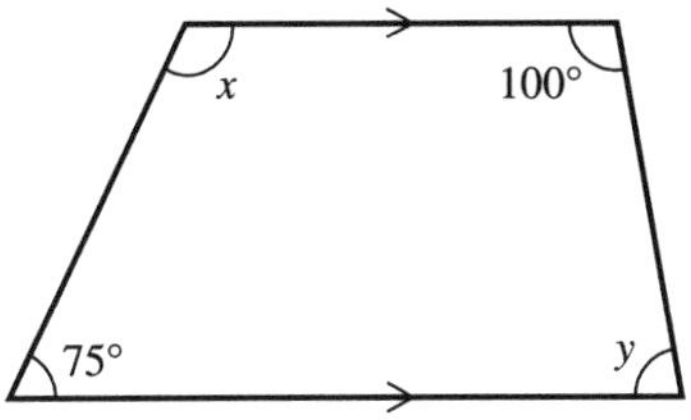

Part C

Find the angle x in each diagram. Show your working.

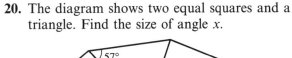

16.

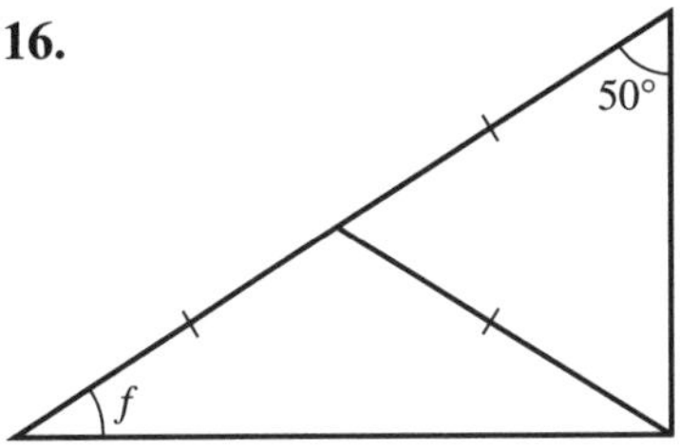

17.

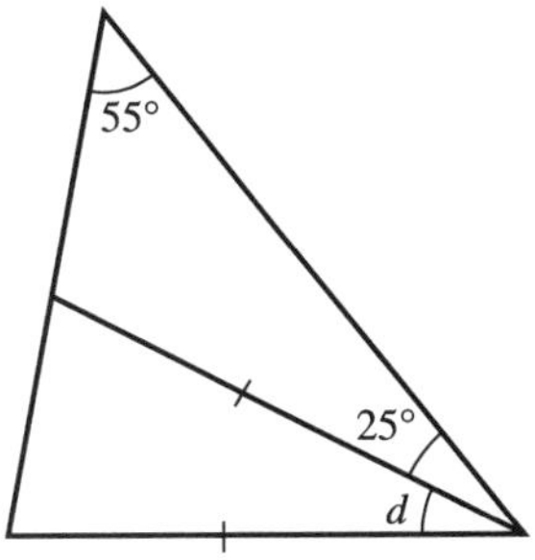

18.

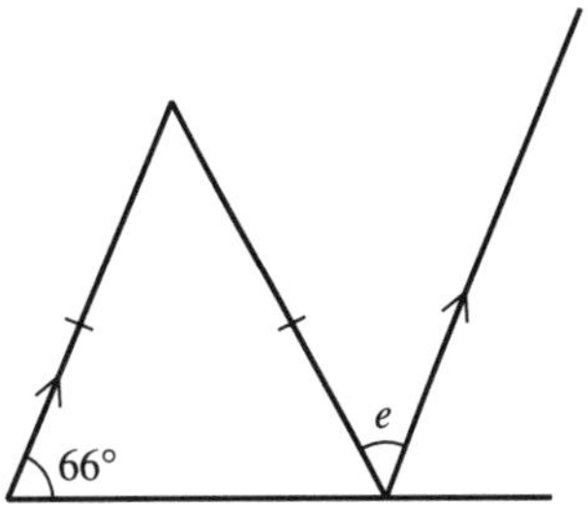

19.

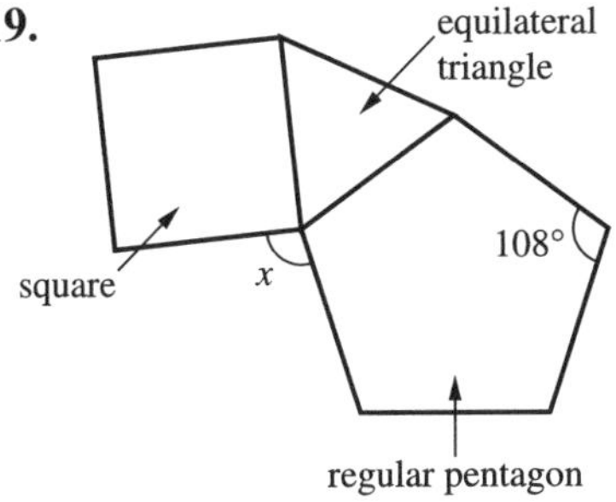

20. The diagram shows two equal squares and a triangle. Find the size of angle x.

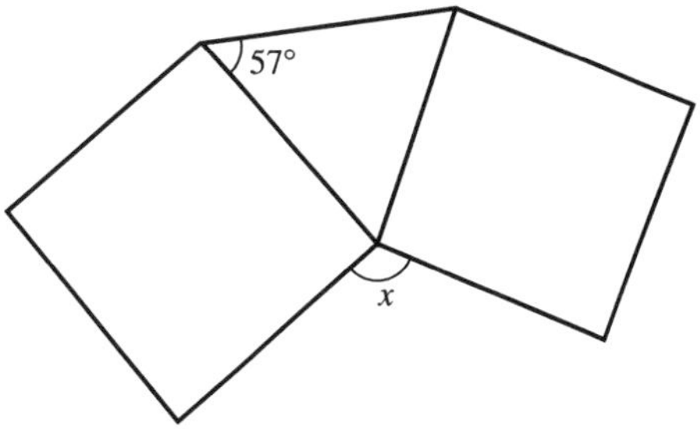

21.

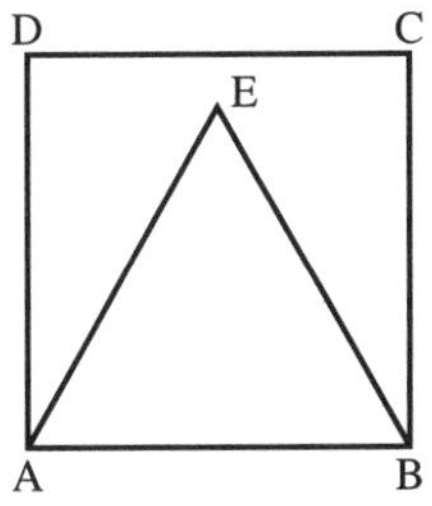

ABE is an equilateral triangle drawn inside square ABCD.
Calculate the size of angle DEC.

Exercise 2

Begin each question by drawing a diagram.

1. Calculate the acute angle between the diagonals of the parallelogram shown.

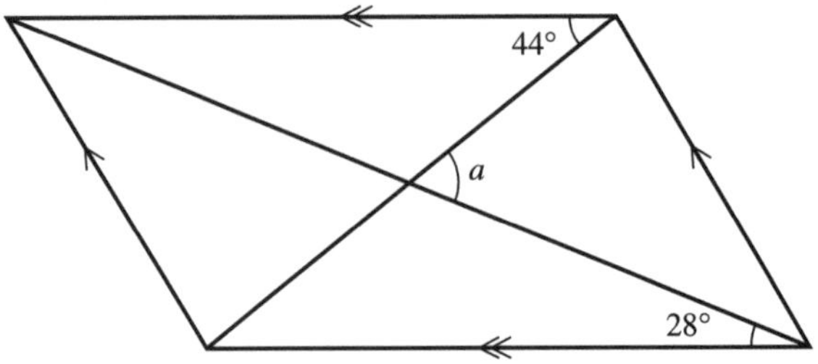

2. In the parallelogram PQRS line QA bisects (cuts in half) angle PQR.
Calculate the size of angle RAQ.

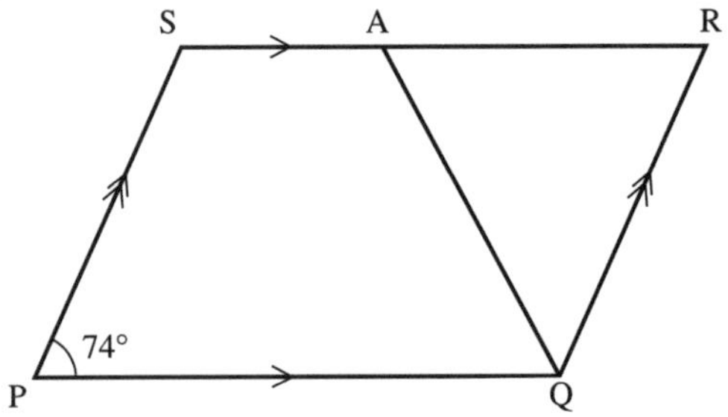

3. 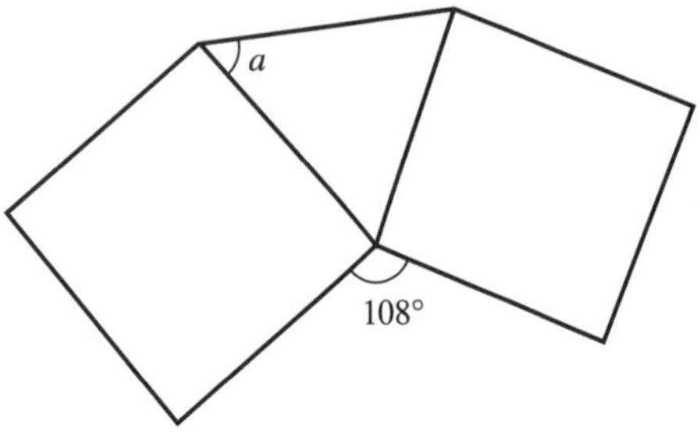

The diagram shows two equal squares and a triangle. Find the size of angle *a*.

4. In the diagram KL is parallel to NM and LJ = LM.
Calculate the size of angle JLM.

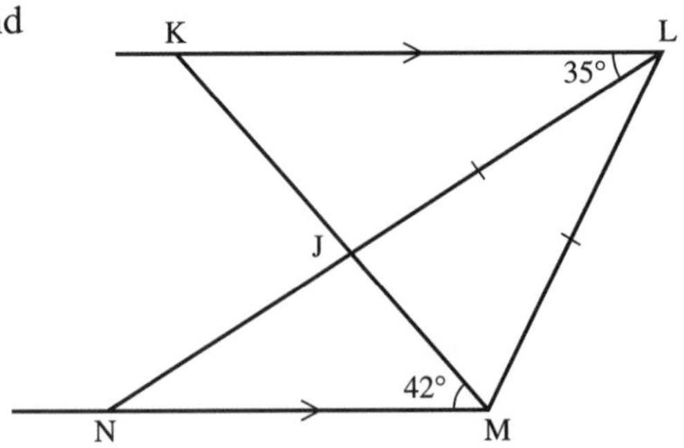

5. The diagram shows a series of isosceles triangles drawn between two lines.
Find the value of *x*.

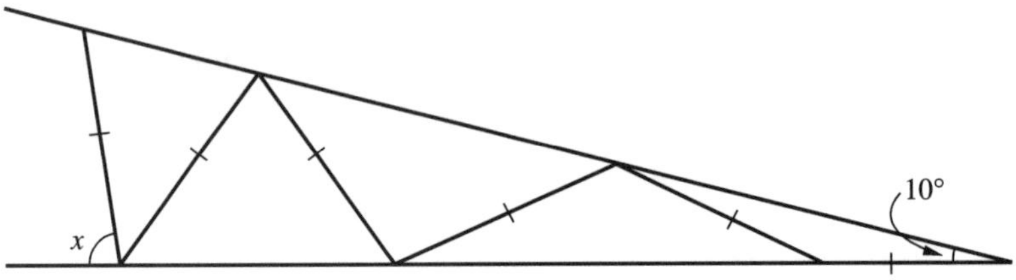

6. Draw a sketch of an isosceles triangle ABC with AB = AC. Point D lies on AC so that $A\hat{D}B = 90°$. If $B\hat{A}C = 40°$ calculate the size of $C\hat{B}D$.

7. 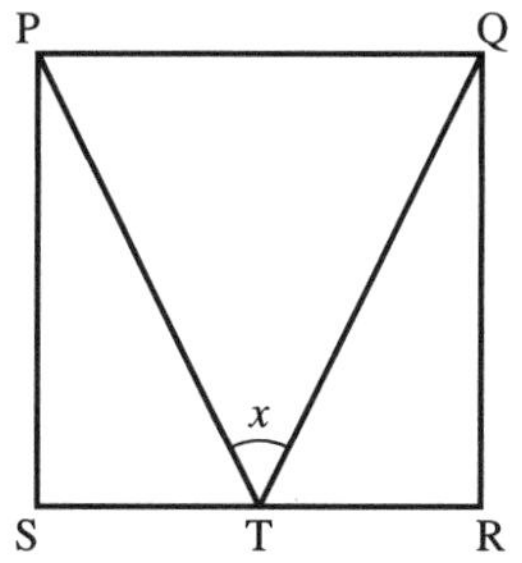

Triangle PQT is drawn inside square PQRS. $P\hat{T}S = 2 \times S\hat{P}T$ and $R\hat{Q}T = 22{\cdot}9°$

Calculate the size of angle x.

8. Draw a sketch of a triangle KLM with KL = KM and $K\hat{M}L = 78°$. Point N lies on KM and line LN bisects $K\hat{L}M$. Calculate the size of angle LNM.

9. In the diagram AC bisects $B\hat{A}D$ and DE = AE. Find the angles a and x.

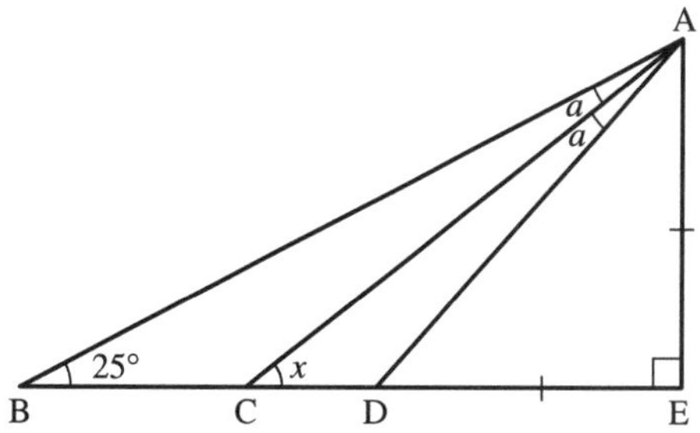

Proving results

- So far we have *demonstrated* that the sum of the angles in a quadrilateral is 360°, by cutting out the angles and rearranging them. A demonstration like this might not work for every conceivable quadrilateral. When we *prove* results it means that the result is true for every possible shape. We often prove one simple result and then use that result to prove further results (and so on).
- Example
  When straight lines intersect, opposite angles are equal.
  By definition, the angle on one whole turn is 360°.
  So $a + b + a + b = 360°$
  $\therefore \quad a + b = 180°$
  This proves that the sum of the angles on a straight line is 180°.

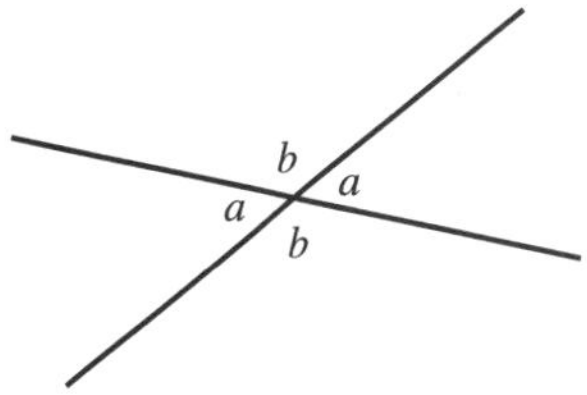

Exercise 3

1. Copy and complete this proof for the sum of the angles in a triangle.

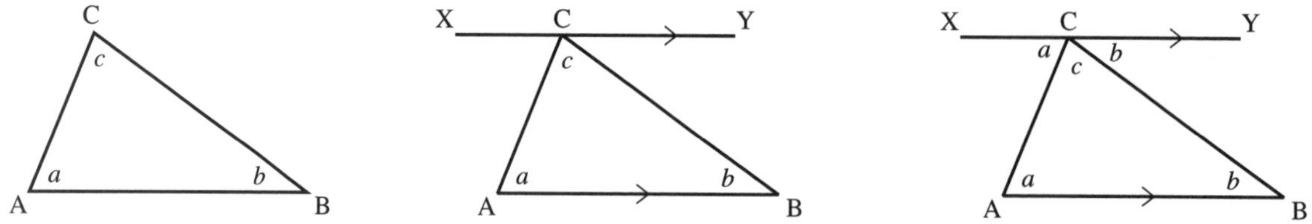

Here is △ABC.

Draw line XCY parallel to AB.

$A\hat{B}C = Y\hat{C}B$ (alternate angles)

$B\hat{A}C = \square$ (alternate angles)

$a + b + c = \square$ (angles on a straight line)

angles in a triangle: $a + b + c = 180°$

2. Copy and complete this proof for the sum of the angles in a quadrilateral.

Draw any quadrilateral ABCD with diagonal BD.

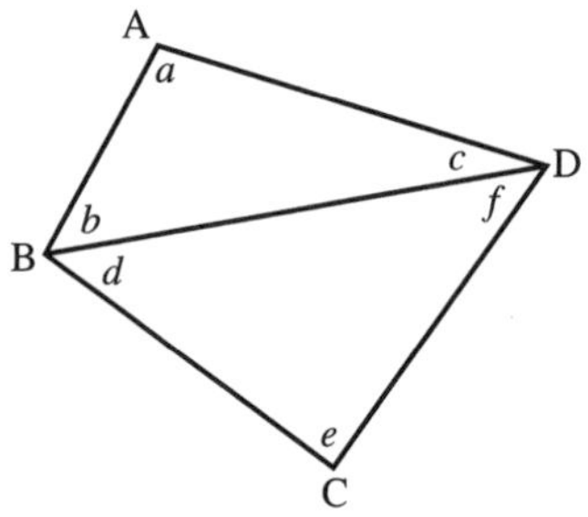

Now $a + b + c = \square$ (angles in a △)

and $d + e + f = \square$ (angles in a △)

$\therefore \quad a + b + c + d + e + f = \square$

This proves the result.

3. To prove that the exterior angle of a triangle is equal to the sum of the two interior opposite angles.

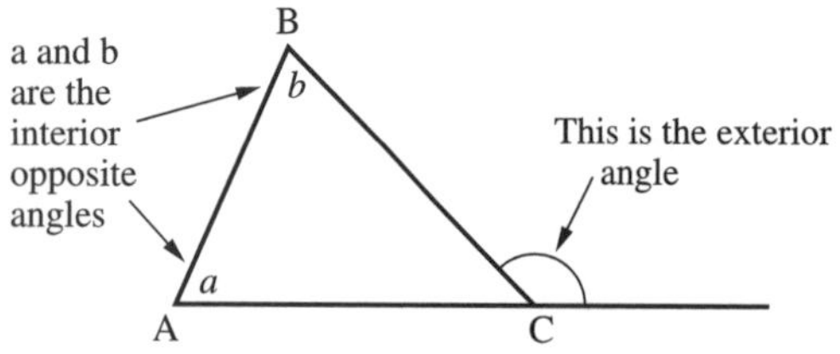

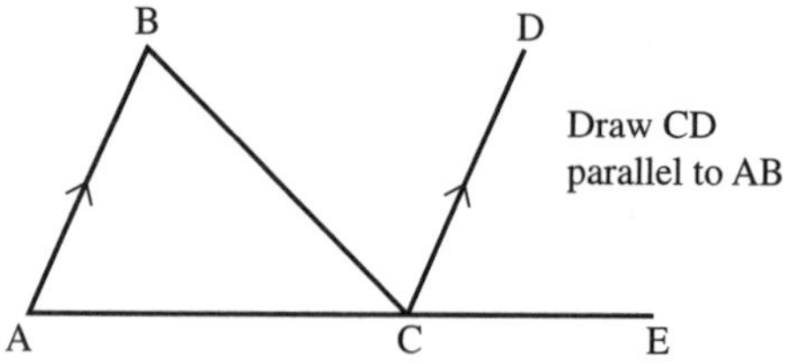

Copy and complete the proof:

$B\hat{A}C = D\hat{C}E$ (corresponding angles) (‘F’ angles)

$A\hat{B}C = \square$ (alternate angles) (‘Z’ angles)

$\therefore \quad \square = \square + \square$

4. Explain why opposite angles of a parallelogram are equal.

[Use alternate and corresponding angles.]

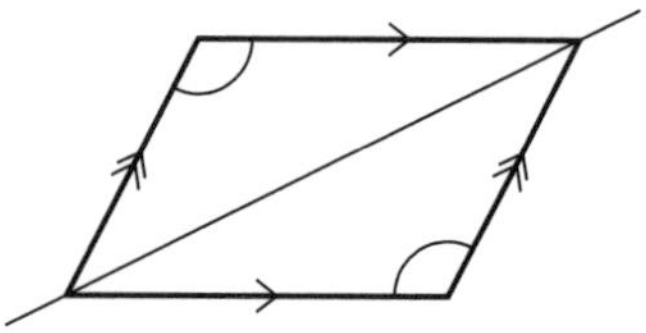

2.4 Construction and locus

Using a ruler, protractor and compasses you can construct the triangles below.

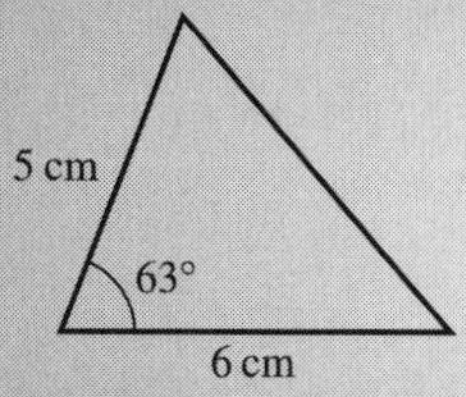

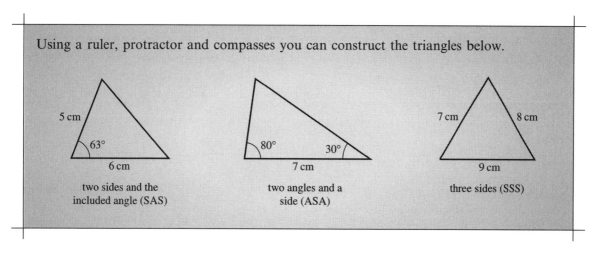

two sides and the included angle (SAS)

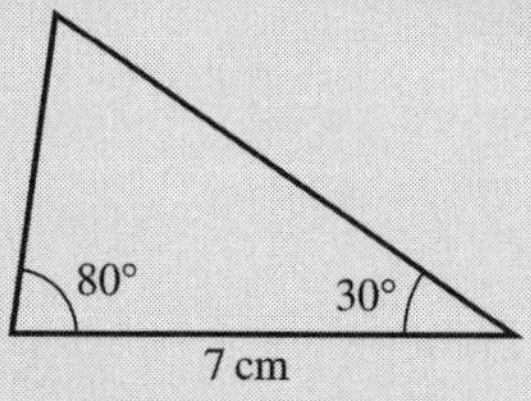

two angles and a side (ASA)

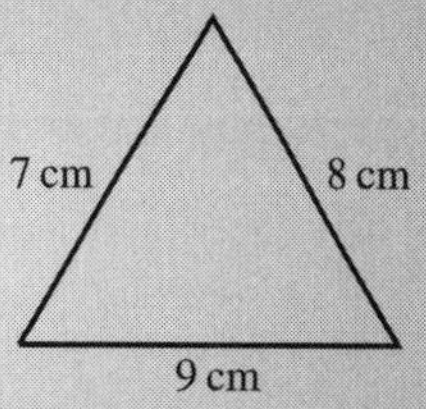

three sides (SSS)

Exercise 1

Construct each shape and measure the side or angle x.

1.

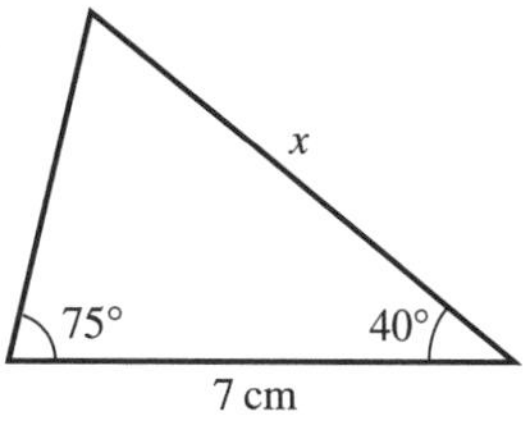

2.

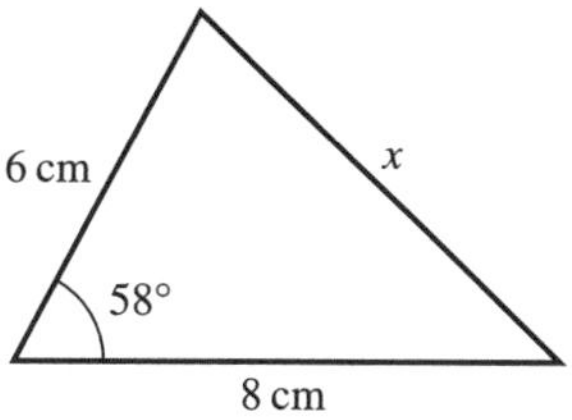

3.

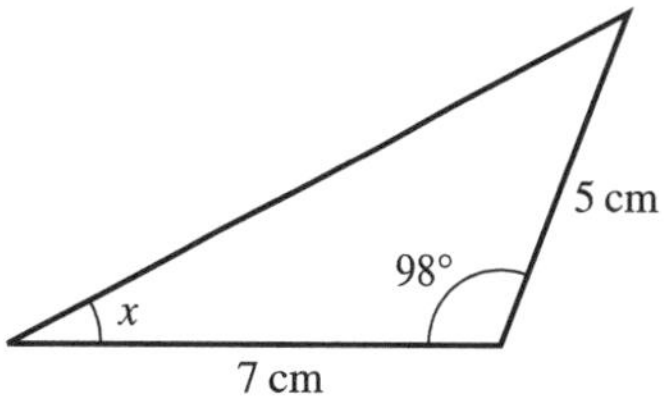

4.

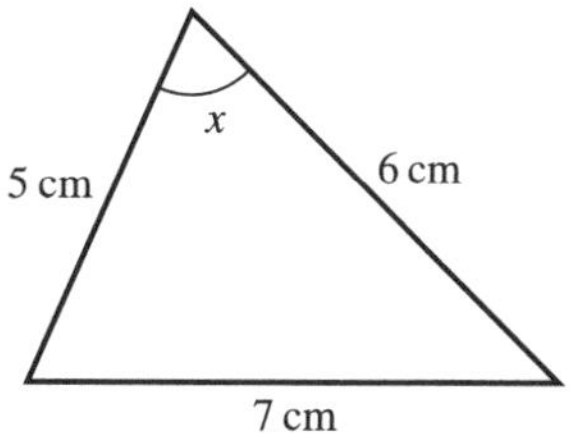

5.

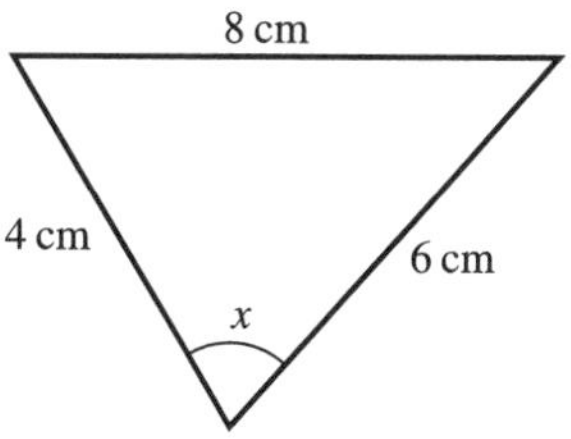

6.

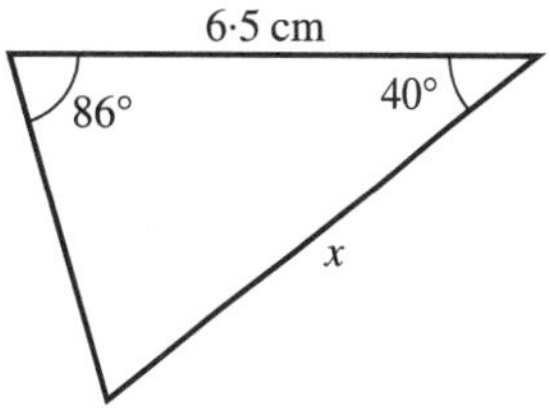

7.

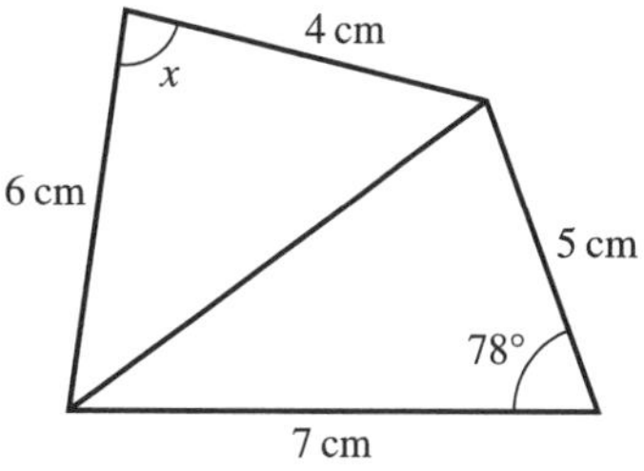

8.

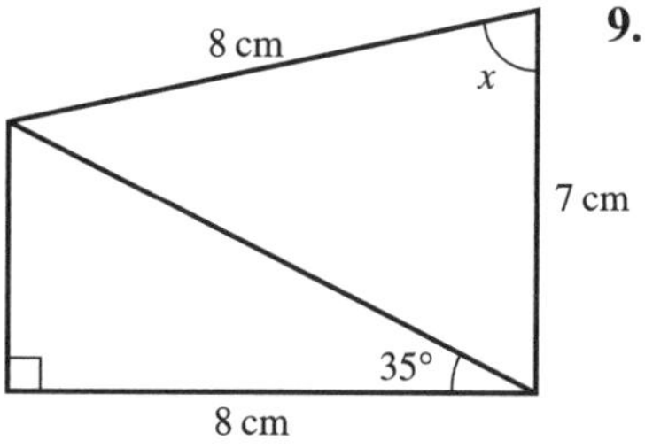

9.

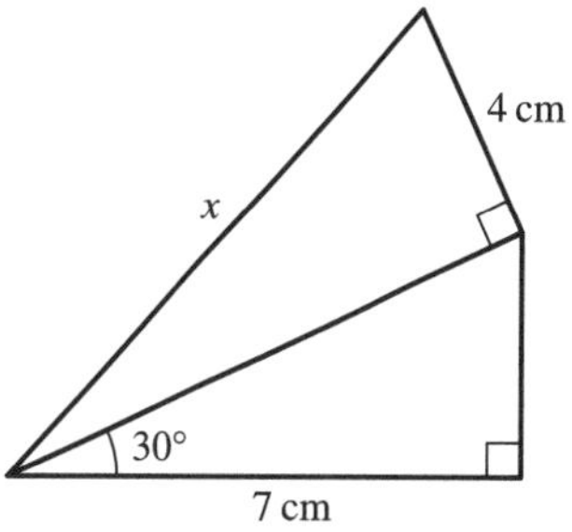

Locus

The *locus* of a point is the path traced out by the point as it moves.

(a) An athlete runs around a track
The locus looks like this

(b) Alan throws a ball to Ben.

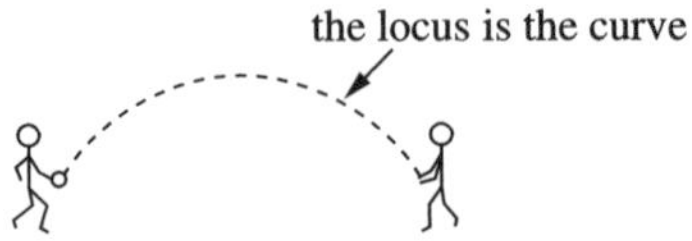

Exercise 2

1. Mark two points A and B, 5 cm apart. Draw crosses at six points which are an equal distance from A and B. The crosses form the locus of points which are an equal distance [equidistant] from A and B.

2. Mark a point C with a dot. Draw crosses at ten points which are all 5 cm from C. The crosses form the locus of points which are 5 cm from C. Describe the locus.

3. With a dot, mark the bottom right corner of the page you are on. Draw crosses at six points which are the same distance from the two edges of the page.
Describe the locus of the crosses you have drawn.

4. Imagine a clock. Describe the locus of the tip of the minute hand as the time goes from 9 o'clock to 10 o'clock.

5. Describe the locus of the tip of the *hour* hand as the time goes from 3 o'clock to 9 o'clock.

6. We trace a locus when we use LOGO. Draw the locus with the following instructions.

   (a) FD 10, RT 90, FD 10, RT 90, FD 10, RT 90, FD 10
   (b) FD 20, RT 120, FD 20, RT 120, FD 20
   (c) REPEAT 6 [FD 10, RT 60]

7. Use LOGO to draw shapes of your own choice. For example: a regular octagon, a rectangle, (more difficult) a spiral

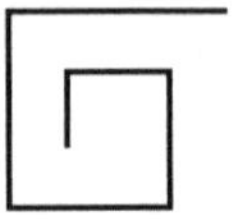

8. 

A car moves forward in a straight line.
Sketch the locus of the valve on one of the wheels

Standard constructions (using compasses)

Exercise 3 [use plain unlined paper]

You are given examples of standard constructions marked A, B, C, D. You are then asked to draw your own constructions using *only* a pencil, a straight edge and a pair of compasses.

A Perpendicular bisector of a line segment AB.

With centres A and B draw two arcs.
The perpendicular bisector is shown as a broken line.

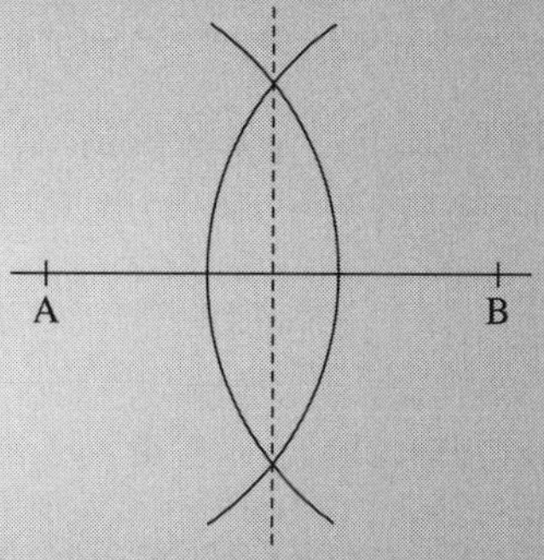

1. Draw a horizontal line AB of the length 6 cm. Construct the perpendicular bisector of AB.

2. Draw a vertical line CD of length 8 cm. Construct the perpendicular bisector of CD.

3. (a) Using a set square,
Draw a right-angled triangle ABC as shown. For greater accuracy draw lines slightly longer than 8 cm and 6 cm and *then* mark the points A, B and C.

(b) *Construct* the perpendicular bisector of AB.

(c) Construct the perpendicular bisector of AC

(d) If done accurately, your two lines from (b) and (c) should cross exactly on the line BC.

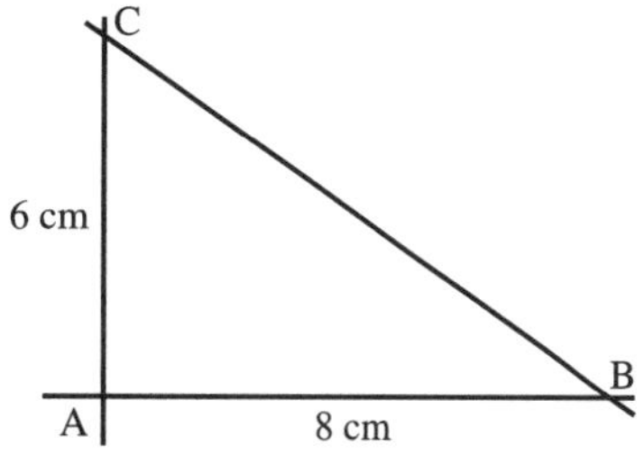

B Perpendicular from point P to a line

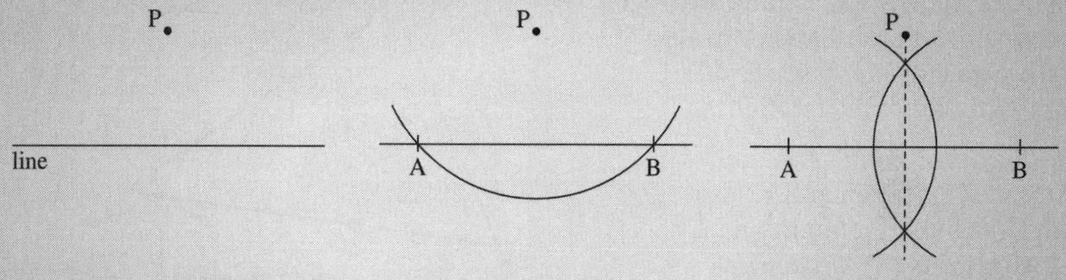

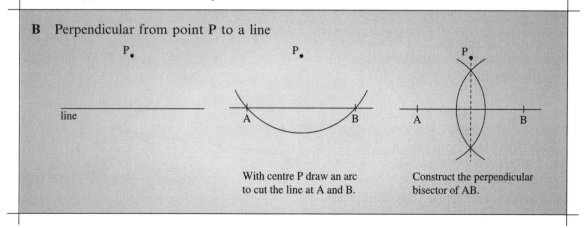

With centre P draw an arc to cut the line at A and B.

Construct the perpendicular bisector of AB.

4. Draw a line and a point P about 4 cm from the line. Construct the line which passes through P which is perpendicular to the line.

C Perpendicular from a point P on a line.

With centre P draw arcs to cut the line at A and B. Now bisect AB as above in (**A**).

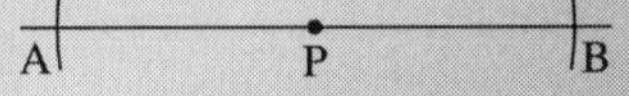

5. Draw a line and a point Q on the line. Construct the perpendicular from the point Q.

D Bisector of an angle

With centre A draw arc PQ.
With centres at P and Q draw two more arcs.
The angle bisector is then drawn.

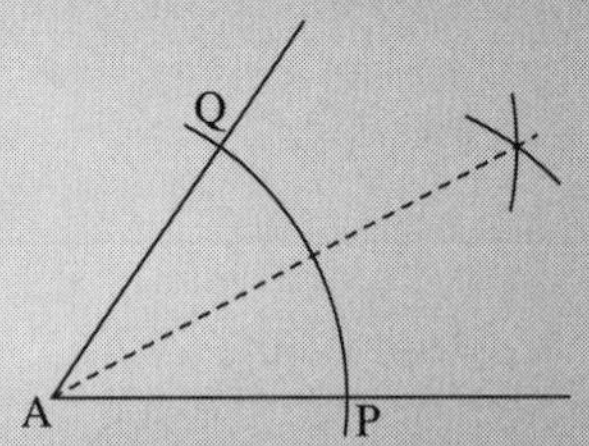

6. Draw an angle of about 70°. Construct the bisector of the angle.

7. Draw an angle of about 120°. Construct the bisector of the angle.

8. Draw any triangle ABC and construct the bisectors of angles B and C to meet at point Y.

With centre at Y draw a circle which just touches the sides of the triangle.
This is the *inscribed* circle of the triangle.

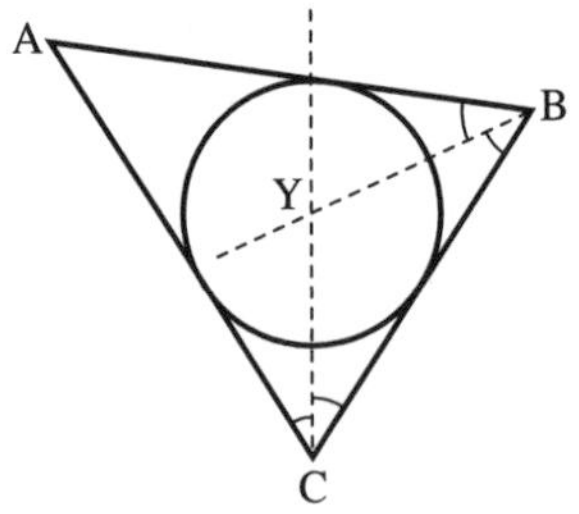

9. Draw *any* triangle KLM and construct
(a) the perpendicular bisector of KM
(b) the perpendicular bisector of KL.
Mark the point of intersection X.

Take a pair of compasses and, with centre at X and radius KX, draw a circle through the points K, L and M. This is the *circumcircle* of triangle KLM.

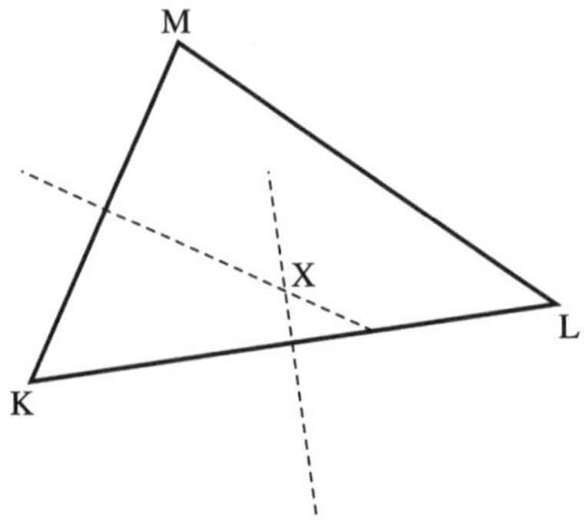

Repeat the construction for another triangle of different shape.

2.5 Circles

Circumference

- The perimeter of a circle is called *circumference*

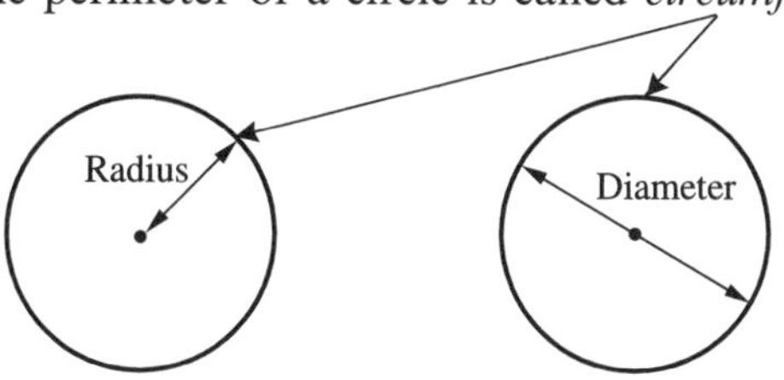

- Find 8 circular objects (tins, plates, buckets, wheels etc.) for each object, measure the diameter and the circumference and write the results in a table. Use a flexible tape measure for the circumference or wrap a piece of string around the object and then measure the string with a ruler. For each pair of readings, work out the ratio (circumference ÷ diameter).

You should find that the number in the $\frac{c}{d}$ column is about the same each time. Work out the mean value of the 8 numbers in the $\frac{c}{d}$ column.

Object	Circumference c	diameter d	$\frac{c}{d}$
Tin of tuna	28·6 cm	8·8 cm	3·25
...			
...			

- 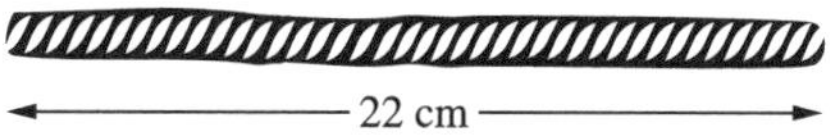

A piece of string 22 cm long will make:

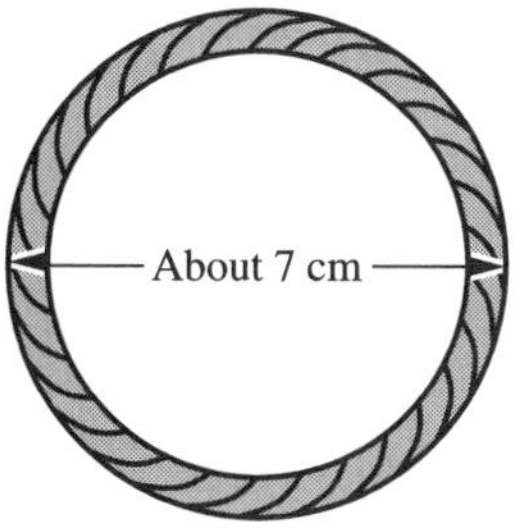

A circle whose diameter is just over 7 cm.

If you divide the circumference of a circle by its diameter the number you obtain is always just over three.

$$\frac{\text{circumference}}{\text{diameter}} \approx 3$$

which means

Circumference ≈ 3 × diameter

This provides a fairly good *estimate* for the circumference of any circle.

Pi

- For any circle, the exact value of the ratio $\left(\frac{\text{circumference}}{\text{diameter}}\right)$ is a number denoted by the Greek letter π.

  Since $\frac{c}{d} = \pi$, we can write $c = \pi \times d$. Learn this formula.

  Most calculators have a $\boxed{\pi}$ button, which will give the value of π correct to at least 7 significant figures: 3·141593.

- The number π has fascinated mathematicians for thousands of years. The Egyptians had a value of 316 in 1500 BC. In about 250 B.C. the Greek mathematician Archimedes showed that π was between $3\frac{10}{71}$ and $3\frac{10}{70}$. He considered regular polygons with many sides. As the number of sides in the polygon increased, so the polygon became nearer and nearer to a circle.

  Ludolph Van Ceulen (1540–1610) obtained a value of π correct to 35 significant figures. He was so proud of his work that he had the number engraved on his tombstone.

Exercise 1

Make a table and complete it for Questions **1** to **12**. Make sure you write the correct units. Give answers correct to one decimal place.

Number	Radius r	Diameter d	Estimated circumference	Calculated circumference
1	2 cm			
2				

1.

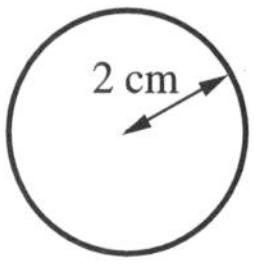

2.

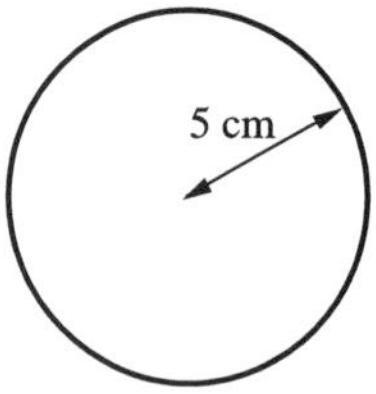

3.

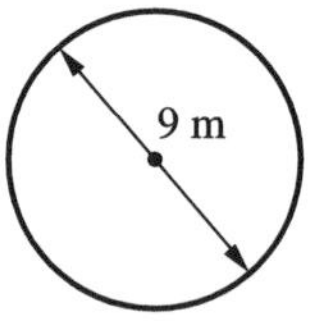

4.

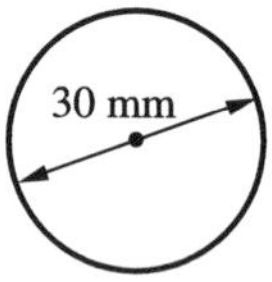

5.

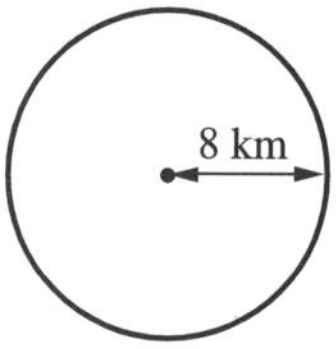

6.

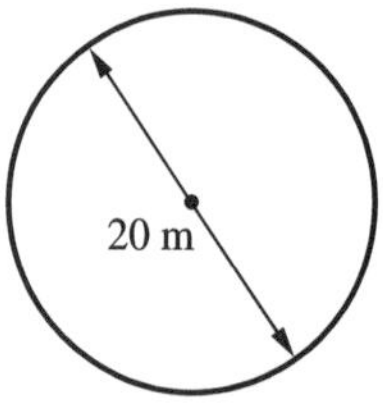

7.

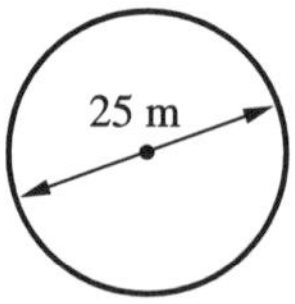

8.

9.

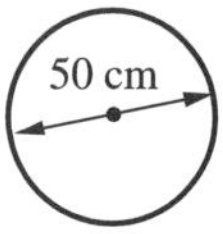

10.

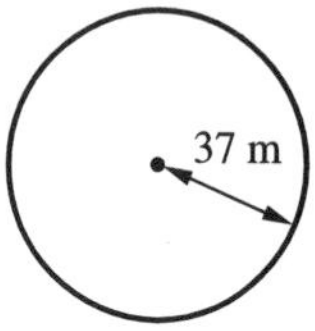

11.

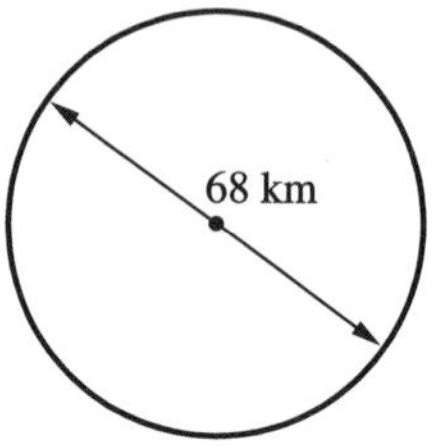

12.

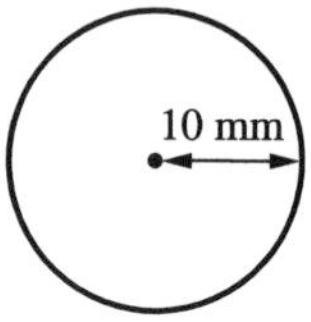

A circular tin of diameter 9 cm rolls along the floor for a distance of 3 m. How many times does it rotate completely?

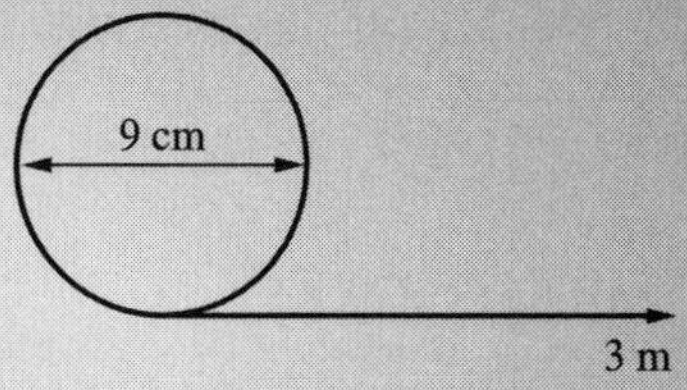

circumference $= \pi \times 9$

$= 28{\cdot}274334$ cm

$3\text{ m} = 300$ cm

$$\text{Number of rotations} = \frac{300}{28{\cdot}274334} = 10{\cdot}61$$

The tin makes 10 *complete* rotations.

Exercise 2

Give your answers correct to 1 decimal place unless told otherwise.

1. The tip of the minute hand of a clock is 8 cm from the centre of the clock face. Calculate the distance moved by the tip of the minute hand in one hour.

2. A bicycle wheel of diameter 80 cm makes 20 complete rotations as the bicycle moves forward in a straight line. Find the circumference of the wheel and work out how far the bicycle moves forward. Give your answers in metres.
3. A tennis ball of diameter 7 cm and a golf ball of diameter 4·25 cm roll in a straight line so that each ball makes 10 complete revolutions. Which ball will go further and by how much? Give your answer to the nearest cm.
4. Which has the longer perimeter and by how much: an equilateral triangle of side 10 cm or a circle of diameter 10 cm?
5. A tin of tomatoes has diameter 7·5 cm. The tin is wrapped in a paper cover which is long enough to allow 1 cm overlap for fixing. How long is the cover?

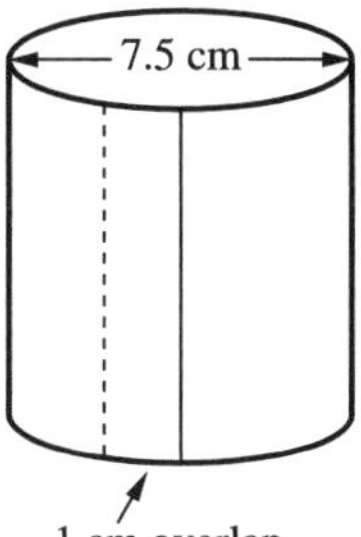

6. The wheels on Gill's bike have a diameter of 62 cm. Gill rolls forward a distance of 1200 cm. Calculate how many times the wheels go round *completely*.
7. In a coin rolling competition Gemma rolls a one pound coin on its edge a distance of 4·2 m. A one pound coin has diameter 2·2 cm. How many times did the coin rotate completely?

8. A car tyre has a radius of 37 cm.
(a) How long is its circumference in cm?
(b) How many complete rotations will the tyre make if the car travels 2 km?

9. A push chair has wheels of diameter 66 cm at the back and wheels of diameter 18 cm at the front. The pushchair travels in a straight line and the rear wheels rotate completely 84 times.

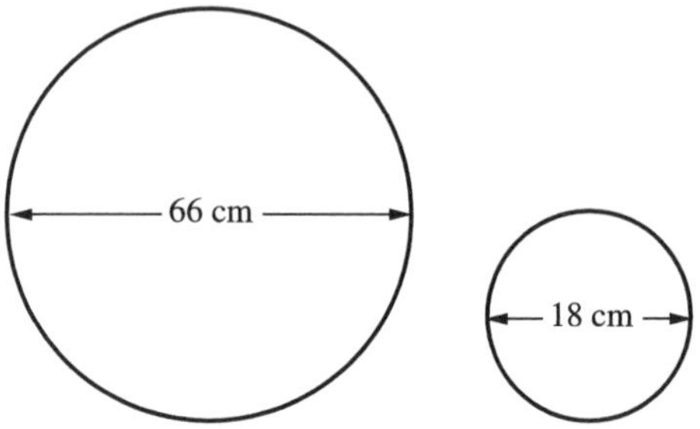

(a) How far in metres does the chair travel?
(b) How many complete rotations do the front wheels make?

10. A newt walks around the edge of a circular pond at a speed of 2 cm/s. How long will it take to walk all the way round if the radius of the pond is 1·3 m?

11. A trundle wheel can be used for measuring distances along roads or pavements. A wheel of circumference one metre is pushed along and distance is measured by counting the number of rotations of the wheel.
Calculate the diameter of the wheel to the nearest mm.

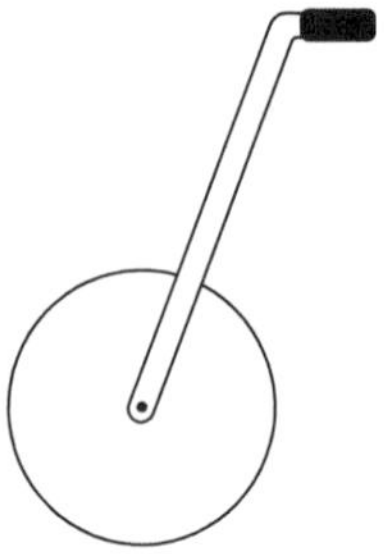

12. The perimeter of a circular pond is 11·7 m. Calculate the diameter of the pond to the nearest cm.

13. The tip of the minute hand of Big Ben is 4·6 m from the centre of the clock face. Calculate the distance, in km, moved by the end of the minute hand in one year (365 days).

Perimeters

Calculate the perimeter of the shape.

The perimeter consists of a semi-circle and 3 straight lines.

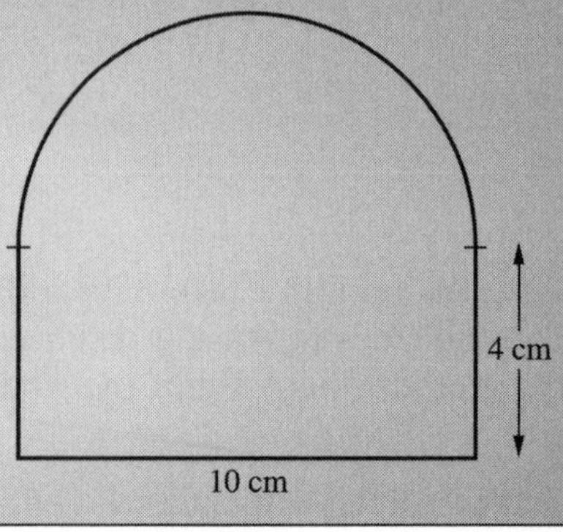

$$\text{Length of semi-circle} = \frac{\pi \times 10}{2}$$
$$= \pi \times 5\,\text{cm}$$

$$\therefore \text{ Perimeter of shape} = (\pi \times 5) + 4 + 10 + 4$$
$$= 33{\cdot}7\,\text{cm (to 1 d.p.)}$$

Exercise 3

Calculate the perimeter of each shape. All arcs are either semi-circles or quarter circles. Give answers correct to 1 d.p.

1.

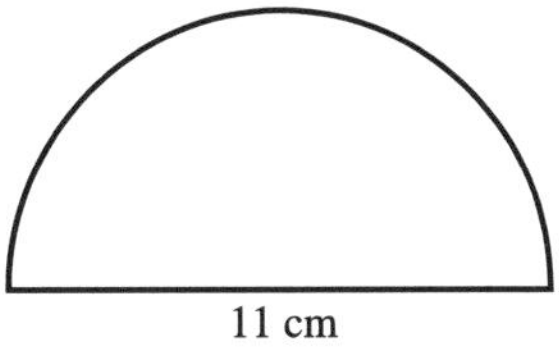

2.

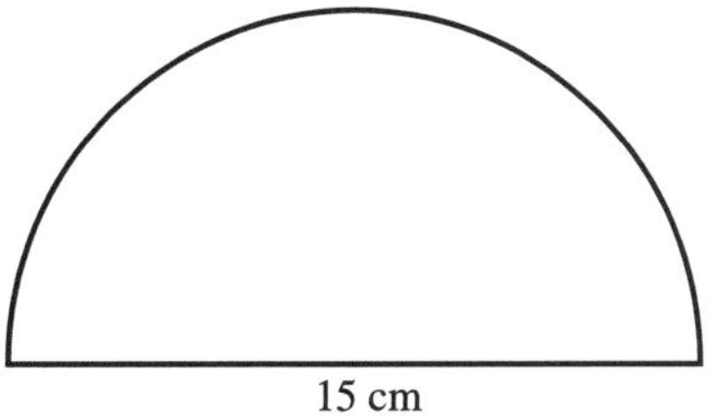

3.

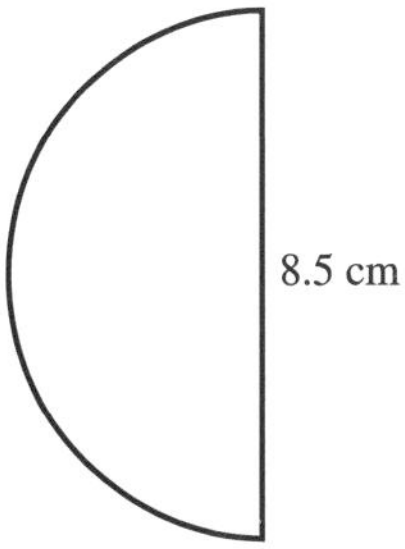

4.

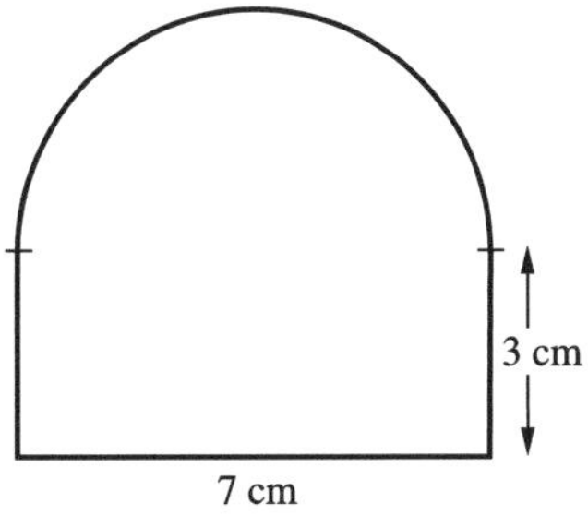

5.

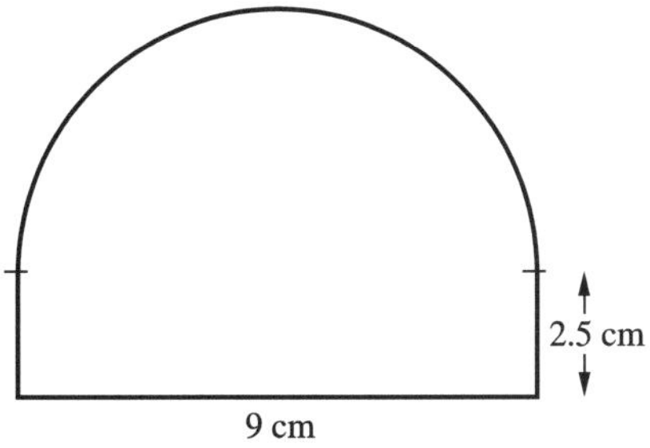

6.

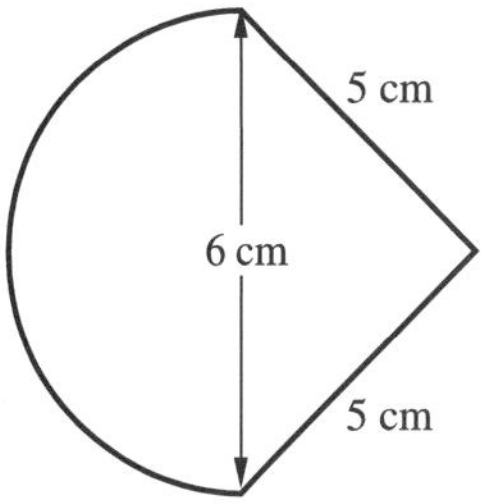

7.

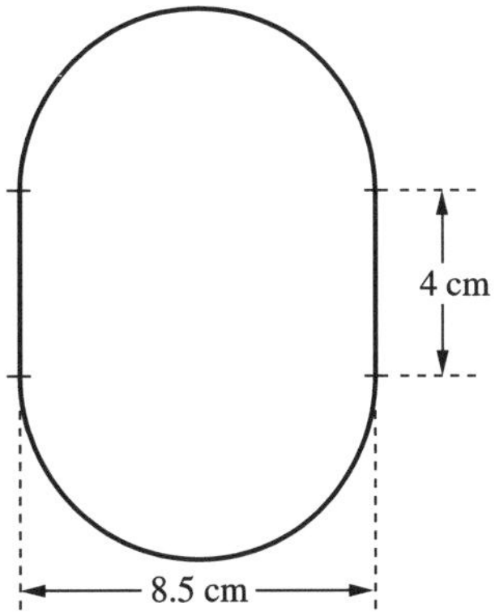

8.

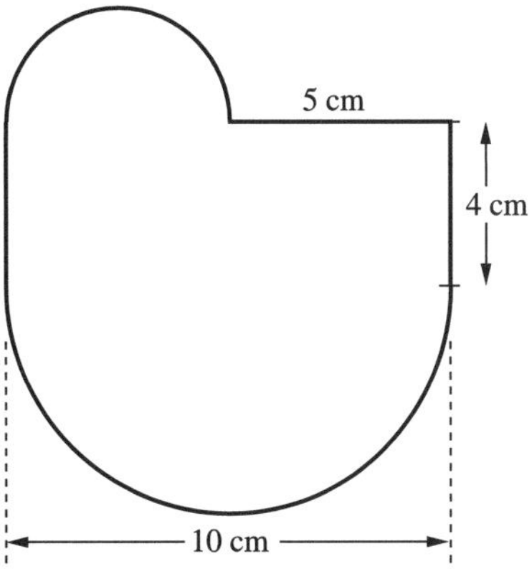

9.

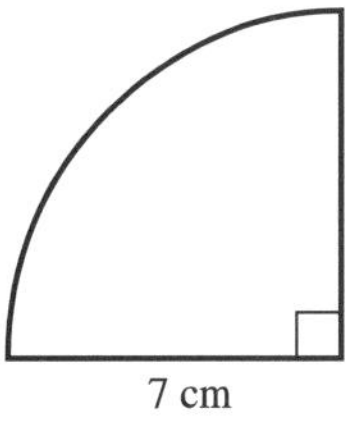

10.

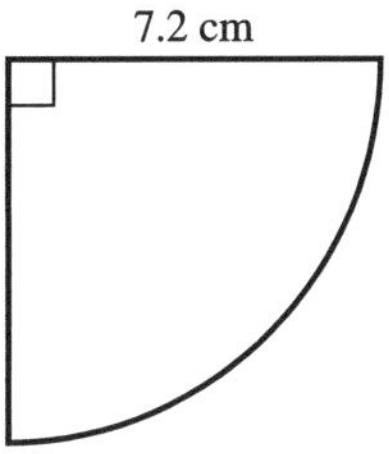

11.

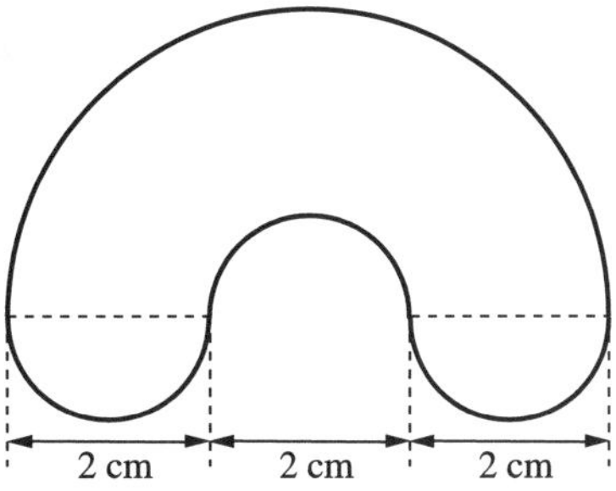

12.

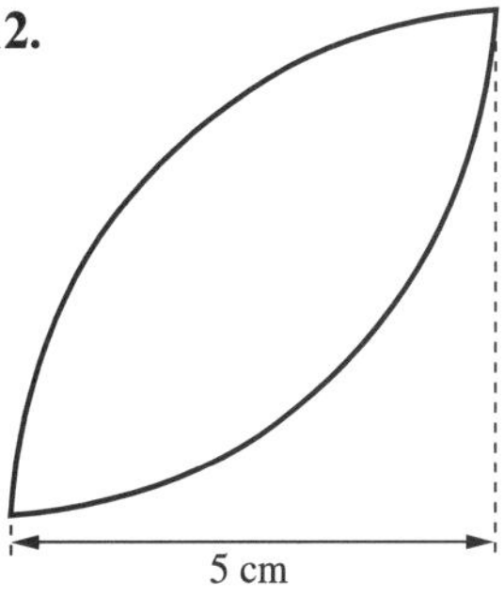

Area of a circle

(a) The circle below is divided into 12 equal sectors

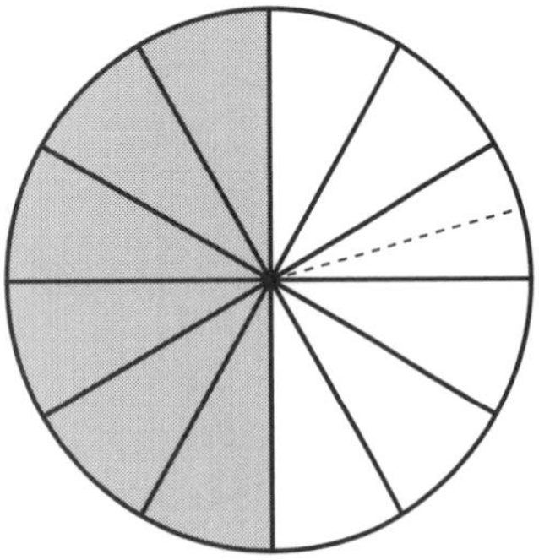

(b) The sectors are cut and arranged to make a shape which is nearly a rectangle. (one sector is cut in half).

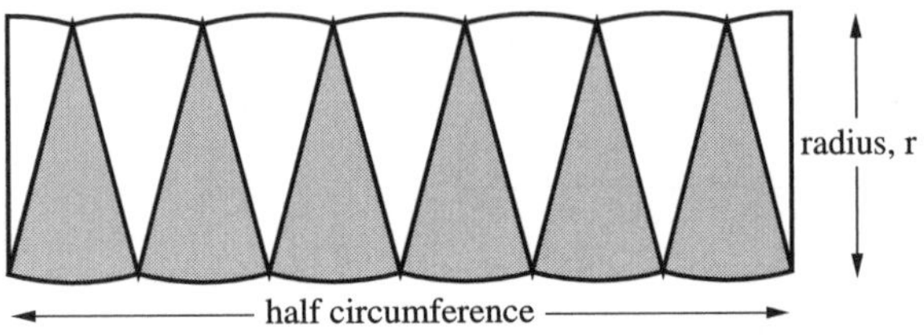

(c) The approximate area can be found as follows:

length of rectangle $\approx$ half circumference of circle

$$\approx \frac{\pi \times 2r}{2}$$

$$\approx \pi r$$

width of rectangle $\approx r$

$\therefore$ area of rectangle $\approx \pi r \times r$

$$\approx \pi r^2$$

If larger and larger numbers of sectors were used, this approximation would become more and more accurate.

This is a demonstration of an important result.

Area of a circle = πr^2 *Learn* this formula.

Note: πr^2 means $\pi(r^2)$.

Find the area of each shape.

(a)

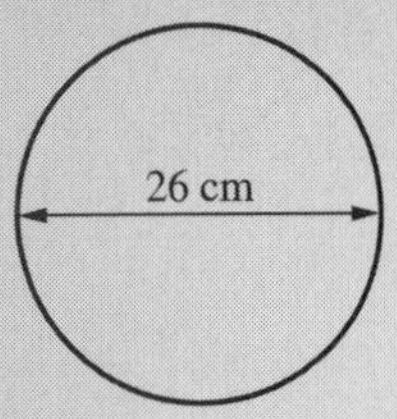

radius = 13 cm

area $= \pi r^2$

$= 530{\cdot}9\,\text{cm}^2$ (1 d.p.)

On a calculator, press:

| 13 | × | 13 | × | π | = |

(b)

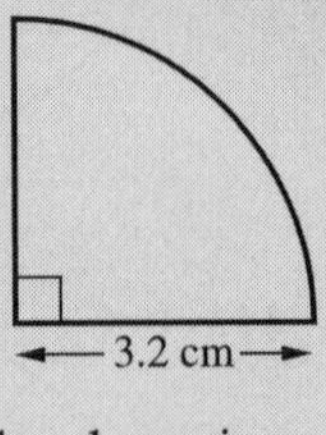

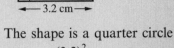

The shape is a quarter circle

area $= \dfrac{\pi(3{\cdot}2)^2}{4}$

$= 8{\cdot}0\,\text{cm}^2$ (1 d.p.)

On a calculator, press:

| 3·2 | × | 3·2 | × | π | ÷ | 4 | = |

Exercise 4

In Questions **1** to **8** calculate the area of each circle correct to 1 d.p.

1.
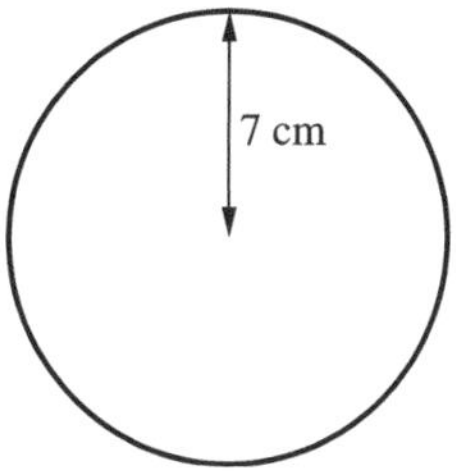

2.
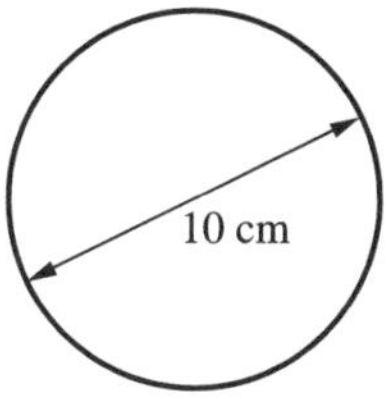

3.
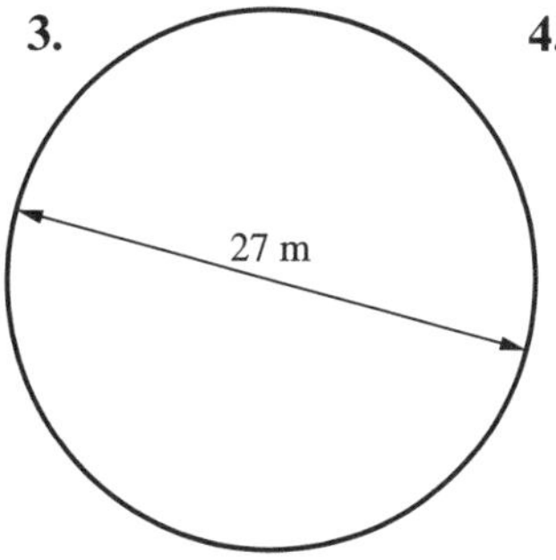

4.
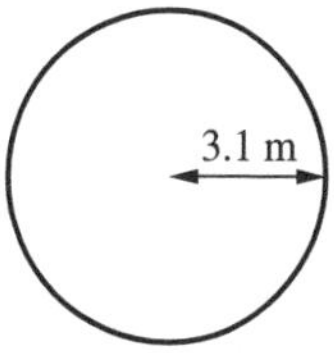

5.
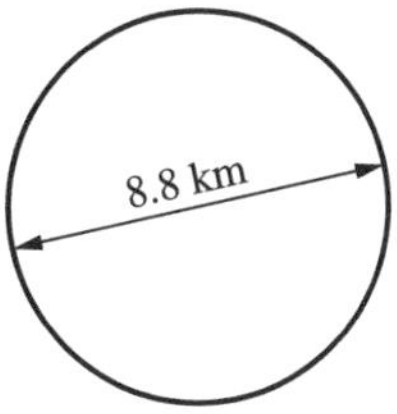

6.
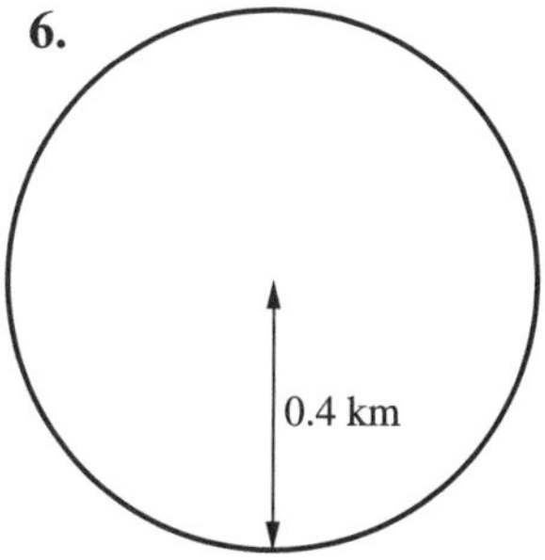

7.
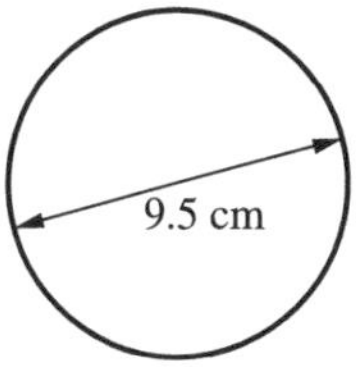

8.
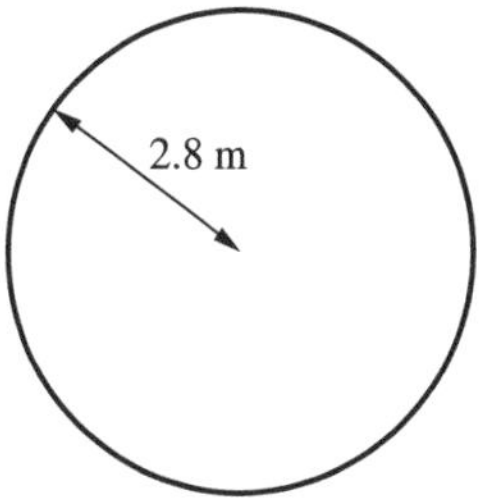

In Questions **9** to **22** give your answers correct to 1 d.p., where necessary.

9. When hunting for food, an eagle flies over a circular region of radius 3·5 km. What is the area of this region in km^2?

10. A carton of 'Verdone' weedkiller contains enough weedkiller to treat an area of $100\,m^2$. A circular lawn at Hampton Court has a radius of 16·5 m. How many cartons of weedkiller are needed to treat this lawn?

In Questions **11** to **14** find the area of each shape. All arcs are either semi-circles or quarter circles and the units are cm.

11.
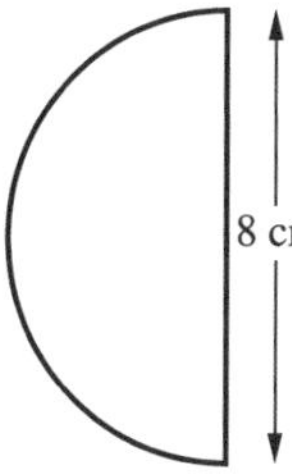

12.
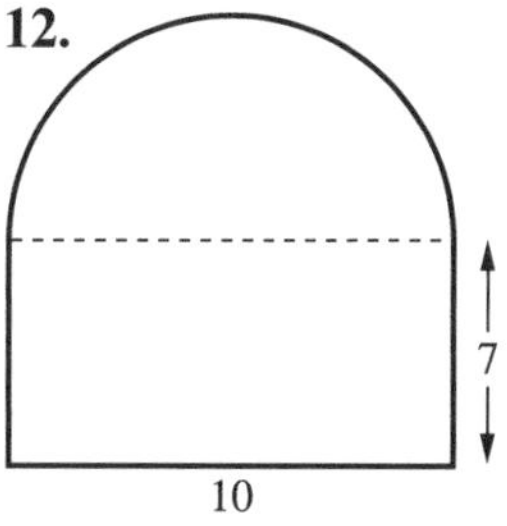

13.
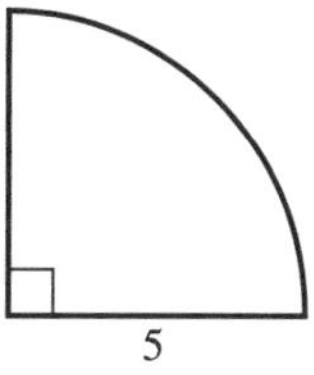

14.
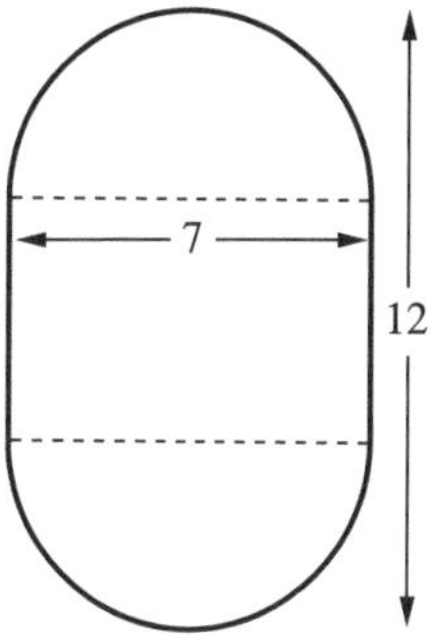

In Questions **15** to **20** find the shaded area. Lengths are in cm.

15.

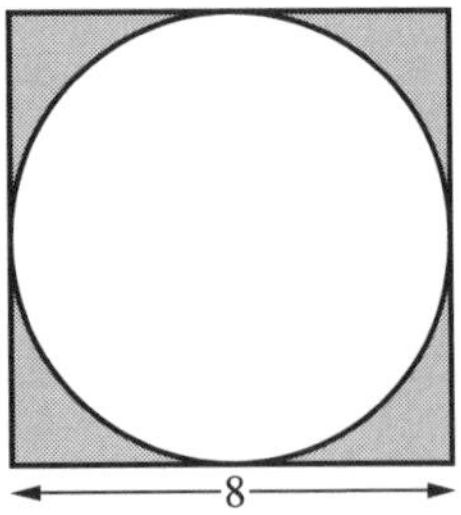

16.

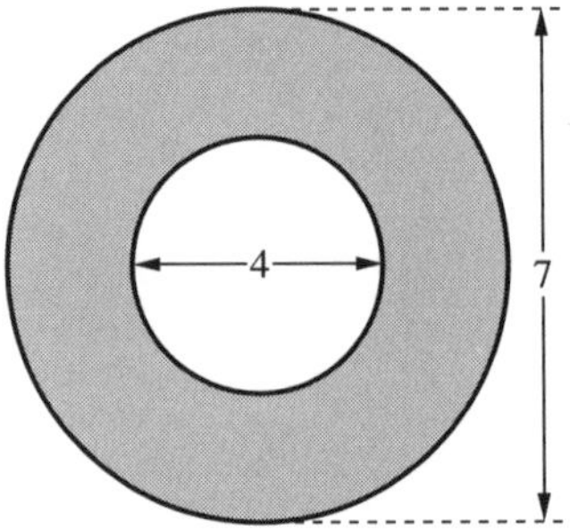

17.

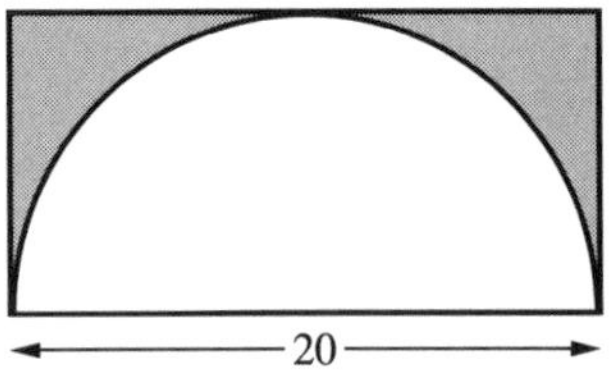

18.

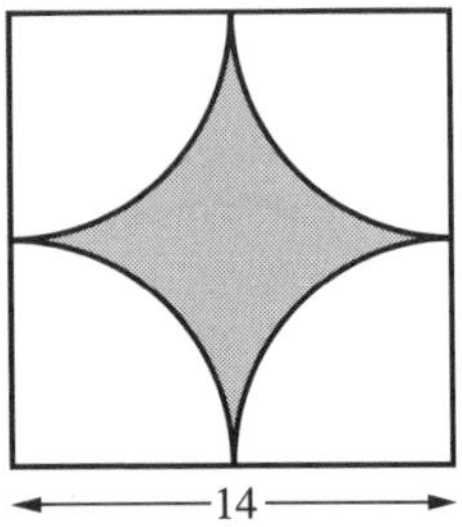

19.

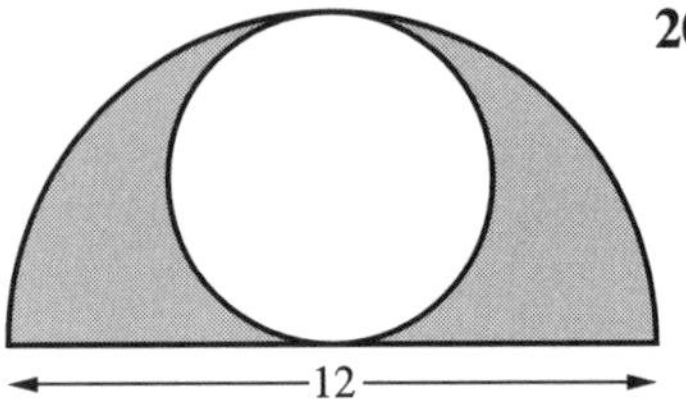

20.

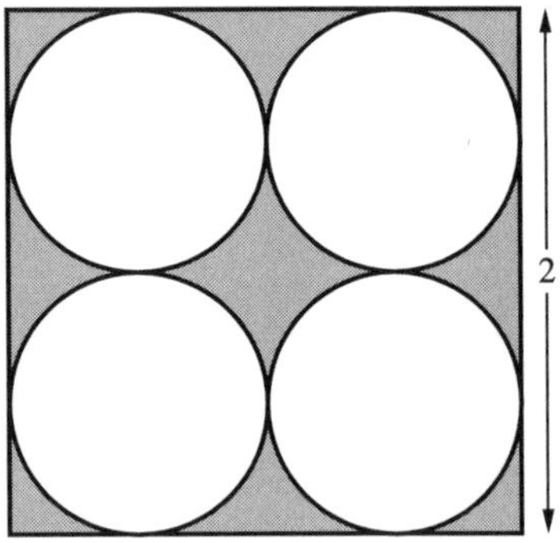

21. An old fashioned telephone dial has the dimensions shown. The diameter of each finger hole is 1 cm.
Calculate the shaded area.

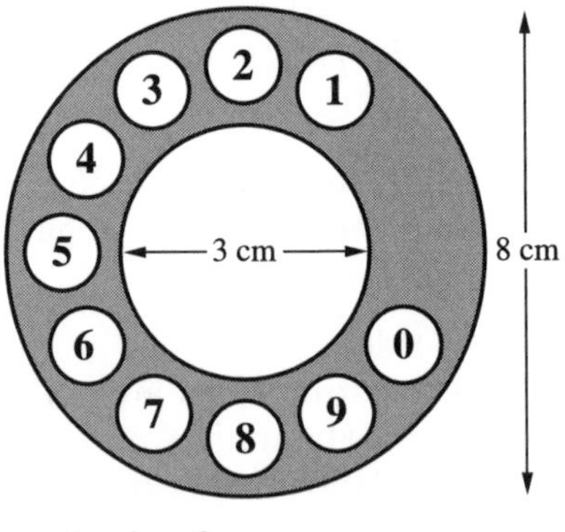

22. A circular pond of radius 3·6 m is surrounded by a concrete path 70 cm wide. Calculate the area of the surface of the path.

23. A cycling track is a circle of diameter 150 m. The wheels of a bicycle have a diameter 82 cm. How many times will the wheels of the bicycle rotate completely when the bicyle travels ten times around the track?

24. The tip of the second hand of an electric clock moves at a speed of 1 cm/s. Calculate the distance x, from the tip of the second hand to the centre of the clock.

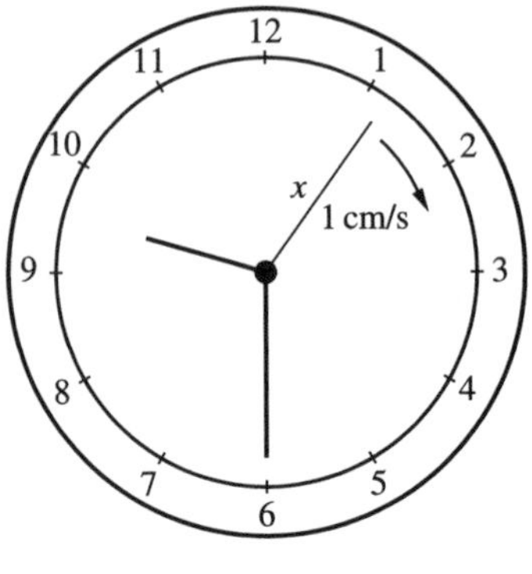

2.6 Mixed problems

Exercise 1

1. Here are some numbers

12	18	30	35	51	70	80

(a) Which numbers divide exactly by 7?
(b) Which numbers divide exactly by both 5 and 2?
(c) Which numbers are multiples of 3?

2. Work out

(a) $-17+4$ (b) $-7-5$ (c) $-3\times(-2)$
(d) $8-(-3)$ (e) $-12\div(3)$ (f) $-8+(-4)$

3. (a) How long does it take the minute hand of a clock to move 180°?
(b) How long does it take the hour hand to move 30°?

4. Write one number at the box in each equation to make it correct.

(a) $55+55=40+\square$ (b) $60\times 100=30\times\square$
(c) $59+58=20+\square$ (d) $110-75=28+\square$
(e) $2000\div 20=200\div\square$ (f) $0{\cdot}3\times 100=90\div\square$
(g) $240-90=15\,000\div\square$ (h) $30^2=20^2+\square$

5. Look at these number cards

[−3] [0] [+2] [−5] [+4] [−6] [+3]

(a) Choose a card to give the answer 2.

[+4] + [−5] + [ ] = 2

(b) Choose a card to give the *lowest* possible answer.

[−3] + [ ] = [ ]

(c) Choose a card to give the *highest* possible answer.

[−5] − [ ] = [ ]

6. The square ACDE is cut into seven pieces. Find the area, in square units, of
(a) triangle EDI
(b) square BJIG
(c) parallelogram FGHE.

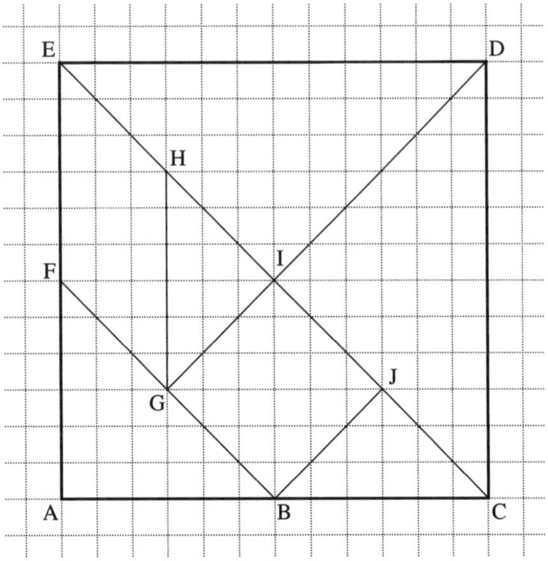

7. The pattern 13579 13579 13579 ...... is continued to form a number with one hundred digits, what is the sum of all one hundred digits?

8. Write each sentence with the number you think is most likely.

(a) The door to the classroom is ☐ high. [80 cm, 2 m, 3 feet]

(b) A large bottle of coke contains ☐ of drink. [20 mℓ, 2 litres, 5 gallons]

(c) This book weighs about ☐. [500 g. 50 g, 5 kg]

9. Work out: (a) A quarter of 30 000
(b) A quarter of 38
(c) A half of 999

10.

> **How odd**
> Next Wednesday will be the first time for 1,112 years that date will be made up entirely of even numbers. 2/2/2000 is the first all-even date since 28/8/888.

This article was in a newspaper in January 2000.
What will be the first date from now made up entirely of *odd* numbers?

Exercise 2

1. Here are four number cards [1] [9] [3] [6]

(i) Use some of the cards to make numbers that are as *close as possible* to the numbers below You must *not* use the same card more than once in each number.
[e.g. 90 ⟶ [9][1]]

(a) 40 (b) 70 (c) 400 (d) 100 (e) 7000

(ii) Use the cards to make the largest possible *even* number.

2. Work mentally to find the missing numbers

(a) $8 \times 7 = \square$ (b) $9 \times \square = 81$ (c) $16 \times \square = 64$

(d) $4 \times 0{\cdot}6 = \square$ (e) $4 \times \square = 168$ (f) $\square \times 9 = 2{\cdot}7$

3. 'Ants can move objects 50 times their own weight.'

(a) If one ant weighs 0·016 grams, find the largest mass it can move.
(b) If ants work together efficiently, how many ants would be needed to move a bag of crisps weighing 32 g?

4. You are given that $3{\cdot}2 \times 25 = 80$
Copy and complete:

(a) $0{\cdot}32 \times \square = 80$ (b) $\square \times 0{\cdot}25 = 800$

5. Fill in the operations to make the answer correct.
You may use any of these signs: $+ \quad - \quad \times \quad \div$

$16 \square 3 \square 25 = 23$

6. Put the correct sign, $<$ or $=$ or $>$, into each number sentence.

(a) $10 \times 0{\cdot}1 \square \frac{1}{2}$ (b) $20 - 4 \square 20 - 5$

(c) $8 - 11 \square -2$ (d) $\frac{1}{2} + \frac{1}{3} \square \frac{2}{5}$

(e) $\frac{3}{4} \times \frac{2}{5} \square 0{\cdot}3$ (f) $\frac{2}{3} \div \frac{1}{3} \square \frac{2}{9}$

7. Jake is working out the height of a lighthouse. He walks up 310 steps from the base to the top of the tower. Each step is 24 cm.

(a) Work out the height of the lighthouse in cm.
(b) Change the height into metres.

8. (a) Work out 15% of £800.
(b) Increase £700 by 7%.
(c) Change $\frac{5}{8}$ to a percentage.

9. A car begins a journey at 11.35 and ends it at 13.05.
(a) How long, in hours, did the journey take?
(b) The car travelled at an average speed of 100 km/h. How far did the car travel?

10. In a magic square each row, column and both main diagonals have the same total. Which of the following numbers should replace n in this magic square [2, 4, 6]?

		7
4		14
		n

Exercise 3

1. Write down the most appropriate *metric* unit for measuring:
(a) the capacity of a car's fuel tank,
(b) the height of the Eiffel Tower,
(c) the mass of a Jumbo Jet,
(d) the area of a small farm.

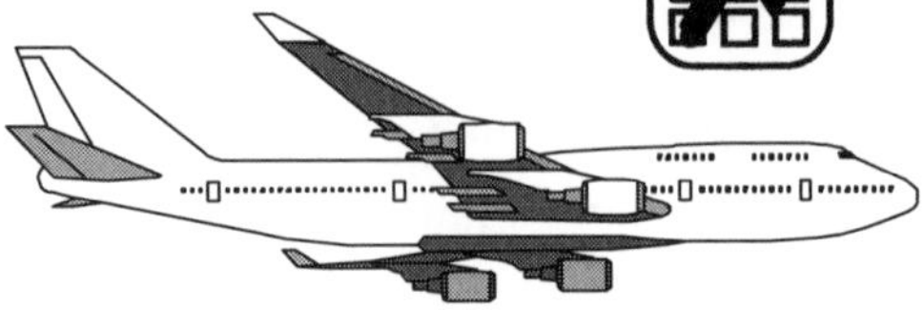

2. For a ten year old child, the recommended dose of 'Calpol' is two spoonfuls. Each spoonful is 5 ml. The whole bottle of 'Calpol' contains 0·25 litres. How many doses can you get from the bottle for a ten year old child?

3. Every year the Government spends about £8·8 billion paying teachers (who deserve every penny they get). A wad of fifty £10 notes is about 5 mm thick.
As a publicity stunt, the Minister of Education decides to make a single pile of £10 notes of total value £8·8 billion. How high would the pile be? [1 billion = 1000 million]

4. Greta has lots of 24p and 19p stamps and she wants to waste as little money as possible when posting 3 packets. Which stamps should she use if the required postage is:
(a) 60p (b) 120p (c) 89p?

5. Six touching circles of radius 5 cm are shown. Calculate the area of the triangle shaded.

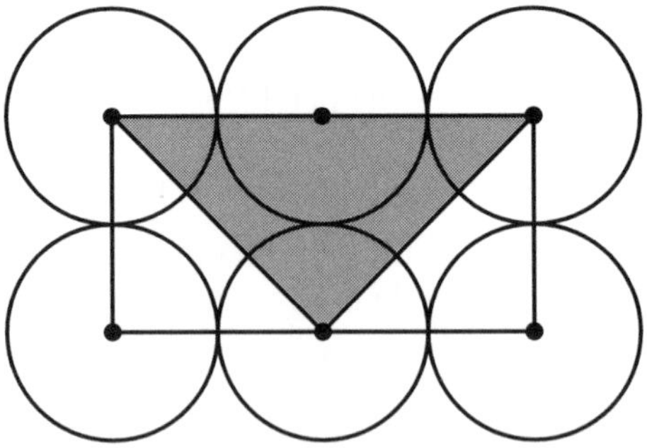

6. Three babies, Petra, Quentin and Rusty, are all weighed on April 1st. After that, Petra is weighed every second day, Quentin every third day and Rusty every fifth day. So, for example, Petra is next weighed on April 3, Quentin is next weighed on April 4 and Rusty is next weighed on April 6. What is the next date when all three babies will be weighed on the same day?

7. A man gives a total of £7 to his two children so that his daughter receives 60p more than his son. How much does his daughter receive?

8. A chef uses 200 ml of oil in 4 days. How many days will a 10 litre drum of oil last?

9. Which is the largest of the following:

$$\sqrt{999}, \qquad 9\sqrt{99}, \qquad 99\sqrt{9}$$

10. Answer 'true' or 'false'.

(a) $0{\cdot}4 = \frac{1}{4}$ (b) $20\text{p} = £0{\cdot}2$ (c) $0{\cdot}02 < 0{\cdot}021$
(d) $(-2)^2 > -2$ (e) $2\% = \frac{1}{50}$ (f) $\frac{1}{2} \times \frac{1}{3} = \frac{1}{6}$

Exercise 4

1. Work out these questions using a calculator. Convert your answer into a number with a fraction: either halves, quarters, fifths, tenths or hundredths. For example: instead of '6·4' write '$6\frac{2}{5}$'.

(a) $237 \div 4$ (b) $678 \div 12$ (c) $48 \div 15$ (d) $238 \div 200$
(e) $478 \div 20$ (f) $76 \div 16$ (g) $408 \div 80$ (h) $403{\cdot}2 \div 8$

2. Find the number indicated by the arrow on the scales below.

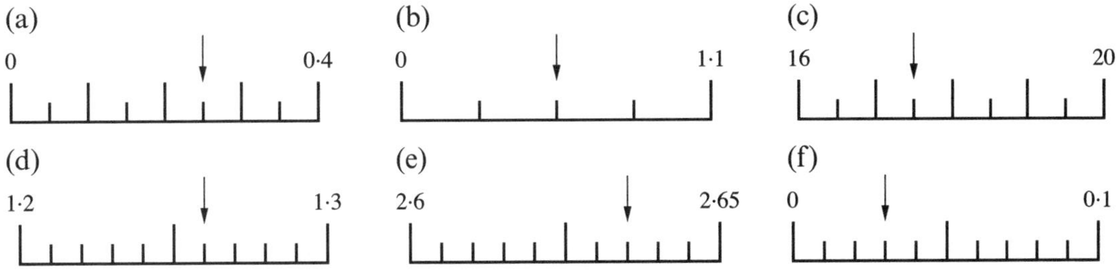

3. Amy is 8 years older than Ben. In 5 years time she will be twice Ben's age. How old is Amy now?

4. Consider the numbers from 1 to 2000 inclusive. In how many of these numbers is the sum of the digits 2?

5. (a) Use a calculator to work out (i) $350 \div 99$
(ii) $350 \div 999$
(iii) $350 \div 9999$

(b) Use your answers to *predict* the answer to (i) $350 \div 99999$, correct to 9 decimal places.

(c) Predict the answer to $350 \div 999999$, correct to 11 decimal places.

6. Neha went to Spain when the exchange rate was 218·40 pesetas to the pound. She bought a C.D. which would cost £10·99 in England. Neha paid 2250 pesetas for the C.D.
How much more or less expensive was the C.D. when bought in Spain? Give your answer to the nearest penny.

7. a and b are positive whole numbers and $a^2 + 15 = b^3$.
Which of the following is a possible value of a?

A 5 B 6 C 7 D 8

8. A 336 g packet of raisins costs £2.25.
How much per 100 g of raisins is this?

9. Using a calculator, express the following as decimals correct to 6 decimal places:

(a) $3\frac{1}{7}$ (b) $\left(\frac{7}{3}+\frac{8}{9}-\frac{8}{99}\right)$

10. Work out one tenth of one half of 5% of the square root of one million.

Exercise 5

1. At the Post Office, stamps are printed on large sheets 38 cm across by 60 cm down. How many stamps are there on each sheet?

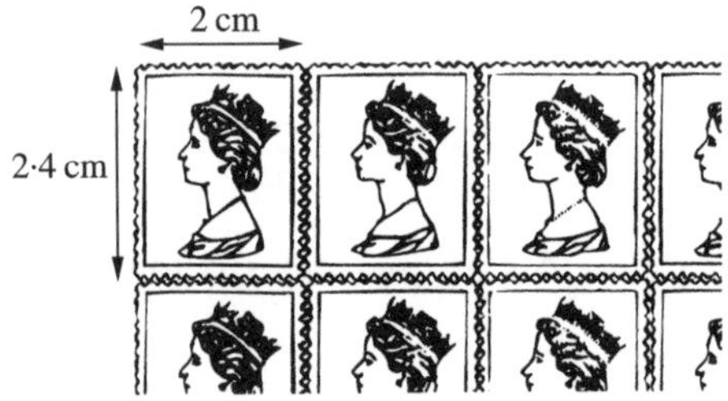

2. A 375 g packet of Bran Flakes costs £1.14. Calculate the cost of a 500 g packet, if both packets represent the same value for money

3. At a European Union conference, all the delegates can speak French or English or both. If 72% can speak English and 45% can speak French, what percentage of the delegates can speak both languages?

4. Canada has an area of 9 980 000 km^2 and a population of 28 200 000.
Hong Kong has an area of 1030 km^2 and a population of 7 300 000.
How many times is Hong Kong more densely populated than Canada?

5. (a) Calculate the total surface area of the solid cuboid shown.
(b) How many of these cuboids could be painted on all faces, using a tin containing enough paint to cover an area of 20 m^2?

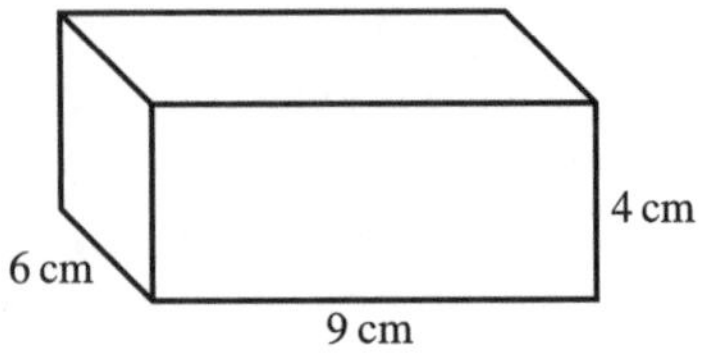

6. 5, 8, 14, 37, 296, 323, 529.
From the list of numbers above, write down
(a) three prime numbers
(b) a square number
(c) a cube number
(d) a number obtained by multiplying together two other numbers in the list.

7. (a) In 2001 Ian was paid £368 per week and 18% of his pay was deducted for tax. What was his 'take home pay' in 2001?
(b) In 2002 Ian received a pay rise of 6% but, in the budget, taxes were raised so that 20% of his pay was deducted. What was his take home pay in 2002?

8. The Day Return train fare from Hatfield to London is £9·40 and an annual season ticket costs £2250. What is the smallest possible number of return journeys a person needs to make in a year so that it is cheaper to buy the season ticket?

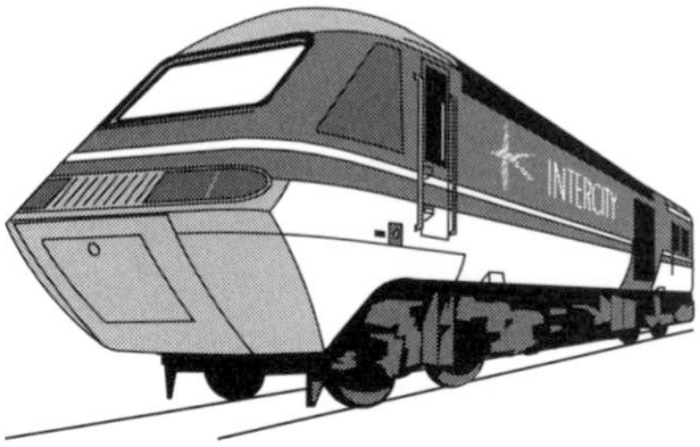

9. The pupils in a school were given a general knowledge quiz.
Some of the results are given in the table
(a) Copy and complete the table with the missing entries.
(b) What percentage of the boys passed the test?

	Passed	Failed	Total
Boys		267	452
Girls		174	
Total		441	821

10. The number N has 8 factors, including 1 and N. Two of its factors are 10 and 14. What is N?

Exercise 6

Some questions in this exercise require a use of the formulas for the circumference and area of a circle.

1. On Mark's watch, the tip of the seconds hand is 13 mm from the centre of the watch.
(a) How far does the tip of the seconds hand move in 1 hour?
(b) Find the speed at which the tip of the seconds hand moves, in mm/s.
(c) The minutes hand is the same length as the seconds hand. At what speed, mm/s, does the tip of the minutes hand move?

2. 'Muirfield' grass seed is sown at a rate of 40 grams per square metre and a 2 kg box of seed costs £6·25. Mrs James wishes to sow a circular lawn and she has up to £50 to spend on seed. Find the radius of the largest circular lawn she can sow.

3. Packets of the same kind of flour are sold in two sizes. A 2 pound bag costs 69p and a 1500 g bag costs £1·05. Given that 1 kg = 2·205 pounds, work out which bag represents the better value for money.

4. The symbols ∗, ∇, □, ○ represent numbers. Use the clues in (a), (b) and (c) to answer part (d).

(a) $* + \nabla = \square$ (b) $* = \nabla + \bigcirc$

(c) $* + * + \nabla = \square + \bigcirc + \bigcirc$ (d) ∇ = how many ○'s?

5. As part of an advertising campaign, the message '*Exercise is good for you*' is taped individually right around 500 000 tennis balls, each of diameter 6·5 cm. Find the total cost of the tape for the campaign, given that a 33 m roll of tape costs 96p.

6. At a steady speed of 70 m.p.h. a car travels 21 miles per gallon of petrol. If petrol costs £4·10 per gallon, work out the cost per minute of driving the car.

7. One square metre of the paper used in this book weighs 80 g. The card used for the cover weighs 240 g per square metre. Measure the size of this book and hence calculate its total weight.
Check how accurate you were by weighing the book on an accurate set of scales.

Part 3

3.1 Written calculations

(a) $56 + 711 + 8$

$$\begin{array}{r} 56 \\ 711 \\ +\quad 8 \\ \hline 775 \\ \hline {}_1 \end{array}$$

(b) $383 - 57$

$$\begin{array}{r} 3\,{}^{7}\!\not{8}\,{}^{1}3 \\ -\quad 57 \\ \hline 326 \\ \hline \end{array}$$

(c) 214×7

$$\begin{array}{r} 214 \\ \times \quad 7 \\ \hline 1498 \\ \hline {}_2\; \end{array}$$

(d) $5{\cdot}6 + 12{\cdot}32$

$$\begin{array}{r} 5{\cdot}60 \\ +12{\cdot}32 \\ \hline 17{\cdot}92 \\ \hline \end{array}$$

← add zero

[Line up the decimal points]

(e) $5{\cdot}26 \times 10$

$= 52{\cdot}6$

Move the digits one place to the left

(f) $28{\cdot}1 \div 100$

$= 0{\cdot}281$

Move the digits two places to the right

(g) 34×200

$= 34 \times 2 \times 100$

$= 6800$

(h) $79{\cdot}2 \div 6$

$$\begin{array}{r} 13{\cdot}2 \\ 6\overline{)\,7^{1}9{\cdot}{}^{1}2} \end{array}$$

(i) $17 - 5{\cdot}4$

$$\begin{array}{r} 1\,{}^{6}\!\not{7}{\cdot}{}^{1}0 \\ -\quad 5{\cdot}4 \\ \hline 11{\cdot}6 \\ \hline \end{array}$$

Exercise 1

Work out, without a calculator

1. 847 + 325	**2.** 7140 + 396	**3.** 294 − 157	**4.** 6293 − 1734
5. 35 × 4	**6.** 73 × 6	**7.** 214 × 8	**8.** 315 × 7
9. 23 × 100	**10.** 315 × 10	**11.** 17 × 1000	**12.** 5·62 × 10
13. 59 ÷ 10	**14.** 647 ÷ 100	**15.** 8·3 ÷ 10	**16.** 219 ÷ 1000
17. 43 × 20	**18.** 26 × 300	**19.** 124 × 200	**20.** 5184 + 2787
21. 5615 − 3916	**22.** 284 + 19 + 564	**23.** 316 × 5	**24.** 56 000 ÷ 20
25. 19·2 − 5·8	**26.** 11 + 5·2	**27.** 173 × 8	**28.** 868 ÷ 7
29. 98·7 ÷ 7	**30.** 0·38 − 0·252	**31.** 73·2 ÷ 100	**32.** 5·1 × 100

33. $42 + 0{\cdot}72 + 5{\cdot}3$	**34.** $5{\cdot}48 \div 4$	**35.** $2900 - 1573$	**36.** $0{\cdot}95 \times 9$
37. $14\,490 \div 6$	**38.** $4000 - 264$	**39.** $5{\cdot}24 \times 0{\cdot}5$	**40.** $8{\cdot}52 \div 4$
41. 52×400	**42.** $234 + 23{\cdot}4$	**43.** $0{\cdot}612 \div 6$	**44.** $5{\cdot}2 \times 2000$
45. $0{\cdot}0924 \div 4$	**46.** $0{\cdot}72 - 0{\cdot}065$	**47.** 73×30	**48.** $5{\cdot}7 \div 100$

Place value

Exercise 2

1. Arrange in order of size, smallest first.
(a) 0·73, 0·718, 0·7 (b) 0·405, 0·5, 0·41
(c) 0·3, 0·035, 0·029 (d) 0·06, 0·058, 0·0511

2. Write the number half way between:
(a) 0·2 and 0·8 (b) 0·4 and 0·5 (c) 0·02 and 0·08
(d) 0·1 and 0·2 (e) 0·06 and 0·07

3. Write each statement with either $>$, $<$ or $=$ in the space.
(a) 0·032 ☐ 0·004 (b) 0·728 ☐ 0·73 (c) 0·3 cm ☐ 3 mm
(d) 0·005 ☐ 0·0006 (e) 0·6 m ☐ 55 cm (f) 0·09 ☐ 0·1

4. (a) What is 0·01 more than 3·29?
(b) What is 0·001 more than 0·628?
(c) What is 0·01 less than 6·4
(d) What is 0·001 less than 0·426?

5. Copy each sequence and fill in the spaces.
(a) 2·67, 2·68, 2·69, ☐, ☐ (b) 1·52, 1·51, 1·5, ☐, ☐
(c) 3·6, 3·8, 4, ☐, ☐ (d) ☐, 5, 5·01, 5·02, ☐

6. What has to be added or subtracted to change:
(a) 3·24 to 3·26 (b) 0·714 to 0·712
(c) 0·142 to 0·152 (d) 0·599 to 0·6

7.

What's in the boot, then?

A MOTORIST who was stopped for a routine police check in Colchester, Essex, was found to be wearing Wellington boots filled with baked beans in tomato sauce.

Officers warned him to choose more suitable footwear. A spokesman said: "We have no idea why he was doing it but it is an offence not to be in proper control of a car. Wearing boots full of baked beans could cause the driver to be distracted and have an accident."

(a) Estimate the number of tins required to fill a pair of wellington boots

(b) Explain why this question is in the section on 'place value'.

Multiplying by 0·1 and 0·01

- Multiplying by 0·1 is the same as multiplying by $\frac{1}{10}$ or dividing by 10.

  Examples:

  $5 \times 0{\cdot}1 = 5 \times \frac{1}{10} = 5 \div 10 = 0{\cdot}5$

  $7 \times 0{\cdot}1 = 7 \times \frac{1}{10} = 7 \div 10 = 0{\cdot}7$

  $0{\cdot}2 \times 0{\cdot}1 = 0{\cdot}2 \times \frac{1}{10} = 0{\cdot}2 \div 10 = 0{\cdot}02$

  $0{\cdot}35 \times 0{\cdot}1 = 0{\cdot}35 \times \frac{1}{10} = 0{\cdot}35 \div 10 = 0{\cdot}035$

- Multiplying by 0·01 is the same multiplying by $\frac{1}{100}$ or dividing by 100.

  Examples:

  $4 \times 0{\cdot}01 = 4 \times \frac{1}{100} = 4 \div 100 = 0{\cdot}04$

  $17 \times 0{\cdot}01 = 17 \times \frac{1}{100} = 17 \div 100 = 0{\cdot}17$

Exercise 3

Work out

1. $8 \times 0{\cdot}1$ **2.** $3 \times 0{\cdot}1$ **3.** $12 \times 0{\cdot}1$ **4.** $26 \times 0{\cdot}1$

5. $0{\cdot}4 \times 0{\cdot}1$ **6.** $0{\cdot}7 \times 0{\cdot}1$ **7.** $0{\cdot}9 \times 0{\cdot}1$ **8.** $0{\cdot}24 \times 0{\cdot}1$

9. $8 \times 0{\cdot}01$ **10.** $6 \times 0{\cdot}01$ **11.** $15 \times 0{\cdot}01$ **12.** $7 \times 0{\cdot}01$

13. $52 \times 0{\cdot}01$ **14.** $63 \times 0{\cdot}01$ **15.** $0{\cdot}6 \times 0{\cdot}001$ **16.** $5{\cdot}2 \times 0{\cdot}01$

17. $11 \times 0{\cdot}1$ **18.** $9 \times 0{\cdot}1$ **19.** $23 \times 0{\cdot}01$ **20.** $0{\cdot}5 \times 0{\cdot}1$

Multiplying decimal numbers

- $5 \times 0{\cdot}3$ is the same as $5 \times \frac{3}{10}$. Work out $(5 \times 3) \div 10 = 15 \div 10 = 1{\cdot}5$

  $4{\cdot}2 \times 0{\cdot}2$ is the same as $4{\cdot}2 \times \frac{2}{10}$. Work out $(4{\cdot}2 \times 2) \div 10 = 8{\cdot}4 \div 10 = 0{\cdot}84$

  $21{\cdot}4 \times 0{\cdot}05$ is the same as $21{\cdot}4 \times \frac{5}{100}$. Work out $(21{\cdot}4 \times 5) \div 100 = 107 \div 100 = 1{\cdot}07$

  Here is a final check:
  When we multiply two decimal numbers together, the answer has the same number of figures to the right of the decimal point as the total number of figures to the right of the decimal point in the question.

  Examples:

  (a) $0{\cdot}3 \times 0{\cdot}4$
  $(3 \times 4 = 12)$
  So $0{\cdot}3 \times 0{\cdot}4 = 0{\cdot}12$

  (b) $0{\cdot}7 \times 0{\cdot}05$
  $(7 \times 5 = 35)$
  So $0{\cdot}7 \times 0{\cdot}05 = 0{\cdot}035$

Exercise 4

1. $7 \times 0{\cdot}2$	**2.** $8 \times 0{\cdot}3$	**3.** $12 \times 0{\cdot}2$	**4.** $5 \times 0{\cdot}03$
5. $0{\cdot}7 \times 3$	**6.** $23 \times 0{\cdot}02$	**7.** $0{\cdot}9 \times 0{\cdot}5$	**8.** $6 \times 0{\cdot}06$
9. $12 \times 0{\cdot}05$	**10.** $0{\cdot}7 \times 0{\cdot}7$	**11.** $8 \times 0{\cdot}1$	**12.** $14 \times 0{\cdot}3$
13. $15 \times 0{\cdot}03$	**14.** $0{\cdot}4 \times 0{\cdot}04$	**15.** $0{\cdot}001 \times 0{\cdot}6$	**16.** $33 \times 0{\cdot}02$
17. $1{\cdot}2 \times 0{\cdot}3$	**18.** $3{\cdot}2 \times 0{\cdot}2$	**19.** $1{\cdot}4 \times 0{\cdot}4$	**20.** $2{\cdot}1 \times 0{\cdot}5$
21. $3{\cdot}61 \times 0{\cdot}3$	**22.** $2{\cdot}1 \times 0{\cdot}6$	**23.** $0{\cdot}31 \times 0{\cdot}7$	**24.** $0{\cdot}42 \times 0{\cdot}02$
25. $0{\cdot}33 \times 0{\cdot}02$	**26.** $3{\cdot}24 \times 0{\cdot}01$	**27.** $8{\cdot}11 \times 0{\cdot}07$	**28.** $16{\cdot}2 \times 0{\cdot}8$
29. $5{\cdot}06 \times 0{\cdot}05$	**30.** $30{\cdot}9 \times 0{\cdot}3$	**31.** $0{\cdot}2^2$	**32.** $0{\cdot}4^2$

- $12{\cdot}2 \times 27$ is approximately $10 \times 30 = 300$

$$12{\cdot}2 \times 27 = (12{\cdot}2 \times 10 \times 27) \div 10$$
$$= (122 \times 27) \div 10$$

	277
	× 27
122 × 20	2440
122 × 7	854
	3294

Answer: $3294 \div 10 = 329{\cdot}4$

- $18{\cdot}4 \times 3{\cdot}2$ is approximately $20 \times 3 = 60$

$$18{\cdot}4 \times 3{\cdot}2 = (18{\cdot}4 \times 10 \times 3{\cdot}2 \times 10) \div 100$$
$$= (184 \times 32) \div 100$$

	184
	× 32
184 × 30	5520
184 × 2	368
	5888

Answer: $5888 \div 100 = 58{\cdot}88$

Exercise 5

Work out, after finding an approximate answer first.

1. $6{\cdot}2 \times 2{\cdot}1$	**2.** $5{\cdot}3 \times 32$	**3.** $4{\cdot}7 \times 15$	**4.** $3{\cdot}8 \times 17$
5. $11{\cdot}4 \times 15$	**6.** $21{\cdot}4 \times 21$	**7.** $15{\cdot}2 \times 13$	**8.** $23{\cdot}6 \times 25$
9. $2{\cdot}3 \times 1{\cdot}2$	**10.** $3{\cdot}5 \times 1{\cdot}5$	**11.** $4{\cdot}3 \times 2{\cdot}3$	**12.** $2{\cdot}4 \times 1{\cdot}8$
13. $6{\cdot}5 \times 3{\cdot}2$	**14.** $8{\cdot}4 \times 4{\cdot}1$	**15.** $0{\cdot}22 \times 1{\cdot}4$	**16.** $0{\cdot}33 \times 1{\cdot}7$
17. $13{\cdot}2 \times 1{\cdot}4$	**18.** $14{\cdot}5 \times 3{\cdot}3$	**19.** $21{\cdot}2 \times 2{\cdot}4$	**20.** $31{\cdot}5 \times 1{\cdot}5$
21. $35{\cdot}6 \times 1{\cdot}9$	**22.** $42{\cdot}3 \times 2{\cdot}7$	**23.** $8{\cdot}64 \times 4{\cdot}7$	**24.** $0{\cdot}332 \times 42$
25. $0{\cdot}32 \times 5{\cdot}6$	**26.** $1{\cdot}52 \times 1{\cdot}7$	**27.** $0{\cdot}35 \times 0{\cdot}13$	**28.** $0{\cdot}51 \times 0{\cdot}24$

Dividing by 0·1 and 0·01

- $1 \div 0{\cdot}1 = 1 \div \frac{1}{10} \ldots$ How many $\frac{1}{10}$s are there in 1? Answer: 10

  $7 \div 0{\cdot}1 = 7 \div \frac{1}{10} \ldots$ How many $\frac{1}{10}$s are there in 7? Answer: 70

  $5{\cdot}2 \div 0{\cdot}1 = 5{\cdot}2 \div \frac{1}{10} \ldots$ How many $\frac{1}{10}$s are there in 5·2? Answer: 52

  $1 \div 0{\cdot}01 = 1 \div \frac{1}{100} \ldots$ How many $\frac{1}{100}$s are there in 1? Answer: 100

  $13 \div 0{\cdot}01 = 13 \div \frac{1}{100} \ldots$ How many $\frac{1}{100}$s are there in 13? Answer: 1300

- We see that: dividing by 0·1 is the same as multiplying by 10,

  dividing by 0·01 is the same as multiplying by 100.

$3 \div 0{\cdot}1 = 3 \times 10 = 30$ $\quad$ $14 \div 0{\cdot}1 = 14 \times 10 = 140$ $\quad$ $0{\cdot}4 \div 0{\cdot}1 = 0{\cdot}4 \times 10 = 4$

$7 \div 0{\cdot}01 = 7 \times 100 = 700$ $\quad$ $52 \div 0{\cdot}01 = 52 \times 100 = 5200$ $\quad$ $0{\cdot}7 \div 0{\cdot}01 = 0{\cdot}7 \times 100 = 70$

Exercise 6

1. $5 \div 0{\cdot}1$ **2.** $9 \div 0{\cdot}1$ **3.** $11 \div 0{\cdot}1$ **4.** $6 \div 0{\cdot}1$

5. $32 \div 0{\cdot}1$ **6.** $0{\cdot}7 \div 0{\cdot}1$ **7.** $0{\cdot}9 \div 0{\cdot}1$ **8.** $1{\cdot}3 \div 0{\cdot}1$

9. $3 \div 0{\cdot}01$ **10.** $11 \div 0{\cdot}01$ **11.** $4 \div 0{\cdot}01$ **12.** $0{\cdot}3 \div 0{\cdot}01$

13. $0{\cdot}8 \div 0{\cdot}01$ **14.** $57 \div 0{\cdot}01$ **15.** $1{\cdot}9 \div 0{\cdot}01$ **16.** $0{\cdot}42 \div 0{\cdot}01$

17. Find the missing numbers

(a) $12 \div 0{\cdot}1 = \square$ (b) $7 \div \square = 70$ (c) $3 \div \square = 300$

(d) $\square \div 0{\cdot}1 = 20$ (e) $1{\cdot}2 \div 0{\cdot}01 = \square$ (f) $1{\cdot}7 \div \square = 17$

Dividing by any decimal number

To divide by any decimal number we transform the calculation into a division by a *whole number*.

Examples $3{\cdot}6 \div 0{\cdot}2 = 36 \div 2 = 18$ [Multiply 3·6 and 0·2 by 10.]

$1{\cdot}5 \div 0{\cdot}03 = 150 \div 3 = 50$ [Multiply 1·5 and 0·03 by 100.]

Since both numbers are multiplied by 10 or 100 the answer is not changed.

Exercise 7

Work out, without a calculator

1. $1{\cdot}46 \div 0{\cdot}2$	**2.** $2{\cdot}52 \div 0{\cdot}4$	**3.** $0{\cdot}942 \div 0{\cdot}3$	**4.** $0{\cdot}712 \div 0{\cdot}2$
5. $0{\cdot}375 \div 0{\cdot}5$	**6.** $0{\cdot}522 \div 0{\cdot}6$	**7.** $6{\cdot}54 \div 0{\cdot}2$	**8.** $1{\cdot}944 \div 0{\cdot}6$
9. $0{\cdot}1368 \div 0{\cdot}04$	**10.** $0{\cdot}228 \div 0{\cdot}04$	**11.** $0{\cdot}498 \div 0{\cdot}06$	**12.** $5{\cdot}04 \div 0{\cdot}7$
13. $3{\cdot}744 \div 0{\cdot}09$	**14.** $0{\cdot}1685 \div 0{\cdot}005$	**15.** $0{\cdot}2846 \div 0{\cdot}2$	**16.** $0{\cdot}0585 \div 0{\cdot}09$
17. $0{\cdot}0257 \div 0{\cdot}005$	**18.** $1{\cdot}872 \div 0{\cdot}08$	**19.** $0{\cdot}268 \div 0{\cdot}4$	**20.** $0{\cdot}39 \div 0{\cdot}006$
21. $0{\cdot}42 \div 0{\cdot}03$	**22.** $7{\cdot}041 \div 0{\cdot}01$	**23.** $0{\cdot}1638 \div 0{\cdot}001$	**24.** $15{\cdot}33 \div 0{\cdot}07$
25. $0{\cdot}993 \div 0{\cdot}3$	**26.** $1{\cdot}05 \div 0{\cdot}6$	**27.** $8{\cdot}4 \div 0{\cdot}02$	**28.** $7{\cdot}52 \div 0{\cdot}4$
29. $4{\cdot}006 \div 0{\cdot}002$	**30.** $17{\cdot}4 \div 0{\cdot}2$	**31.** $54 \div 0{\cdot}3$	**32.** $32 \div 0{\cdot}4$

33. (a) Start in the top left box.
(b) Work out the answer to the calculation in the box.
(c) Find the answer in the top corner of another box.
(d) Write down the letter in that box.
(e) Repeat steps (b), (c) and (d) until you arrive back at the top left box. What is the message?

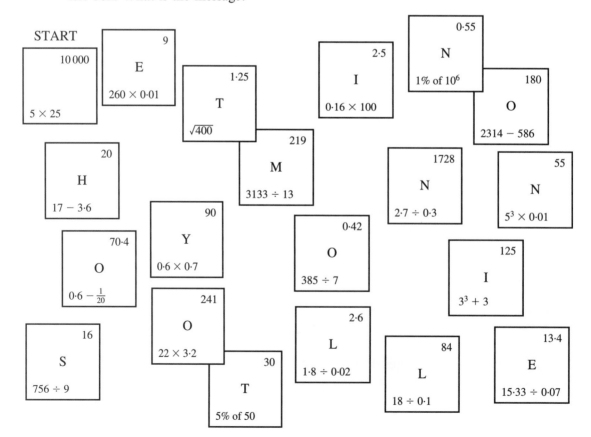

START

Top corner	Letter	Calculation
10 000		5×25
9	E	$260 \times 0{\cdot}01$
1·25	T	$\sqrt{400}$
2·5	I	$0{\cdot}16 \times 100$
0·55	N	1% of 10^6
180	O	$2314 - 586$
219	M	$3133 \div 13$
20	H	$17 - 3{\cdot}6$
1728	N	$2{\cdot}7 \div 0{\cdot}3$
55	N	$5^3 \times 0{\cdot}01$
90	Y	$0{\cdot}6 \times 0{\cdot}7$
0·42	O	$385 \div 7$
70·4	O	$0{\cdot}6 - \frac{1}{20}$
125	I	$3^3 + 3$
241	O	$22 \times 3{\cdot}2$
2·6	L	$1{\cdot}8 \div 0{\cdot}02$
16	S	$756 \div 9$
30	T	5% of 50
84	L	$18 \div 0{\cdot}1$
13·4	E	$15{\cdot}33 \div 0{\cdot}07$

3.2 Averages and range

The mean
All the data is added and the total is divided by the number of items. In everyday language the word 'average' usually stands for the mean.

The median
When the data is arranged in order of size, the median is the one in the middle. If there are two 'middle' numbers, the median is in the middle of these two numbers [i.e. the mean of the two numbers].

The mode
The mode is the number or quality (like a colour) which occurs most often. Sometimes a set of data will have no mode, two modes or even more and this is a problem which we cannot avoid.

Range
The range is not an average but is the difference between the largest value and the smallest value in a set of data. It is useful in comparing sets of data when the *spread* of the data is important.

Exercise 1

1. (a) Find the mean of the numbers 4, 13, 5, 7, 9, 6, 5
(b) Find the median of the numbers 6, 20, 1, 16, 2, 12, 6, 3, 8, 6, 8
(c) Find the mode of the numbers 13, 2, 11, 2, 10, 4, 5, 10, 8, 10

2. In several different garages the cost of one litre of petrol is
55p, 52·8p, 56·4p, 53·1p, 59p, 53·8p, 57p.
What is the median cost of one litre of petrol?

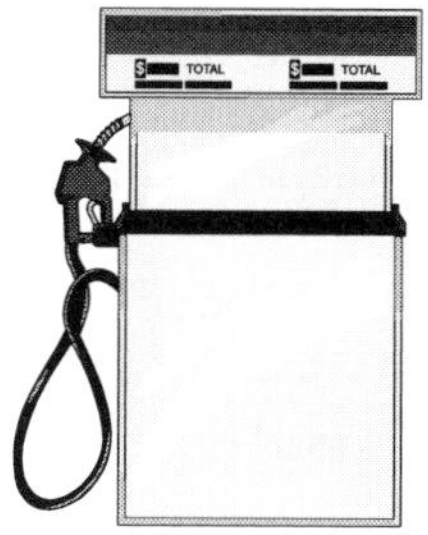

3. Six girls have heights of 1·48 m, 1·51 m, 1·47m, 1·55 m, 1·40 m and 1·59 m.
(a) Find the mean height of the six girls.
(b) Find the mean height of the remaining five girls when the tallest girl leaves.

4. The temperature was recorded at 04.00 in seven towns across the U.K. The readings were 0°, 1°, −4°, 1°, −2°, −5°, −4°. What was the median temperature?

5. The test results for a class of 30 pupils were as follows:

Mark	3	4	5	6	7	8
Frequency	2	5	4	7	6	6

What was the modal mark?

6. Find the range of the following sets of numbers:
(a) 4, 11, 3, 8, 22, 5, 7, 30, 18
(b) 9, 18, 100, 64, 11, 26
(c) 4, −2, 6, 4, 5, 10, 3.

7. The range for nine numbers on a card is 60. One number is covered by a piece of blu-tac. What could that number be? [There are two possible answers.]

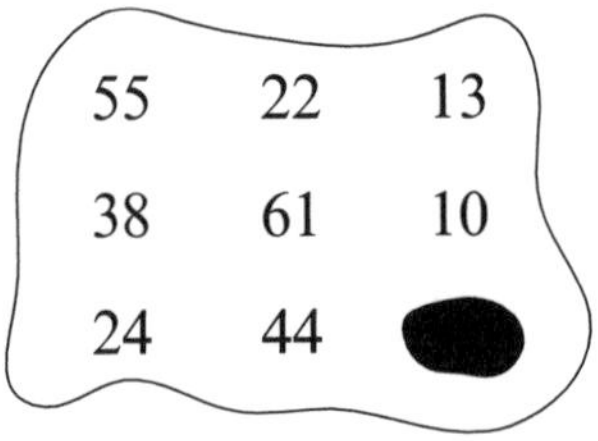

8. Lauren has five cards. The five cards have a mean of 7 and a range of 4. What are the missing numbers?

9. For the set of numbers below, find the mean and the median.

1, 3, 3, 3, 4, 6, 99.

Which average best describes the set of numbers?

10. In a history test, Andrew got 62%. For the whole class, the mean mark was 64% and the median mark was 59%. Which 'average' tells him whether he is in the 'top' half or the 'bottom' half of the class?

11. Write down five numbers so that:
the mean is 7
the median is 6
the mode is 4.

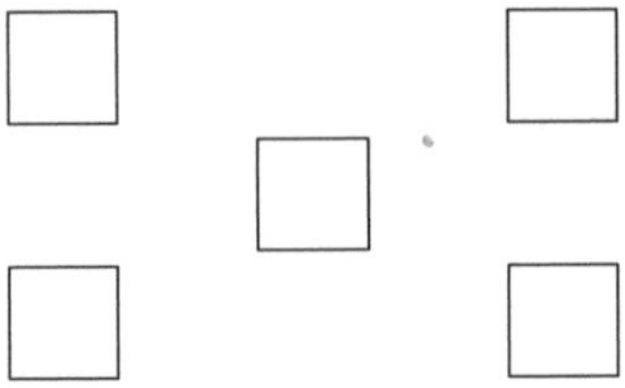

12. The mean of the eight numbers 6, 6, 9, 3, 8, 11, 5, 2 is $6\frac{1}{4}$.

When a number x is added, the new mean of the nine numbers is 7. Find x.

13. Tom and Wendy both do three tests and their marks have the same mean.
The range of Tom's marks is twice the range of Wendy's marks.
Copy and complete the table.

Tom's marks		60	
Wendy's marks	55	60	65

14. The mean age of three people is 22 and their median age is 20. The range of their ages is 16. How old is each person?

15. Here are 4 cards and you are told that x is a positive whole number.

$5x + 1$	$x - 1$	$x + 3$	$x + 9$

(a) Find, in terms of x,
 (i) the range of the 4 cards.
 (ii) the median of the 4 cards
 (iii) the mean of the 4 cards.

(b) The mean is 2 greater than the median. Find the value of x.

16. The mean height of n people is h cm. One person of height x cm leaves the group and one person of height y cm joins the group. Find an expression for the new mean height

Frequency tables

When a set of data consists of many numbers it is convenient to record the information in a frequency table. It is possible to find the mean, median and mode directly from the table as shown in the example below.

The frequency table shows the number of goals scored in 15 football matches.

number of goals	0	1	2	3	4	5 or more
frequency	2	5	4	3	1	0

(a) We *could* find the mean as follows:

$$\text{mean} = \frac{(0+0+1+1+1+1+1+2+2+2+2+3+3+3+4)}{15}$$

A better method is to multiply the number of goals by the respective frequencies.

$$\text{mean} = \frac{(0 \times 2) + (1 \times 5) + (2 \times 4) + (3 \times 3) + (4 \times 1)}{15}$$

mean $= 1{\cdot}73$ goals (correct to 2 d.p.)

(b) The median is the 8th number in the list, when the numbers are arranged in order. The median is, therefore, 2 goals.

(c) The modal number of goals is 1, since more games had 1 goal than any other number.

Exercise 2

1. The frequency table shows the weights of 30 eggs laid by the hens on a free range farm.

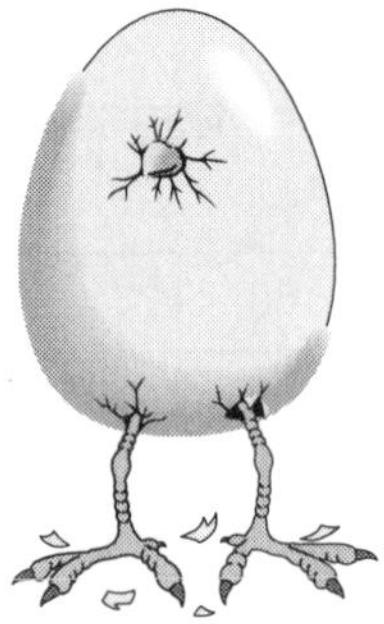

weight	44 g	48 g	52 g	56 g	60 g
frequency	5	6	7	9	3

Find the mean weight of the eggs.

2. The frequency table shows the weights of the 40 pears sold in a shop.

weight	70 g	80 g	90 g	100 g	110 g	120 g
frequency	2	7	9	11	8	3

Calculate the mean weight of the pears.

3. The frequency table shows the price of a Mars bar in 30 different shops.

price	49p	50p	51p	52p	53p	54p
frequency	2	3	5	10	6	4

Calculate the mean price of a Mars bar.

4. The marks, out of 10, achieved by 25 teachers in a spelling test were as follows:

mark	5	6	7	8	9	10
frequency	8	7	4	2	3	1

Find (a) the mean mark
(b) the median mark
(c) the modal mark.

5. A golfer played the same hole 30 times with the following results.

score	3	4	5	6	7	8
frequency	2	11	5	5	3	4

(a) Find his mean score, median score and modal score on the hole.
(b) Which average best represents the data? Explain why.

6. The table shows the weights of 50 coins.
Find the weight x if the mean weight of the 50 coins is 1 gram more than the median weight.

weight	frequency
2 g	4
4 g	7
5 g	16
x	10
9 g	13

7. The number of bedrooms in the houses in a street is shown in the table
(a) If the mean number of bedrooms is 3·6, find x.
(b) If the median number of bedrooms is 3, find the largest possible value of x.
(c) If the modal number of bedrooms is 3, find the largest possible value of x.

number of bedrooms	frequency
2	5
3	12
4	x

8. The weights of 20 ear-rings were measured. Copy and complete the table below so that the mean weight is 6·3 g, the median weight is 6 g and the modal weight is 7 g.

weight of ear-ring	5 g	6 g	7 g	8 g
frequency	5			2

Stem and leaf diagrams

Data can be displayed in groups in a stem and leaf diagram.
Here are the marks of 20 girls in a science test.

47	53	71	55	28	40	45	62	57	64
33	48	59	61	73	37	75	26	68	39

We will put the marks into groups 20–29, 30–39.:... 70–79.
We will choose the tens digit as the 'stem' and the units as the 'leaf'.

The first four marks are shown [47, 53, 71, 55]

Stem (tens)	Leaf (units)
2	
3	
4	7
5	3 5
6	
7	1

The complete diagram is below ...... and then with the leaves in numerical order:

Stem	Leaf
2	8 6
3	3 7 9
4	7 0 5 8
5	3 5 7 9
6	2 4 1 8
7	1 3 5

Stem	Leaf
2	6 8
3	3 7 9
4	0 5 7 8
5	3 5 7 9
6	1 2 4 8
7	1 3 5

The diagram shows the shape of the distribution. It is also easy to find the mode, the median and the range.

Exercise 3

1. The marks of 24 children in a test are shown

41	23	35	15	40	39	47	29
52	54	45	27	28	36	48	51
59	65	42	32	46	53	66	38

Stem	Leaf
1	
2	3
3	5
4	1
5	
6	

Draw a stem and leaf diagram. The first three entries are shown.

2. Draw a stem and leaf diagram for each set of data below

(a)

24	52	31	55	40	37	58	61	25	46
44	67	68	75	73	28	20	59	65	39

(b)

30	41	53	22	72	54	35	47
44	67	46	38	59	29	47	28

Stem	Leaf
2	
3	
4	
5	
6	
7	

3. Here is the stem and leaf diagram showing the masses, in kg, of some people on a bus.
(a) Write down the range of the masses
(b) How many people were on the bus?
(c) What is the median mass?

Stem (tens)	Leaf (units)
3	3 7
4	1 2 7 7 8
5	1 6 8 9
6	0 3 7
7	4 5
8	2

4. In this question the stem shows the units digit and the leaf shows the first digit after the decimal point.
Draw the stem and leaf diagram using the following data:

2·4	3·1	5·2	4·7	1·4	6·2	4·5	3·3
4·0	6·3	3·7	6·7	4·6	4·9	5·1	5·5
1·8	3·8	4·5	2·4	5·8	3·3	4·6	2·8

key
3|7 means 3·7

Stem	Leaf
1	
2	
3	
4	
5	
6	

(a) What is the median?
(b) Write down the range.

3.3 Mental calculations

Mental calculation strategies

In Book 7 we discussed three strategies for mental calculation. Here is a reminder of each technique.

A 'Easy-to-add' numbers

$16 + 57 + 24 = 16 + 24 + 57 = 40 + 57 = 97$
$23 + 68 + 7 = 23 + 7 + 68 = 30 + 68 = 98$
$45 + 108 + 35 = 45 + 35 + 108 = 80 + 108 = 188$

B Splitting numbers

$33 + 48$: $30 + 40 = 70$ and $3 + 8 = 11$
So $33 + 48 = 70 + 11 = 81$
$264 + 38$: $260 + 30 = 290$ and $4 + 8 = 12$
So $264 + 38 = 290 + 12 = 302$

C Add/subtract 9, 19, 29 . . . 11, 21, 31 . . . , adjusting by one

$57 + 19 = 57 + 20 - 1 = 77 - 1 = 76$
$109 + 39 = 109 + 40 - 1 = 149 - 1 = 148$
$65 - 29 = 65 - 30 + 1 = 35 + 1 = 36$
$111 - 59 = 111 - 60 + 1 = 51 + 1 = 52$

Practice questions

A

1. $7 + 13 + 49$ **2.** $18 + 57 + 12$ **3.** $25 + 37 + 25$ **4.** $31 + 55 + 29$
5. $28 + 2 + 67$ **6.** $55 + 99 + 25$ **7.** $17 + 13 + 68$ **8.** $64 + 16 + 27$
9. $42 + 56 + 8$ **10.** $23 + 25 + 17$ **11.** $16 + 9 + 44$ **12.** $91 + 54 + 9$

B

1. $23 + 35$ **2.** $51 + 37$ **3.** $44 + 37$ **4.** $32 + 69$
5. $57 + 59$ **6.** $67 + 27$ **7.** $108 + 58$ **8.** $124 + 33$
9. $63 + 74$ **10.** $125 + 62$ **11.** $45 + 68$ **12.** $53 + 84$

C

1. $55 + 19$ **2.** $64 + 39$ **3.** $87 + 9$ **4.** $55 + 31$
5. $27 + 41$ **6.** $74 + 29$ **7.** $25 + 61$ **8.** $84 - 19$
9. $74 - 59$ **10.** $93 - 61$ **11.** $87 - 29$ **12.** $113 - 81$

New strategies

D Doubling large numbers: work from the left

- double 63 = double 60 + double 3 = 120 + 6 = 126
- double 79 = double 70 + double 9 = 140 + 18 = 158
- double 127 = double 100 + double 20 + double 7 = 200 + 40 + 14 = 254
- double 264 = double 200 + double 60 + double 4 = 400 + 120 + 8 = 528

E (a) Multiplying by doubling and then halving:

- 23×5 $23 \times 10 = 230$ $230 \div 2 = 115$
- 7×45 $7 \times 90 = 630$ $630 \div 2 = 315$
- 11×15 $11 \times 30 = 330$ $330 \div 2 = 165$

(b) To multiply by 50, multiply by 100, then halve the result.

- 23×50 $23 \times 100 = 2300$ $2300 \div 2 = 1150$
- 38×50 $38 \times 100 = 3800$ $3800 \div 2 = 1900$

(c) To multiply by 25, multiply by 100, then divide by 4

- 44×25 $44 \times 100 = 4400$ $4400 \div 4 = 1100$
- 56×25 $56 \times 100 = 5600$ $5600 \div 4 = 1400$

F Multiplying by 19 or 21 . . . or by 49 or 51 . . . or by 99 or 101

- $15 \times 21 = (15 \times 20) + 15 = 300 + 15 = 315$
- $14 \times 51 = (14 \times 50) + 14 = 700 + 14 = 714$
- $23 \times 101 = (23 \times 100) + 23 = 2300 + 23 = 2323$
- $17 \times 19 = (17 \times 20) - 17 = 340 - 17 = 323$
- $16 \times 49 = (16 \times 50) - 16 = 800 - 16 = 784$
- $19 \times 99 = (19 \times 100) - 19 = 1900 - 19 = 1881$

Practice questions

D

1. double 54   **2.** double 38   **3.** double 67   **4.** double 73

5. double 28   **6.** double 79   **7.** double 115   **8.** double 126

9. double 87   **10.** double 66   **11.** double 237   **12.** double 342

E

1. 22×50 **2.** 32×50 **3.** 24×25 **4.** 16×25

5. 8×35 **6.** 8×15 **7.** 7×45 **8.** 9×35

9. 14×50 **10.** 13×20 **11.** 18×50 **12.** 12×25

F

1. 7×21 **2.** 9×51 **3.** 11×41 **4.** 23×31

5. 9×19 **6.** 6×29 **7.** 7×99 **8.** 15×99

9. 12×101 **10.** 55×101 **11.** 23×1001 **12.** 15×999

Mental arithmetic tests

There are several sets of mental arithmetic questions in this section. It is intended that a teacher will read out each question twice, with all pupils' books closed. The answers are written down without any written working. Only a pencil or pen may be used.

Test 1

1. Add together 15, 25 and 70.
2. How many millimetres are there in a kilometre?
3. Find the length of the perimeter of a regular hexagon of side 20 cm.
4. Find the change from £10 when you buy two magazines for 75p each.
5. Give a rough estimate for the square root of 405.
6. Find the cost of 60 eggs at £1 per dozen.
7. A car is travelling at a steady speed of 30 m.p.h. How far does it go in 30 minutes?
8. Find the difference between $8\frac{1}{2}$ and 20.
9. Work out $1 + 2^2 + 3^3$.
10. Through what angle does the minute hand of a clock move between 8·50 and 9·00?
11. Work out roughly the area of a circle of radius 10 cm.
12. A bridge was built in Paris in 1780. How many years ago was that?
13. What is 40% as a fraction?
14. How many items costing £25 each can you buy with £200?
15. What five coins make 75p?
16. Calculate the length of the perimeter of a rectangular field measuring 110 m by 80 m.
17. Work out 0·03 multiplied by 1000.
18. Increase a price of £700 by 1%.
19. Answer true or false: $\left(\frac{1}{3}\right)^2$ is greater than $\frac{1}{3}$.
20. A large brick weighs 1 kg. Roughly what does it weigh in pounds?
21. Work out 1% of £150.
22. A plant grows 5 cm every day. How many days will it take to grow 60 cm?
23. A charity collection is made into a pile of 1000 20p coins. How much was collected?
24. Add together 67 and 77.
25. True or false: At a steady speed of 30 m.p.h. you go 1 mile every 2 minutes.
26. Glen has one of each of the coins from 1 p to 1 pound. What is their total value?
27. Three angles of a quadrilateral are 80°, 120° and 60°. What is the fourth angle?
28. How many inches are there in a foot?
29. A pie chart has a pink sector representing 25% of the whole chart. What is the angle of the sector?
30. Write down the next prime number after 31.

Test 2

1. Which of these fractions is the larger: $\frac{2}{3}$ or $\frac{3}{4}$?
2. True or false: a weight of 5 stones is less than 50 kg.
3. Work out 1% of £45.
4. Write in words the answer to $10 \times 100 \times 1000$.
5. Add together 5, 6, 7 and 8.
6. A car travels 30 miles in 30 minutes. How far will it travel at this speed in $\frac{3}{4}$ hour?
7. Sam spends 40% of his money on tapes and 50% of his money on clothes. If he had £5 left, how much did he have at first?
8. Write as a decimal: $\frac{1}{5}$ plus $\frac{1}{10}$.
9. A bucket contains 2 litres of milk. How much is left, in ml, after 100 ml is removed?
10. How many hours and minutes is it from 8·15 a.m. until noon?
11. One bag weighs 250 g. How many bags weigh 5 kg?
12. If 20 drinks cost £28, find the cost of 5.
13. A magazine costing 47p was paid for with a £1 coin. Which three coins were given as change?

14. What is the number which is 200 less than 2000?

15. Find the change from a £5 note after buying 3 pounds of apples at 20p per pound.

16. A girl faces West and turns clockwise through 1 right angle. In which direction is she now facing?

17. A film, lasting $1\frac{1}{2}$ hours, starts at 6·20. When does it finish?

18. Work out $100 - 4{\cdot}9$.

19. Name the date which is 4 months before the 1st of February.

20. Write down the next prime number after 20.

21. Write $\frac{9}{10}$ as a percentage.

22. Of the people in a room, a half were French, ten per cent were German and the rest were Irish. What percentage were Irish?

23. In January, Steve weighs 70 kg. By July his weight is reduced by 10%. What does he weigh in July?

24. Find the total surface area of a cube of side 1 cm.

25. Work out $98 + 67$.

26. Write 1·6 recurring correct to one decimal place.

27. A 10p coin is 1·7 mm thick. What is the height of a pile of coins worth £1?

28. Estimate the length of a side of a square of area 50 cm^2.

29. Work out $\frac{2}{3}$ of £120.

30. True or false: 15 cm is about 6 inches.

Test 3

1. If I have 35 pence change from a ten pound note, how much have I spent?

2. My train leaves at 16.18. How many minutes do I have to wait if I arrive at the station at 15.55?

3. The area of a triangle is 20 cm^2. Its base measures 10 cm. What is the height of the triangle?

4. One eighth of the children in a class walk to school. What percentage of the class is this?

5. A man was born in 1939. How old was he in the year 2000?

6. A piece of string 54 cm long is cut into four equal parts. How long is each part?

7. True or false: Five miles is about the same as eight km.

8. The time in Miami is 5 hours earlier than the time in England. If I want to telephone Miami at 13.30 their time, what time will it be here?

9. I think of a number, multiply it by 2 and subtract 8. The result is 12. What number am I thinking of?

10. A plank of wood measures 2 metres by 50 cm. What is the area of the plank in square metres?

11. Which is largest: $\frac{1}{9}$ or 10%?

12. A bar of chocolate costs 18p. I buy as many as I can for 50p. How much change will I receive?

13. Add together 1, 2, 3, 4, 5, 6.

14. Write down ten million millimetres in kilometres.

15. By how much does a half of 130 exceed 49?

16. Work out two squared plus three squared.

17. Work out 5% of £40.

18. Two angles in a quadrilateral are each 80° and a third angle is 100°. What is the fourth angle?

19. Give an *estimate* for $291{\cdot}4 \times 0{\cdot}486$.

20. What number is a quarter of 140?

21. What is a half of a half of £60?

22. Rosie is going on a 2 week holiday. She leaves on the 5th of July. On what date will she return?

23. What is 2% as a simplified fraction?

24. What is the fraction exactly half way between $\frac{1}{4}$ and $\frac{1}{2}$?

For the last six questions you may write down the numbers in the question.

25. Work out 15% of £60.

26. I think of a number, subtract 8 and then divide by 2. The result is 1. What number am I thinking of?

27. My newspaper costs 45p per day from Monday to Friday and 50p on Saturday. How much do I spend on papers from Monday to Saturday?

28. The coordinates of the 4 corners of a rectangle are (1, 1), (5, 1), (5, 4) and (1, 4). What is the area of the rectangle in square units?

29. How many seconds are there in 1 hour?

30. A train journey of 480 miles took 4 hours. What was the average speed of the train?

Test 4

1. How many 20 pence coins are needed to make £8?

2. What number is mid-way between 0·1 and 0·2?

3. Work out 5% of £320.

4. True or false: one yard is approximately one metre.

5. Work out 2·2 divided by 10.

6. One sector of a pie chart represents 10% of the whole chart. what is the angle of the sector?

7. Find the approximate area of a circle of diameter 6 cm.

8. I pay for a pen costing £3.40 with a £20 note. What change do I receive?

9. Who is taller: Jan who is 5 feet tall or Sam who is 1 metre 10 tall?

10. A jar contains 1000 5p coins. Find the total value of the coins.

11. A rectangle measures 2·4 m by 10 cm. What is its perimeter in cm?

12. A rope of length 1 foot 4 inches is cut in half. How long is each piece?

13. A film started at 7·10 and finished at 10·55. How long was the film in hours and minutes?

14. Which has the longer perimeter: a square of side 10 cm or a circle of diameter 10 cm?

15. What fraction is equivalent to 40%?

16. Find the cost of 4 litres of wine at £1·25 per litre.

17. How many 24p stamps can be bought for £3?

18. Add together 34 and 164.

19. How long will it take to travel 60 miles at a speed of 30 m.p.h.?

20. Work out 3 × 30 × 30.

21. What is the angle between the hands of a clock at 4 o'clock?

22. Find the cost of buying a newspaper for 40 days if each paper costs 20p.

23. Work out two fifths of £40.

24. How many prime numbers are there between 10 and 20?

25. I am thinking of a number. If I double it, add one and then square the result the answer is 25. What number am I thinking of?

26. Work out $\frac{1}{4}$ plus $\frac{1}{2}$ and give the answer as a decimal.

27. Divide one million by 100.

28. A rectangle has area 12 cm^2. What is the area of a rectangle whose sides are twice as long as those of this rectangle?

29. In a quiz, David got 15 out of 20. What percentage is that?

30. Increase a price of £300 by 10%.

KS3 tests

The next 2 tests are written in the form of the Key Stage 3 mental arithmetic tests.

Each question will be repeated once. You have 5 seconds to answer questions 1 to 6, 10 seconds to answer questions 7 to 20 and 15 seconds to answer the remaining questions. You will be told to put down your pen after the correct time interval for each question.

Work out the answer to each question in your head and write down only the answer. Sometimes other useful information, such as the numbers used in the question, has been written down to help you. Look at the sheets on page 87.

Test 1

- Time: 5 seconds

1. Look at the numbers on your answer sheet. What is half their total?
2. Change one hundred and forty millimetres into centimetres.
3. What is sixty-three divided by nine?
4. Look at the equation. Write down the value for *n*.
5. Your answer sheet shows a fraction. Write the fraction in its simplest form.
6. Write four fifths as a decimal number.

- Time: 10 seconds

7. Look at the expression. What is its value when x equals six?
8. A TV film starts at five minutes to seven. It lasts forty-five minutes. At what time does the film finish?
9. What is one hundred and forty minus eighty?
10. On a coach there are fifty pupils. Thirty of the pupils are girls. A pupil is chosen at random. What is the probability that a girl is chosen?
11. Look at your answer sheet. Work out the answer.
12. Ten per cent of a number is eight. What is the number?
13. A pond is fifteen feet long. About how many metres is that?
14. Write the number two and a half million in figures.
15. Look at the equation. Use it to work out the value of $2x$.
16. Estimate the size of this angle in degrees.
17. Estimate the value of fifty-two per cent of sixteen pounds ninety pence.
18. How many halves are there altogether in four and a half?
19. What is five hundred minus forty-five?

20 n stands for a number. Write an expression for the following: 'add six to n, then multiply the result by three'.

- Time: 15 seconds

21. Pete and Bob share some money in the ratio of one to two. Pete's share is fifteen pounds. How much money is Bob's share?
22. What is one quarter of two hundred thousand?
23. Write two consecutive numbers that add up to thirty-five.
24. Use the calculation on your answer sheet to help you to work out how many seventeens there are in two thousand two hundred and ten.
25. Divide twenty-two pounds between four people. How much money does each person get?
26. Write an approximate answer to the calculation on your answer sheet.
27. Find *n*, if two times *n* minus one equals eleven.
28. Your answer sheet shows the marks by four pupils in a test. What is the mean mark?
29. Work out three plus four plus five all squared.
30. A man's heart beats 80 times in 1 minute. How many times does it beat in one hour?

Test 2

- Time: 5 seconds

1. Write the number one thousand, five hundred and sixty-seven to the nearest hundred.
2. What is five point two multiplied by one thousand?
3. Work out five per cent of four hundred.
4. Simplify the expression on your answer sheet.
5. What is the sum of the numbers on your answer sheet?
6. What is one tenth of half a million?

- Time: 10 seconds

7. Look at the expression. What is its value when *x* equals four?
8. Tim's height is one point seven metres. Greg's height is one hundredth of a metre more than Tim's height. What is Greg's height?
9. Twenty per cent of a number is eleven. What is the number?
10. Two angles in a triangle are each sixty-five degrees. What is the size of the third angle?
11. In a group of sixty-three children, twenty-eight are girls. How many are boys?
12. What is the area of this triangle?
13. The value of four *x* plus *y* is sixteen.
    Write the value of eight *x* plus two *y*.

14. Divide two by nought point one.

15. Michelle got thirty out of fifty on a test. What percentage did she get?

16. Work out one plus two plus three plus four all squared.

17. Look at the inequalities on your answer sheet. Write down one possible value for x.

18 How many twelths are there in three quarters?

19. Multiply six point nought two by one thousand.

20. On the answer sheet find the missing number.

- Time: 15 seconds:

21. What is the cost of three items at two pounds ninety-nine pence each?

22. Look at these numbers. Put a ring around the smallest number.

23. Write an approximate answer to the calculation on your answer sheet.

24. Each side of a square is thirty-two centimetres. What is the perimeter of the square?

25. Look at these pairs of numbers. Between which pair of numbers does the square root of thirty-three lie? Put a ring around the correct pair.

26. Look at the calculation on your answer sheet.
What is thirty-two multiplied by thirty-eight?

27. A map has a scale of one to ten thousand.
What is the actual length of a path which is 8 cm long on the map?

28. Look at the expression on your answer sheet. Write down the value of the expression when x equals nought.

29. Which has the longer perimeter: a square of side 10 cm or an equilateral triangle of side 15 cm?

30. A film started at eight fifty p.m. and ended two and a quarter hours later. When did it finish?

Test 1 Answer sheet

Time: 5 seconds

Question	Answer	
1		18 22
2	cm	
3		
4		$3n = 12$
5		$\frac{14}{21}$
6		

Time: 10 seconds

7		$5x$
8		
9		
10		50 pupils, 30 girls
11		$32 - (12 + 7)$
12		
13	m	
14		
15		$x - 3 = 30$
16		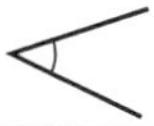
17		52% £16.90
18		
19		
20		

Time: 15 seconds

21		1:2 £15
22		
23		
24		$17 \times 260 = 4420$, 2210
25		£22 4
26		$41{\cdot}22 \times 9{\cdot}87$
27		
28		1, 3, 4, 4
29		$(3 + 4 + 5)^2$
30		

Test 2 Answer sheet

Time: 5 seconds

Question	Answer	
1		1567
2		5·2
3		
4		$a \times a \times a$
5		2·3 2·7 2·3 2·7
6		

Time: 10 seconds

7		$2(x + 1)$
8		1·7 m $\frac{1}{100}$ m
9		
10		
11		
12	cm^2	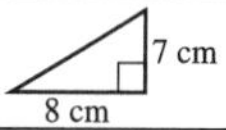
13	m	$4x + y$ $8x + 2y$
14		2 0·1
15	%	
16		$(1 + 2 + 3 + 4)^2$
17		$-4 < x < 0$
18		
19		6·02
20		$3 \times \square - 1 = 65$

Time: 15 seconds

21	£	
22	0·3 0·18 0·35 0·332 0·2	
23		$497{\cdot}3 \div 1{\cdot}97$
24		
25		3, 4 4,5 5,6 6,7 7,8
26		$32 \times 19 = 608$
27		1 : 10000 8 cm
28		$(x - 3)(x + 2)$
29		
30		8.50 pm $2\frac{1}{4}$

3.4 Using a calculator

Order of operations

Some people use the word 'BIDMAS' to help them remember the correct order of operations.

Brackets
Indices
Divide
Multiply
Add
Subtract

Here are four examples

- $8 + 6 \div 6 = 8 + 1 = 9$
- $20 - 8 \times 2 = 20 - 16 = 4$
- $(13 - 7) \div (6 - 4) = 6 \div 2 = 3$
- $20 - 8 \div (5 + 3) = 20 - 8 \div 8 = 19$

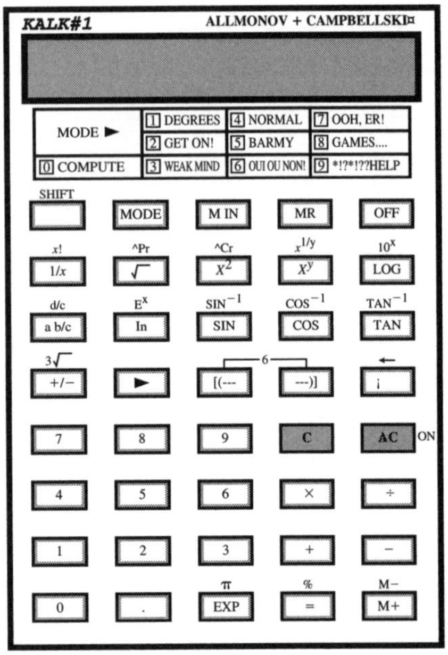

Exercise 1

Use a calculator and give the answer correct to two decimal places.

1. $3{\cdot}4 \times 1{\cdot}23$ **2.** $20{\cdot}4 - 5{\cdot}7412$ **3.** $0{\cdot}341^2$

4. $0{\cdot}17 + 2{\cdot}89 - 1{\cdot}514$ **5.** $3{\cdot}2^2 - 2{\cdot}8$ **6.** $4{\cdot}6 \times 1{\cdot}9 + 8{\cdot}05$

7. $0{\cdot}54 \times 0{\cdot}87 - 0{\cdot}1$ **8.** $8{\cdot}7 \div 2{\cdot}73$ **9.** $12{\cdot}5 - 0{\cdot}516 + 1{\cdot}2$

10. $\dfrac{8{\cdot}9}{7{\cdot}4}$ **11.** $\dfrac{20{\cdot}2}{5{\cdot}6} + 8{\cdot}2$ **12.** $\dfrac{8{\cdot}65}{6} - 0{\cdot}12$

In Questions **13** to **30** remember 'B I D M A S'.

13. $2{\cdot}6 + 2{\cdot}7 \times 1{\cdot}9$ **14.** $8{\cdot}01 + 0{\cdot}8 \times 3{\cdot}2$ **15.** $7{\cdot}93 + 5 \div 12$

16. $8{\cdot}6 \div 0{\cdot}7 - 5{\cdot}55$ **17.** $8 \div 0{\cdot}55 + 2{\cdot}33$ **18.** $8{\cdot}06 + 1{\cdot}4 \times 1{\cdot}5$

19. $3{\cdot}5 + \dfrac{8{\cdot}5}{1{\cdot}34}$ **20.** $1{\cdot}53^2 + 2{\cdot}53$ **21.** $6{\cdot}4 + \dfrac{1{\cdot}7}{0{\cdot}85}$

22. $8{\cdot}65 + 30 \div 8{\cdot}2$ **23.** $5{\cdot}44 + 1{\cdot}37^2$ **24.** $6{\cdot}4^2 \div 19$

25. $0{\cdot}751 - 0{\cdot}14 \times 0{\cdot}9$ **26.** $2{\cdot}3^3$ **27.** $10 + 10 \times 10$

28. $8{\cdot}9 + \dfrac{19{\cdot}6}{15}$ **29.** $\dfrac{2{\cdot}7 + 5{\cdot}65}{3{\cdot}3}$ **30.** $\dfrac{11{\cdot}2 - 5{\cdot}67}{1{\cdot}9}$

Using brackets

Most calculators have brackets buttons like these `[(---`, `---)]`.

When you press the left hand bracket button `[(---` you may see

 ignore this.

When the right hand bracket button is pressed you will see that the calculation inside the brackets has been performed. Try it.

Don't forget to press the `=` button at the end to give the final answer.

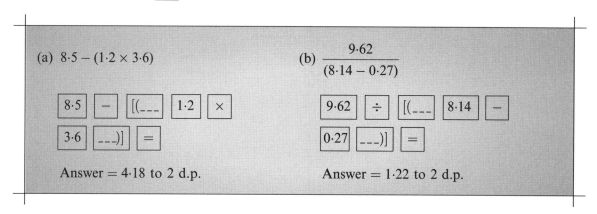

(a) $8\cdot5 - (1\cdot2 \times 3\cdot6)$

`8·5` `−` `[(---` `1·2` `×`
`3·6` `---)]` `=`

Answer = 4·18 to 2 d.p.

(b) $\dfrac{9\cdot62}{(8\cdot14 - 0\cdot27)}$

`9·62` `÷` `[(---` `8·14` `−`
`0·27` `---)]` `=`

Answer = 1·22 to 2 d.p.

Exercise 2

Work out and give the answer correct to 2 decimal places.

1. $11\cdot52 - (3\cdot14 \times 2\cdot6)$

2. $12\cdot5 + (3\cdot8 \div 6)$

3. $(5\cdot27 + 8\cdot2) \div 2\cdot7$

4. $9\cdot6 + (8\cdot7 \div 11)$

5. $(9\cdot5 \div 7) - 0\cdot44$

6. $13\cdot7 - (8\cdot2 \times 1\cdot31)$

7. $6\cdot31 - \left(\dfrac{8\cdot2}{1\cdot9}\right)$

8. $\left(\dfrac{7\cdot65}{1\cdot5}\right) - 3\cdot06$

9. $\dfrac{3\cdot63}{3\cdot9 + 0\cdot121)}$

10. $(2\cdot26 + 3\cdot15 + 8\cdot99) \div 1\cdot45$

11. $5\cdot89 \times (1\cdot8 - 0\cdot633)$

12. $17\cdot8 \div (5\cdot8 - 4\cdot95)$

13. $(11\cdot2 \div 7) \times 2\cdot43$

14. $(3\cdot65 + 1\cdot4 - 2\cdot34) \times 2\cdot6$

15. $35 - (8\cdot7 \times 2\cdot65)$

16. $\dfrac{(9\cdot37 + 8\cdot222)}{2\cdot47}$

17. $\dfrac{11\cdot23}{(9\cdot7 - 6\cdot66)}$

18. $\dfrac{(114 - 95\cdot6)}{14}$

19. $2{\cdot}7^2 - 1{\cdot}56$ **20.** $0{\cdot}73^2 \times 5{\cdot}2$ **21.** $6{\cdot}6 + 4{\cdot}1^2$

22. $(1{\cdot}5 + 2{\cdot}61)^2$ **23.** $(8{\cdot}2 - 6{\cdot}93)^2$ **24.** $(2{\cdot}4 \times 0{\cdot}15)^2$

25. $8{\cdot}9 - (1{\cdot}35)^2$ **26.** $(2{\cdot}7^2 - 3{\cdot}3) \div 5$ **27.** $2{\cdot}1^2 + 3{\cdot}11^2$

28. $\left(\frac{4{\cdot}5}{8}\right) + \left(\frac{4{\cdot}7}{7}\right)$ **29.** $3{\cdot}2^2 - \left(\frac{4{\cdot}2}{3{\cdot}7}\right)$ **30.** $\frac{2{\cdot}6^2}{(1{\cdot}4 + 1{\cdot}91)}$

Hint: Use the x^2 key

Fractions

- The $a\,{}^{b}\!/_{c}$ key is used for fractions.

To enter $\frac{3}{4}$, press 3 $a\,{}^{b}\!/_{c}$ 4. You see 3⌟4

To enter $5\frac{1}{3}$, press 5 $a\,{}^{b}\!/_{c}$ 1 $a\,{}^{b}\!/_{c}$ 3. You see 5⌟1⌟3

Exercise 3

Work out

1. $\frac{2}{3} + \frac{1}{4}$ **2.** $\frac{5}{6} + \frac{1}{3}$ **3.** $\frac{8}{9} + \frac{1}{3}$ **4.** $\frac{4}{15} + \frac{1}{2}$

5. $\frac{3}{5} - \frac{1}{2}$ **6.** $\frac{7}{8} - \frac{1}{16}$ **7.** $\frac{5}{7} - \frac{1}{2}$ **8.** $\frac{5}{6} - \frac{1}{5}$

9. $\frac{9}{10} + \frac{1}{20}$ **10.** $\frac{11}{12} - \frac{3}{4}$ **11.** $\frac{4}{9} \times \frac{1}{2}$ **12.** $\frac{3}{11} \times \frac{1}{4}$

13. $2\frac{1}{4} + \frac{2}{3}$ **14.** $3\frac{2}{3} - 1\frac{1}{2}$ **15.** $4\frac{1}{2} + \frac{5}{8}$ **16.** $\frac{1}{6} + 3\frac{3}{4}$

17. $3\frac{1}{5} \times 1\frac{1}{2}$ **18.** $4\frac{1}{2} \div \frac{3}{4}$ **19.** $3\frac{1}{2} \div \frac{2}{5}$ **20.** $21 \div 5\frac{1}{4}$

21. Copy and complete.

(a) $1\frac{1}{4} + 2\frac{1}{5} = \square$ (b) $\square + 3\frac{1}{3} = 4\frac{1}{2}$ (c) $\square + \frac{5}{6} = 1\frac{3}{4}$

(d) $\square - \frac{3}{7} = \frac{3}{4}$ (e) $\square \div \frac{2}{3} = 2$ (f) $\square \times 1\frac{2}{5} = \frac{1}{2}$

22. Copy and complete.

(a)

+		$\frac{3}{5}$		$1\frac{3}{4}$
	$\frac{5}{8}$		$\frac{5}{6}$	
$\frac{1}{4}$				
$2\frac{1}{2}$	$2\frac{5}{8}$			
			$\frac{11}{15}$	

(b)

×			$\frac{5}{8}$	$2\frac{1}{5}$
$\frac{4}{5}$	$\frac{2}{5}$			
			$\frac{5}{24}$	
	$\frac{1}{8}$	$\frac{1}{6}$		
$1\frac{1}{2}$				

Negative numbers

- On a calculator the [+/−] key changes the sign of a number from (+) to (−) or from (−) to (+).
- On most calculators we press [+/−] *after* the number.

  On graphics calculators we press it before the number, though this varies according to the model.

On a calculator work out:

(a) $-5{\cdot}2 + 7{\cdot}81$

Press the keys

[5·2] [+/−] [+] [7·81] [=]

Answer = 2·61

(b) $7{\cdot}5 \div (-0{\cdot}04)$

[7·5] [÷] [0·04] [+/−] [=]

Answer = −187·5

Notice that we do not *need* the brackets buttons. You may use them if you prefer.

Exercise 4

Work out the following. Give the answer correct to one decimal place where appropriate.

1. -7×3	**2.** $-5 \times (-2)$	**3.** $8 \div (-4)$
4. $10 \times (-4)$	**5.** $-2 \times (-2)$	**6.** $-12 \div 3$
7. $-5 \times (-4)$	**8.** $-8 - 11$	**9.** $-7 + 2$
10. $-9 + 30$	**11.** $-20 \div 4$	**12.** $-16 - 15$
13. $-3{\cdot}4 \times (-2{\cdot}5)$	**14.** $-0{\cdot}5 \times 6{\cdot}8$	**15.** $12{\cdot}5 - (-2{\cdot}5)$
16. $-1{\cdot}1 \times (-1{\cdot}1)$	**17.** $-8 \div (-0{\cdot}25)$	**18.** $-6{\cdot}8 \div 0{\cdot}1$
19. $\dfrac{-8 \times (-3)}{4}$	**20.** $\dfrac{12}{(3 \times (-2))}$	**21.** $\dfrac{20}{(-2)} + 8$
22. $-11{\cdot}4 + 1{\cdot}71$	**23.** $-9{\cdot}2 - 7{\cdot}4 + 15{\cdot}2$	**24.** $-4{\cdot}74 - (-13{\cdot}08)$
25. $\dfrac{(-8{\cdot}23) \times (-1{\cdot}24)}{3{\cdot}6}$	**26.** $\dfrac{5{\cdot}1 \times (-1{\cdot}42)}{(-1{\cdot}7)}$	**27.** $\dfrac{(-2{\cdot}3 \times (-2{\cdot}8)}{(-3{\cdot}5)}$
28. $(-3{\cdot}6)^2 + 2{\cdot}7$	**29.** $(-3{\cdot}91)^2 - 7$	**30.** $17{\cdot}4 - (-7{\cdot}2)^2$
31. $-6{\cdot}2 + (-8{\cdot}4)$	**32.** $-91 + (-8{\cdot}1)^2$	**33.** $-2{\cdot}5 \times (-1{\cdot}7)$
34. $-7{\cdot}2 + \left(\dfrac{4{\cdot}3}{1{\cdot}5}\right)$	**35.** $-8{\cdot}7 \times \left(\dfrac{7{\cdot}2}{11}\right)$	**36.** $(-7{\cdot}2 + 4)^2$

Other useful buttons

M+	Adds the number to the current memory. This key is useful when several numbers are to be added together.
x^y	Raises the number to a power.

(a) $5{\cdot}2 + (7{\cdot}2 \times 1{\cdot}4) + (8{\cdot}63 \times 1{\cdot}9)$

[0] [Min] [5·2] [M+] [7·2] [×] [1·4] [=] [M+] [8·63] [×] [1·9] [=] [M+] [MR]

Answer = 31·7 (to 3 s.f.)

(b) $15{\cdot}2 \times 6{\cdot}3 - 4{\cdot}2^3$

[4·2] [x^y] [3] [=] [Min] [15·2] [×] [6·3] [=] [−] [MR] [=]

Answer = 21·7 (to 3 s.f.)

Exercise 5

Work out correct to 1 decimal place, unless told otherwise.

Use the [M+] button in Questions **1** to **10**. Don't forget to clear the memory each time!

1. $(1{\cdot}3 \times 2{\cdot}4) + (5{\cdot}3 \times 0{\cdot}7) + (8{\cdot}6 \times 0{\cdot}61) + 11{\cdot}7$

2. $(0{\cdot}8 \times 0{\cdot}7) + (1{\cdot}1 \times 3{\cdot}5) + 6{\cdot}23 + (1{\cdot}9 \times 0{\cdot}8)$

3. $(1{\cdot}8 \times 1{\cdot}9 \times 3{\cdot}1) + (0{\cdot}91 \times 5{\cdot}6) + (4{\cdot}71 \times 1{\cdot}9)$

4. $(8{\cdot}9 \times 1{\cdot}5) + 7{\cdot}1^2 + 5{\cdot}3^2 + 31{\cdot}4$

5. $8{\cdot}21 + (9{\cdot}71 \times 2{\cdot}3) + (8{\cdot}2 \times 1{\cdot}4) + 2{\cdot}67$

6. $(8{\cdot}9 \times 1{\cdot}1) + (1{\cdot}2 \times 1{\cdot}3 \times 1{\cdot}4) + (0{\cdot}76 \times 3{\cdot}68)$

In questions **7** to **10** find the total bill, correct to the nearest penny.

7. 5 tins at 42p each
4 jars of jam at 69p each
48 eggs at £1·55/dozen
3 packets of tea at £1·19 each
4 grapefruit at 33p each

8. 200 g of cheese at £5·20/kg
1 bottle of ketchup at £1·19
3 jars of coffee at £2·45 each
4 lemons at 29p each
8lb potatoes at 32p/lb

9. 14 bolts at 22p each
30 m of cable at 15p/metre
3 sacks of fertilizer at £5·35 each
200 tiles at £2·30 for 10
5 plugs at 49p each

10. 1 tube of glue at £1·35
3 tins of paint at £4·20 each
100 m of wire at 11p/metre
100 g of nails at £8/kg
3 boxes of seed at £3·35 each

In questions **11** to **19** use the x^y button, where needed.

11. $3{\cdot}7^3$ **12.** $2{\cdot}1^4$ **13.** $3{\cdot}1^5 + 112$

14. $1{\cdot}64^5$ **15.** $(1{\cdot}81 + 2{\cdot}43)^4$ **16.** $19{\cdot}8 + 1{\cdot}96^3$

17. $1{\cdot}7^3 + 2{\cdot}4^3$ **18.** $200 - 3{\cdot}7^4$ **19.** $3{\cdot}2 + 3{\cdot}2^2 + 3{\cdot}2^3$

In Questions **20** to **34** think ahead and use your calculator as efficiently as possible.

20. $\dfrac{5{\cdot}65}{1{\cdot}21 + 3{\cdot}7}$ **21.** $\dfrac{8{\cdot}7}{13} + \dfrac{4{\cdot}9}{15}$ **22.** $14{\cdot}6 - (3{\cdot}9 \times 2{\cdot}62)$

23. $12{\cdot}94 - \sqrt{8{\cdot}97}$ **24.** $\dfrac{5{\cdot}41 + 7{\cdot}82}{9{\cdot}82 - 3{\cdot}99}$ **25.** $\sqrt{\dfrac{100{\cdot}9}{9{\cdot}81 + 56}}$

26. $11{\cdot}2\%$ of $9{\cdot}6^3$ **27.** $\frac{2}{7}$ of $\left(\dfrac{4{\cdot}2}{1{\cdot}95 - 0{\cdot}713}\right)$ **28.** $\frac{1}{6} + \frac{1}{7} + \frac{1}{8} + \frac{1}{9}$

29. $\dfrac{\sqrt{8{\cdot}74} + \sqrt{7{\cdot}05}}{\sqrt{3{\cdot}14} + \sqrt{2{\cdot}76}}$ **30.** $\dfrac{900}{101 - 2{\cdot}9^4}$ **31.** $(15\%$ of $22{\cdot}36)^3$

32. 18% of $9{\cdot}1\%$ of 1150 **33.** $2{\cdot}8^5 - \sqrt{\dfrac{9{\cdot}7}{11{\cdot}4}}$ **34.** $\frac{2}{3}$ of $\left(\dfrac{9{\cdot}81}{1{\cdot}25^2}\right)^3$

Calculator words

- When you hold a calculator display upside down some numbers appear to form words: [4506] spells "Gosh"

  [0.710] spells "Old"

  (ignoring the decimal point)

Exercise 6

Translate this passage using a calculator and the clues below:

'(1) ___!', (2) ___, (3) ___, climbing out of (4) ___. 'It's raining. I can't take (5) ___ and (6) ___ for a walk now.' (7) ___ and (8) ___ were her (9) ___ and they loved to (10) ___ up the (11) ___ and roll about, covering their (12) ___ (13) ___ in mud.

From the window of her small (14) ___, she saw a lady coming down the (15) ___. '(16) ___ (17) ___!' said (18) ___. 'It's (19) ___, come to (20) ___ her (21) ___ (22) ___. I'll ask her in for a chat.' '(23) ___, (24) ___. (25) ___! I'm wetting your floor,' (26) ___ (27) ___, taking of her coat and (28) ___ and giving (29) ___ the basket of (30) ___ (31) ___ (32) ___. 'I'll (33) ___ the eggs now', said (34) ___. 'Do you want some?' 'Yes please' smiled (35) ___. 'I'll eat anything that is (36) ___.' 'Did you know that the (37) ___ of the

(38) ____ garage was ill and (39) ____ so the garage is closed until it is (40) ____ to someone (41) ____.'
'(42) ____. The (43) ____ (44) ____ are ready.' 'Is that a new (45) ____ in your garden?' asked (46) ____.
Gardening was one of (47) ____ (48) ____ and she could (49) ____ away hours with her plants and her pet (50) ____. As it wasn't raining anymore she decided to let the (51) ____ (52) ____ in the garden.

(53) ____ had to go, so she put on her (54) ____ (55) ____ and coat. Picking up her basket, (56) ____ (57) ____, 'My basket has so many (58) ____. It doesn't (59) ____ (60) ____ properly anymore. It (61) ____.'

With that (62) ____ left, saying (63) ____, just in time to (64) ____ another downpour.

Clues to passage

(1): $2 \times 2 \times 2 \times 5$
(2): $0{\cdot}4 - 0{\cdot}05085$
(3): $22 \times 23 \times 24 \times 25 + 15\,230$
(4): $0{\cdot}6^2 + (2 \times 0{\cdot}1 \times 0{\cdot}1)$
(5): $0{\cdot}3 \times 0{\cdot}5$
(6): $(9 \times 10 \times 11) - (2 \times 7 \times 13)$
(7): $0{\cdot}4^2 - 0{\cdot}1^2$
(8): $(10^2 + 1) \times 2^3$
(9): $1234 + 5678 - 1012$
(10): $(5 \times 6 \times 5 \times 6) + (1 + 2 + 3 + 4)$
(11): $203 \times 7 \times 5$
(12): $1000 - (3^4 + 1)$
(13): $728 \times 729 + 8 \times 37$
(14): $3 \times 13 \times 10^3 + (3{\cdot}5 \div 0{\cdot}5)$
(15): $2570 + 2571 + 2572 + 1^{74}$
(16): $10^3 \div 5^2$
(17): $9 \div 1000$
(18): $333\,333 - 12345 - 2158$
(19): $(67 \times 68 \times 69) + (34 \times 35) - (2^4)$
(20): $5 \times 7 \times (11 \times 20 + 1)$
(21): $5 \times 5 \times 5 \times 5 \times 2 \times 2 \times 2 \times 7 + 9$
(22): $6000 - 7$
(23): $0{\cdot}1234 + 0{\cdot}65$
(24): $11 \times 2 \times 8 \times 3 \times 23 \times 5^2 + (2 \times 7615)$
(25): $(3^2 - 1^2) \times 5$
(26): $5 \times 3 \times 23$
(27): $0{\cdot}38 - 0{\cdot}000081$
(28): $123 \times 432 - 91$
(29): $320\,000 - 1170$
(30): $30 \times 200 - 8 + 1$
(31): $567 + 345 - 567$
(32): $0{\cdot}7 + 0{\cdot}004 + 0{\cdot}03$
(33): 1777×2^2
(34): $321\,123 - 2293$
(35): $561 \times 562 + 2^8$
(36): $377\,777 + 321 + 5$
(37): $33\,048 \div (4{\cdot}7 + 1{\cdot}3)$
(38): $12345 + (5 \times 13 \times 10^3)$
(39): $0{\cdot}31 + 0{\cdot}00034$
(40): $0{\cdot}047 \times 5 \times 3$
(41): $60^2 - 3^3$
(42): $68 \times 69 \times 70 + (22 + 45) \times 100$
(43): $0{\cdot}61^2 - 0{\cdot}00102$
(44): $10^4 - 4007$
(45): $(23 \times 5 \times 3) \div 1000$
(46): $105\,180 + 105\,181 + 105\,177$
(47): $47 \times 48 \times 49 \times 50 - 208\,370$
(48): $(23 \times 10^2 \times 209 \times 11) + 31\,104$
(49): $503 \times \sqrt{(108 \div 3)}$
(50): $448 \times 449 \times 450 - 79\,366$
(51): $41\,300 \div (0{\cdot}32 + 0{\cdot}61 + 6{\cdot}07)$
(52): $(0{\cdot}7 \div 0{\cdot}1) + (5 \times 7 \times 10^3)$
(53): $16^2 + 562 \times 561$
(54): $0{\cdot}33333 + 0{\cdot}04001$
(55): $(10^4 + 609) \times 5$
(56): $(4^2 - 1^2) \times (30 - 7)$
(57): $0{\cdot}6^2 - 0{\cdot}1^2 - 0{\cdot}00085$
(58): $(999 - 40) \times 2^3 \times 7$
(59): $0{\cdot}011 \times \sqrt{4096}$
(60): $5678 + 630 \div 2$
(61): $1 - 0{\cdot}3 + 0{\cdot}000551$
(62): $315\,513 + (10^3 \div 40)$
(63): $146 \times 147 \times 148 + (3 \times 1211)$
(64): $[1001 \div (7 \times 11)] \times 10^3 \times 3$

3.5 Reflection

Reflections are quite common in everyday life.
Think of examples of reflections:

- in the classroom
- at home
- anywhere

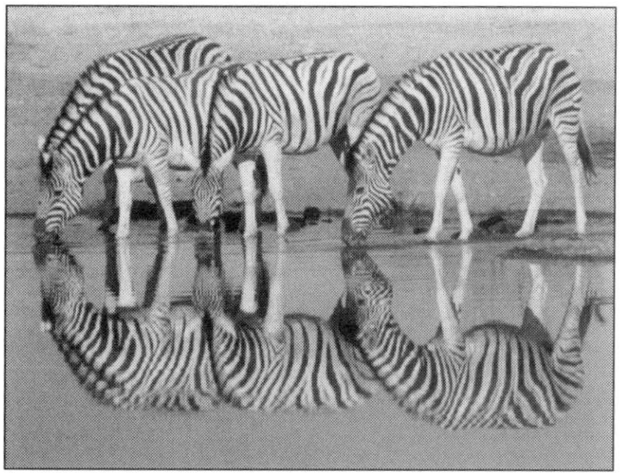

- The shape on the right has line symmetry. This can be checked by either paper folding, using tracing paper or by using a mirror. In a mathematical reflection we imagine a line of symmetry which acts like a double-sided mirror.

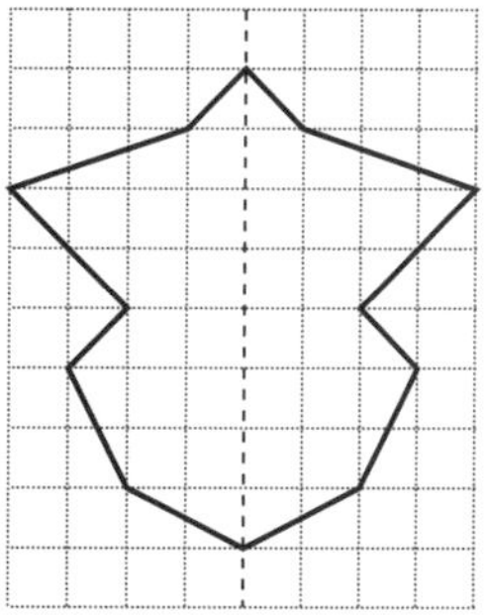

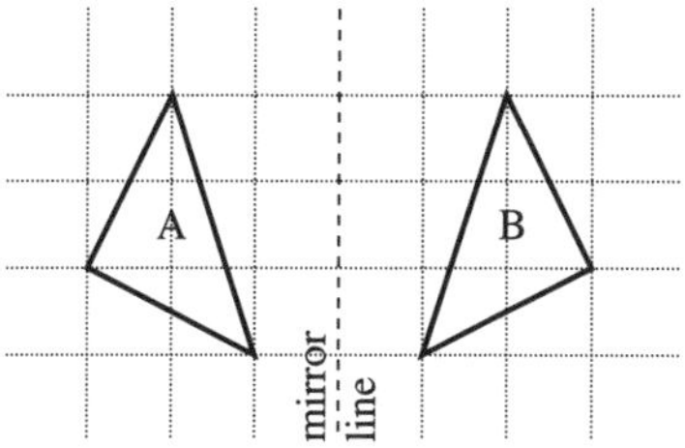

- Triangle B is the image of triangle A under reflection in the mirror line. Similarly triangle A is the image of triangle B under reflection in the same line.

- In the reflection on the right, the image of the shape ABCD is the shape A′B′C′D′. Notice that the perpendicular distance from A to the mirror line is the same as the perpendicular distance from A′ to the mirror line. Similarly B, C and D are the same perpendicular distances from the line as B′, C′ and D′ respectively.

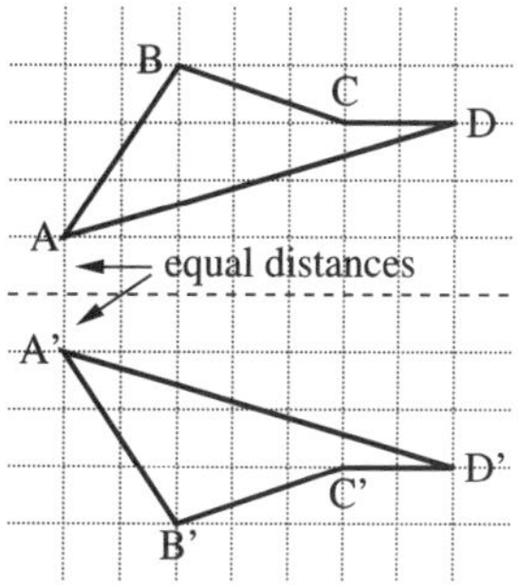

- Extra care is required when the mirror line lies along a diagonal.
  Notice that the line PP′ is perpendicular to the mirror line.

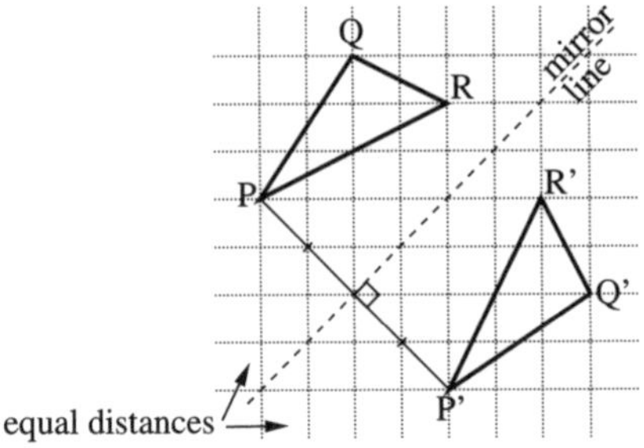

- The mirror line can pass through the shape which is being reflected, as shown here.

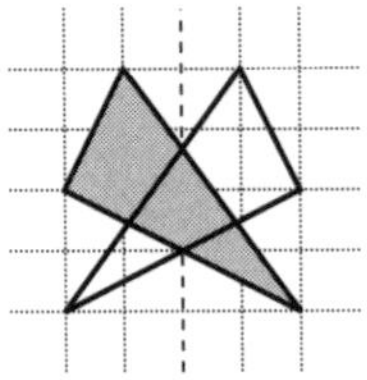

Exercise 1

Copy each shape on squared paper and draw the image after reflection in the broken line.

1. 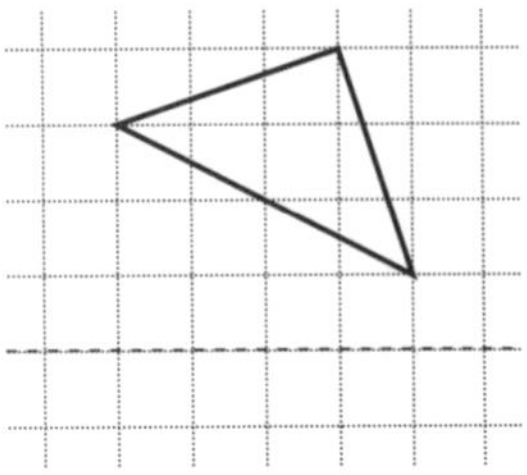
2. 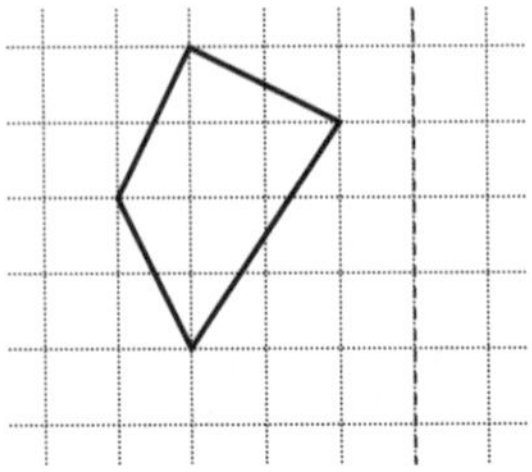
3. 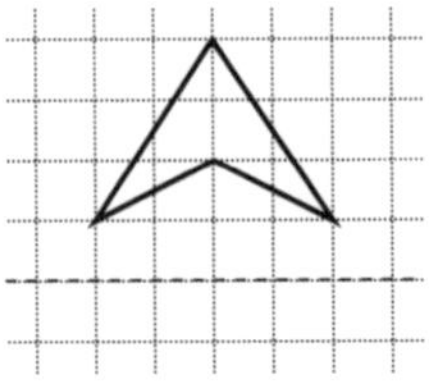
4. 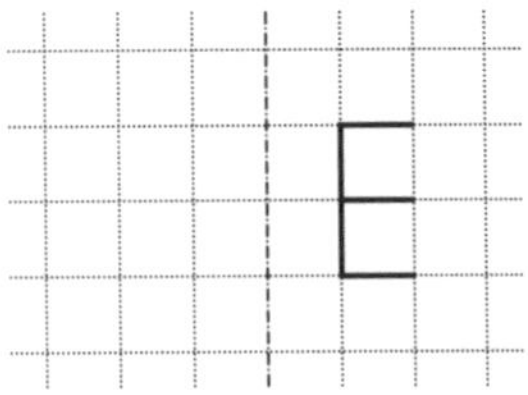
5. 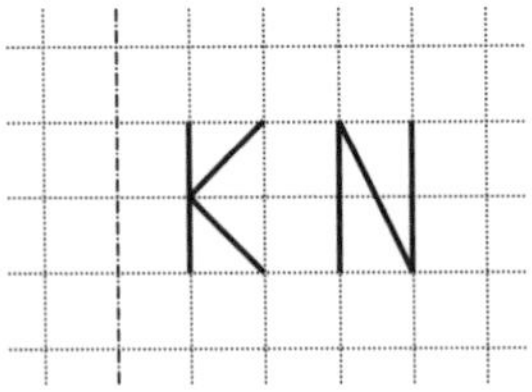
6. 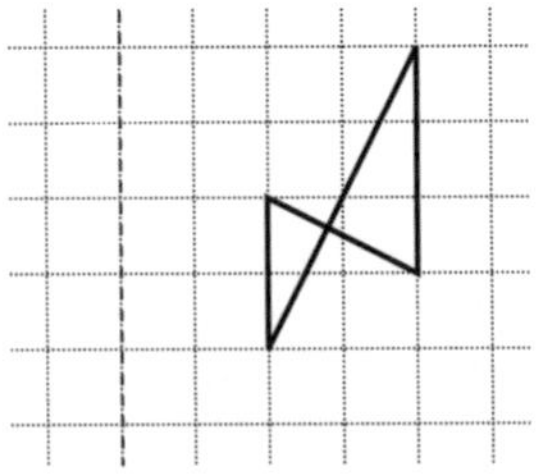
7. 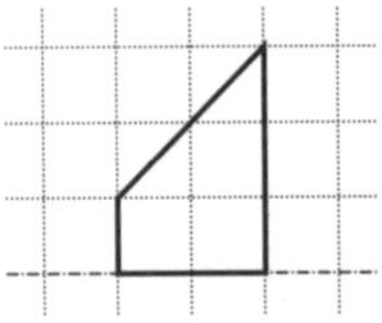
8. 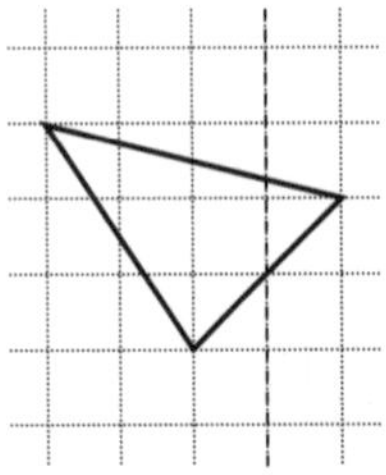
9. 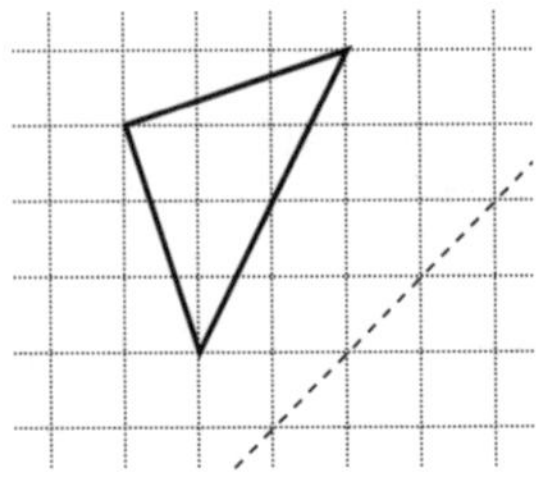

10.

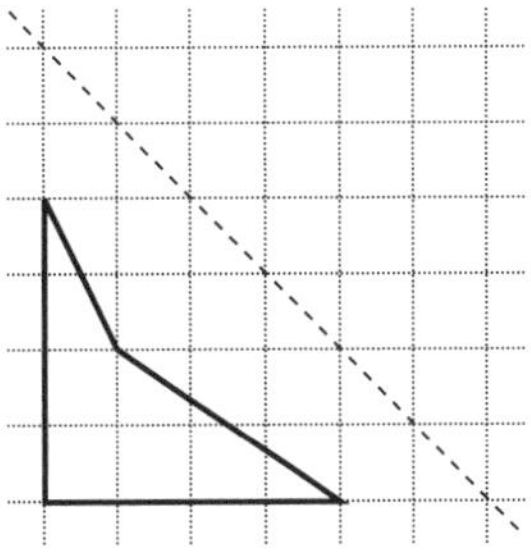

11.

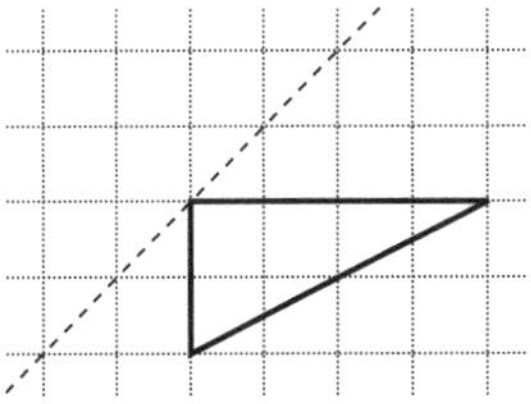

12.

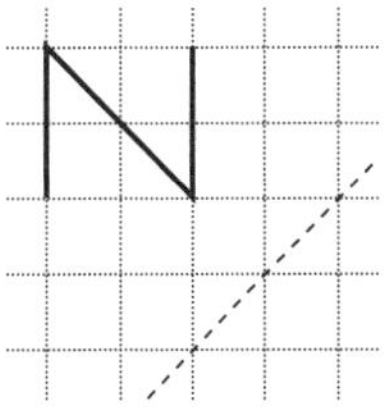

13. Write your own name in capital letters and then reflect the letters in a horizontal line.

14. Draw any shape of your own design (not too complicated!) and then reflect it in either a horizontal, vertical or diagonal line.

In Questions **15** to **17** first reflect the shape in line 1 and then reflect the image in line 2.

15.

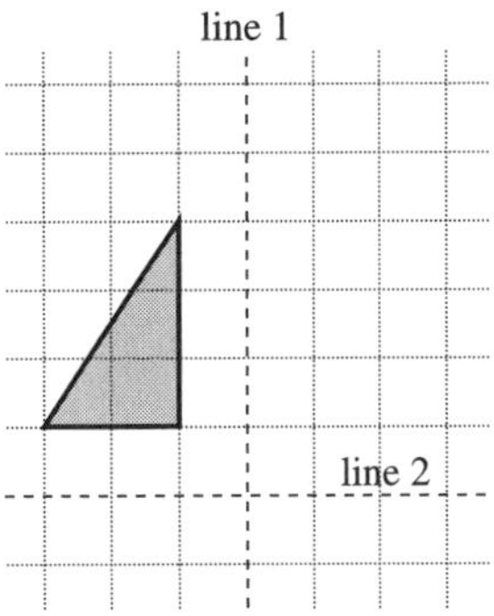

16.

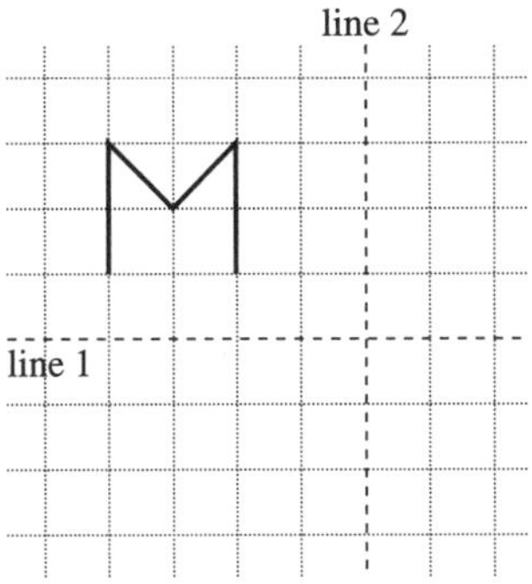

17.

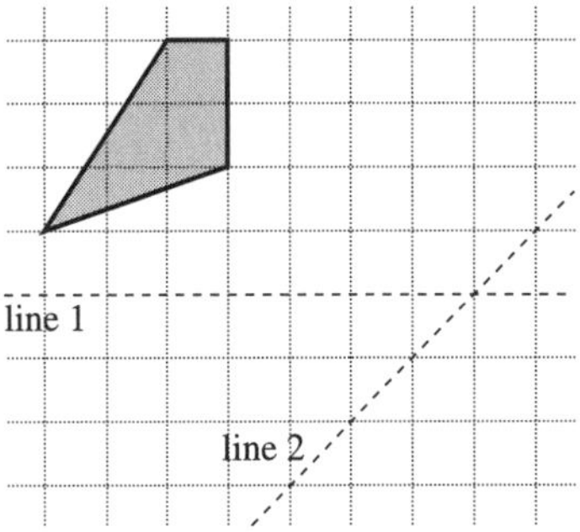

Questions **18** to **20** are more difficult reflections. Copy each shape and draw the image after reflection in the broken line.

18.

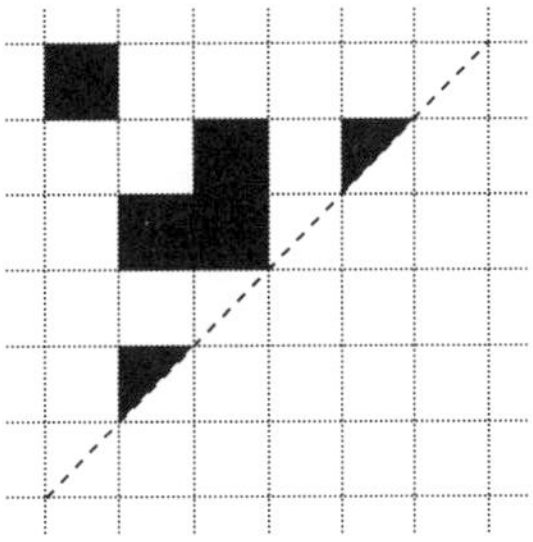

19.

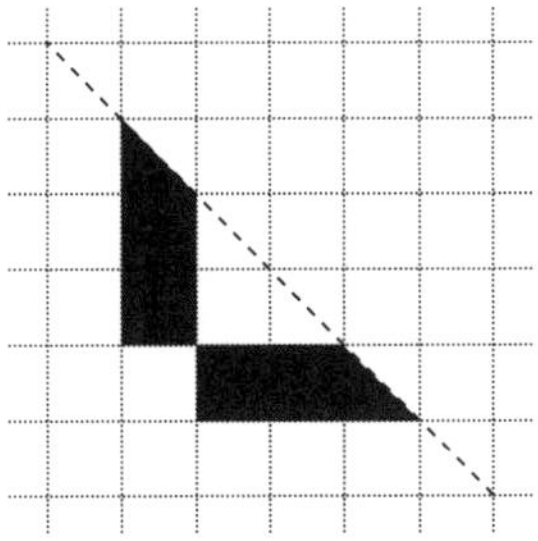

20.

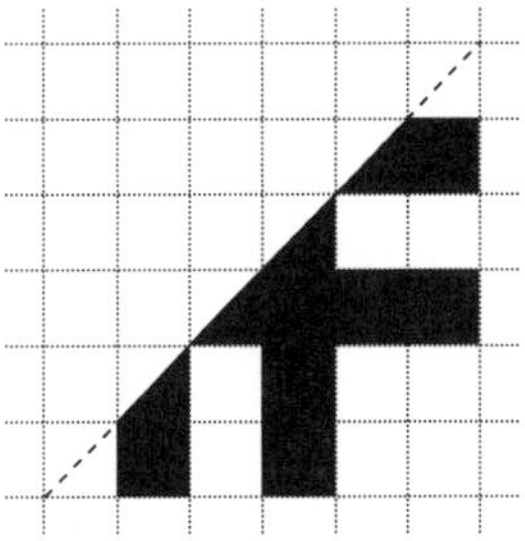

Using coordinates

(a) Triangle 2 is the image of triangle 1 under reflection in the *x axis*.

We will use the shorthand '△' for 'triangle'.

(b) △3 is the image of △2 under reflection in the line $x = -1$.

(c) △4 is the image of △1 under reflection in the line $y = x$.

Teacher's note. There is work on equations of lines in section 5.1, 'Graphs of straight lines'.

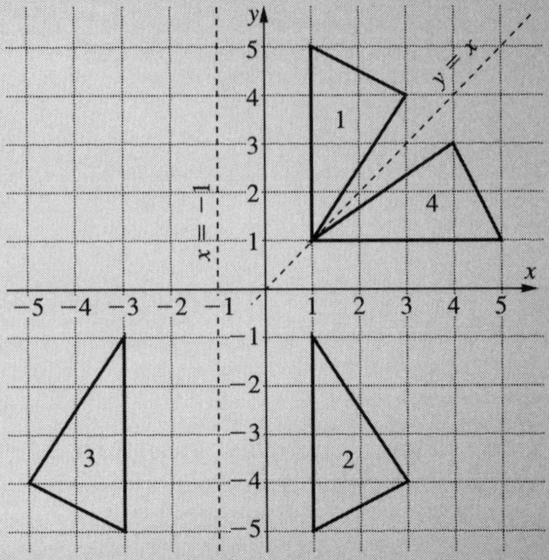

Exercise 2

1. 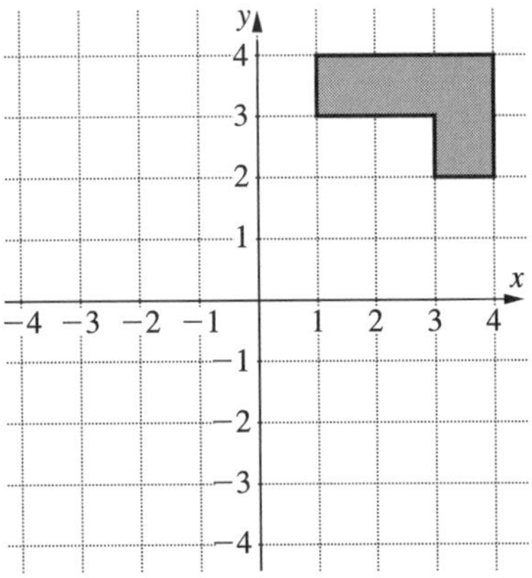

Copy the diagram.

(a) Reflect the shape in the x axis. Label the image A.

(b) Reflect the shape in the y axis. Label the image B.

2. Copy the diagram onto squared paper.

(a) Reflect the shaded triangle in $y = 2$. Label the image A.

(b) Reflect the shaded triangle in $x = 1$. Label the image B.

(c) Reflect the shaded triangle in the x axis. Label the image C.

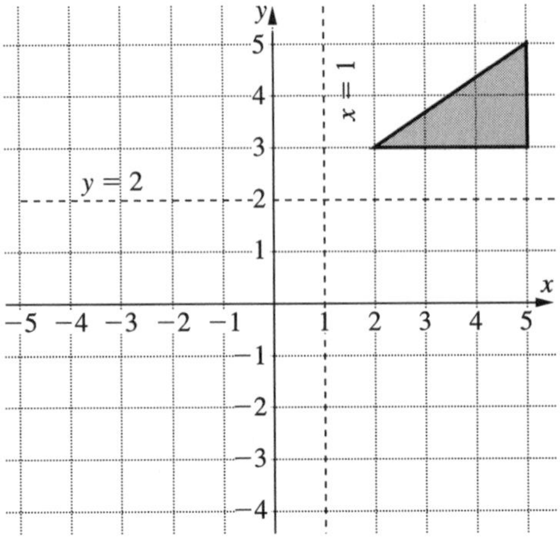

3. Copy the diagram onto squared paper.
Draw the image of the shaded triangle under reflection in:
(a) $y = 1$, label it $\triangle$A
(b) $x = -1$, label it $\triangle$B
(c) $y = x$, label it $\triangle$C

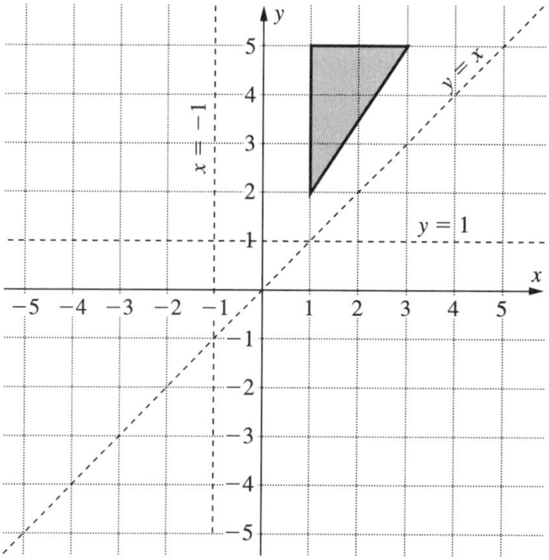

4. (a) Draw x and y axes with values from -6 to $+6$ and draw shape A which has vertices at (3, 1), (5, 3), (5, 1), (4, 0)
(b) Reflect shape A in the x axis onto shape B.
(c) Reflect shape A in the y axis onto shape C.
(d) Reflect shape A in the line $y = x$ onto shape D.

5. (a) Draw x and y axes with values from -6 to $+6$ and draw shape A which has vertices at (1, −2), (3, −3), (3, −4), (1, −6)
(b) Reflect shape A in the y axis onto shape B.
(c) Reflect shape B (not shape A!) in the line $y = x$ onto shape C.
(d) Reflect shape C in the line $y = 1\frac{1}{2}$ onto shape D.
(e) Write down the coordinates of the vertices of shape D.

6. (a) Draw x and y axes with values from -6 to $+6$ and draw shape P which has vertices at (−4, 2), (−4, 3), (−3, 5), (−3, 2).
(b) Reflect shape P in the line $y = 2$ onto shape Q.
(c) Reflect shape Q in the y axis onto shape R.
(d) Reflect shape R in the line $y = x$ onto shape S.
(e) Write down the coordinate of the vertices of shape S.

7. Write down the equation of the mirror line for the following reflections:

(a) $\triangle A \rightarrow \triangle C$
(b) $\triangle A \rightarrow \triangle B$
(c) $\triangle D \rightarrow \triangle G$
(d) $\triangle F \rightarrow \triangle E$
(e) $\triangle F \rightarrow \triangle D$

Remember:
The x axis is also the line $y = 0$,
The y axis is also the line $x = 0$.

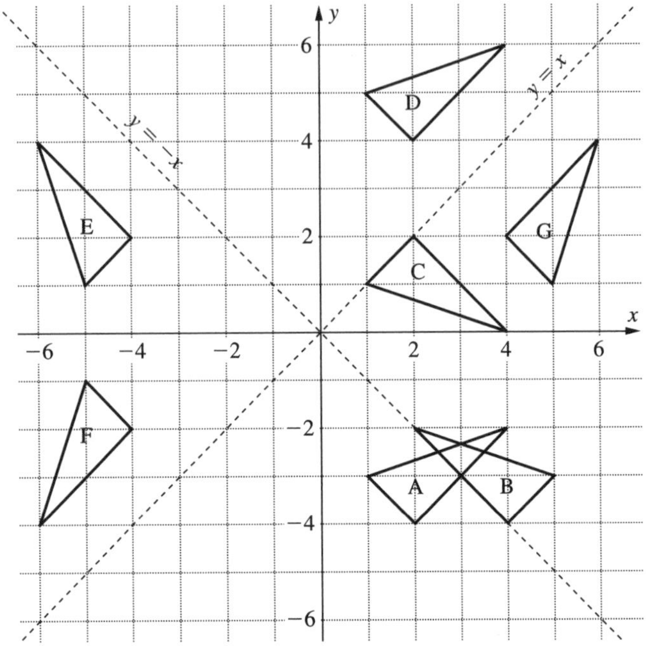

8. (a) Draw x and y axes with values from -6 to $+6$ and draw $\triangle 1$ with vertices at (3, 1), (6, 1), (6, 3).
(b) Reflect $\triangle 1$ in the line $y = x$ onto $\triangle 2$.
(c) Reflect $\triangle 1$ in the y axis onto $\triangle 3$.
(d) Reflect $\triangle 2$ in the y axis onto $\triangle 4$.
(e) Find the equation for the reflection $\triangle 3$ onto $\triangle 4$.

9. (a) Draw $\triangle 1$ with vertices at $(-4, 4)$, $(-4, 6)$, $(-1, 6)$.
(b) Reflect $\triangle 1$ in the line $x = -\frac{1}{2}$ onto $\triangle 2$.
(c) Reflect $\triangle 2$ in the line $y = x$ onto $\triangle 3$.
(d) Reflect $\triangle 1$ in the line $y = x$ onto $\triangle 4$.
(e) Find the equation for the reflection $\triangle 3$ onto $\triangle 4$.

10. (a) In what country did 'Napoleon' live?
Write your answer in "mirror writing".
(b) Whose statue is on top of a column in Trafalgar Square?
(c) Which famous mathematician made a discovery after an apple fell on his head?

11. The word 'AMBULANCE' is to be printed on the front of an ambulance so that a person in front of the ambulance will see the word written the right way round, when viewed in the driver's mirror. How should the word be printed on the front of the ambulance?

12. Draw a circle, with radius about 4 cm, and mark any three points A, B and C on the circumference. Draw lines through AB, BC and CA as shown.
Mark a fourth point P anywhere on the circumference. Use a set square and ruler to find the images of P after reflection in the lines through AB, BC and CA.
What do you notice? Compare your result with that of other people.

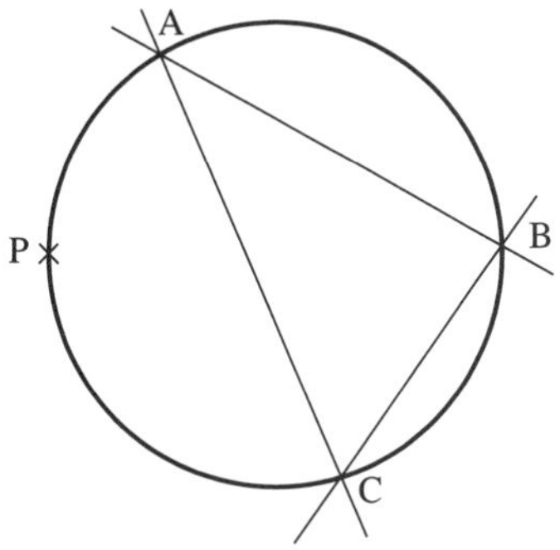

13.* (a) Find the image of the point (1, 6) after reflection in the line:
(i) $x = 5$ (ii) $x = 50$ (iii) $y = 2$
(iv) $y = 200$ (v) $y = x$ (vi) $y = -x$
(b) Find the image of the point (63, 207) after reflection in the line:
(i) $y = x$ (ii) $y = -x$.
(c) Find the image of the point (a, b) after reflection in the x axis.
(d) Find the image of the point (a, b) after reflection in the y axis.

14.* The line segment AB can be made into a 2×2 square using three successive reflections as shown below.

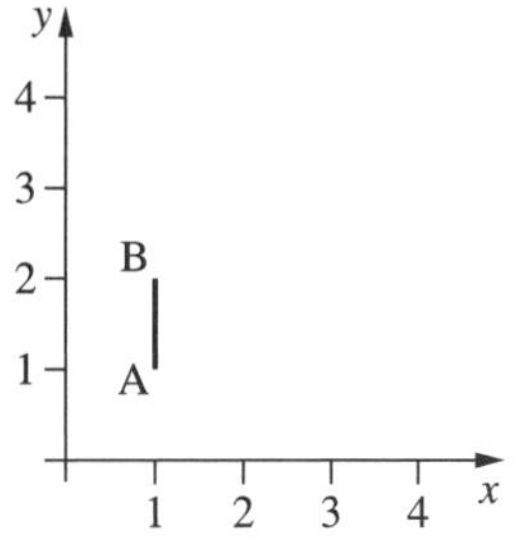

(a) reflect in $y = 2$

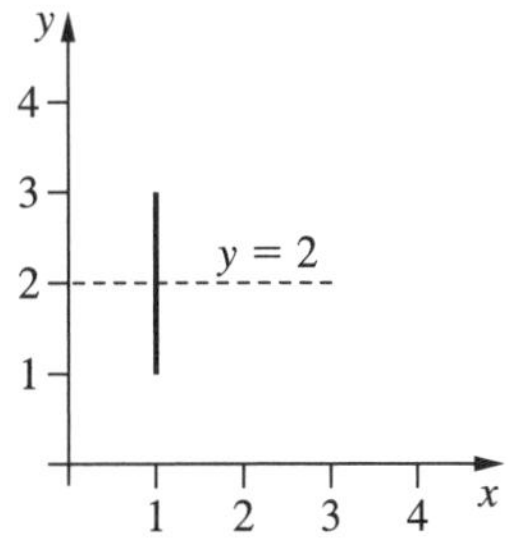

(b) reflect in $x + y = 4$

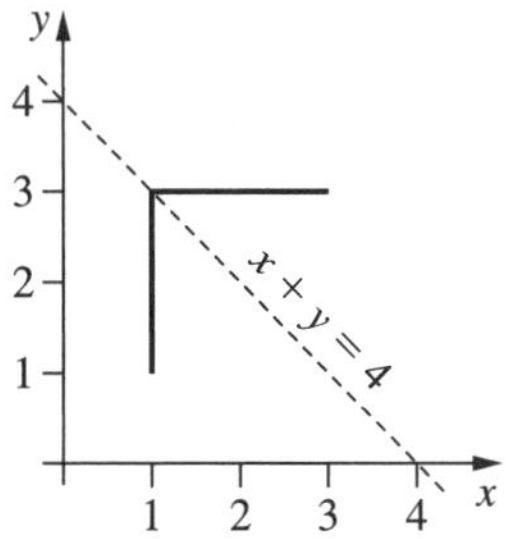

(c) reflect in $y = x$

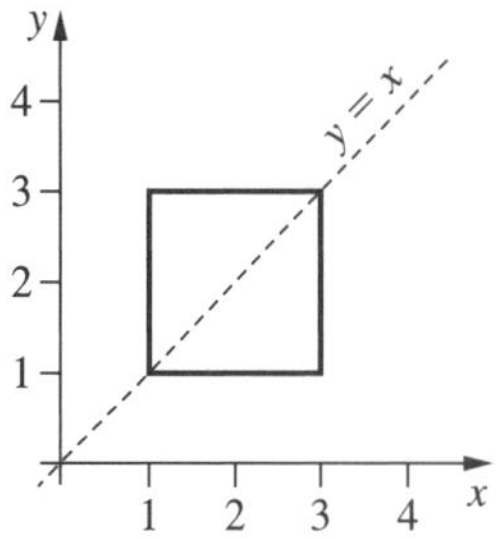

Show how the same line segment AB can be made into a 3×3 square with four successive reflections. Give the equations for all the mirror lines.

3.6 Formulas and expressions

Substituting into a formula

(a) In the formula $s = ut$, s, u and t are variable quantities.

s is for distance,
u is for speed,
t is for time taken.

When $u = 3$ and $t = 10$, $s = ut$

$s = 3 \times 10 = 30$

(b) When the wind velocity is v, the cost of damage, £C, is given by the formula

$C = 500\,v + 20\,000$

When $v = 100$, $C = 500 \times 100 + 20\,000$

$C = 70\,000$

The cost of damage = £70 000

Exercise 1

In Questions **1** to **12** you are given a formula. Find the value of the letter required in each case.

1. $x = 3y + 2$
Find x when $y = 4$

2. $a = 4b + 1$
Find a when $b = 5$

3. $c = \frac{d}{5} + 3$
Find c when $d = 15$

4. $e = \frac{f}{2} - 4$
Find e when $f = 8$

5. $g = 8h + 7$
Find g when $h = 6$

6. $i = 5j - 3$
Find i if $j = 7$

7. $k = \frac{l}{3} + 4$
Find k when $l = 21$

8. $m = \frac{n}{4} - 2$
Find m when $n = 32$

9. $p = 6q + 5$
Find p when $q = 13$

10. $r = \frac{s}{6} - 8$
Find r when $s = 66$

11. $t = \frac{4u + 3}{5}$
Find t when $u = 3$

12. $v = 3(5w - 6)$
Find v when $w = 2$

13. x and y are connected by the formula $x = 3(y - 4)$
Find x when $y = 8$

14. a and b are connected by the formula $a = 100 - 5b$
Find a when $b = 20$.

Exercise 2

1. Here are some polygons.

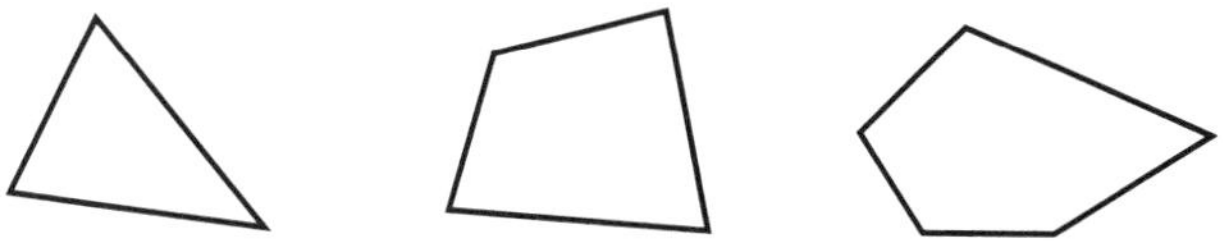

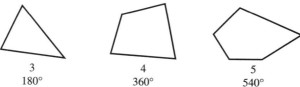

Number of sides:	3	4	5
Sum of angles:	180°	360°	540°

The sum of the angles in a polygon with n sides is given by the formula, $\text{sum of angles} = (n - 2) \times 180°$

(a) Find the sum of the angles in a hexagon (6 sides).
(b) Find the sum of the angles in a polygon with 102 sides.
(c) Show that the formula gives the correct answer for the sum of the angles in a pentagon (5 sides).

2. Here is a formula $h = 5t - 4$.
Find the value of h when
(a) $t = 2$ (b) $t = 10$ (c) $t = 6$

3. Using the formula $p = 100 + 2x$, find the value of p when
(a) $x = 3$ (b) $x = 100$ (c) $x = \frac{1}{2}$

4. Suppose you add the numbers from 1 to 50: $1 + 2 + 3 + \ldots + 49 + 50$.
The answer is $\dfrac{50 \times 51}{2} = 1275$.
If you add the numbers from 1 to any number n the answer is given by the formula $\text{sum} = \dfrac{n(n+1)}{2}$.

(a) Use the formula to find the sum of the numbers from 1 to 10. (i.e. $1 + 2 + 3 + \ldots + 9 + 10$).
(b) Check your answer by adding the numbers in the normal way.
(c) Use the formula to find the sum of the numbers from 1 to 99.

5. Below are several different formulas for z in terms of x.
Find the value of z in each case.
(a) $z = 10x - 6$, $x = 5{\cdot}5$
(b) $z = \dfrac{5x + 3}{2}$, $x = 3$
(c) $z = 3(2x + 5)$, $x = 2$

6. In the formulas below t is given in terms of n and a. Find the value of t in each case.
(a) $t = 5a + 2n$; $a = 3$, $n = 4$
(b) $t = 6a + 3n - 10$; $a = 2$, $n = 1$
(c) $t = an + 7$; $a = 5$, $n = 2$

7. Here is a sequence of shapes made from sticks

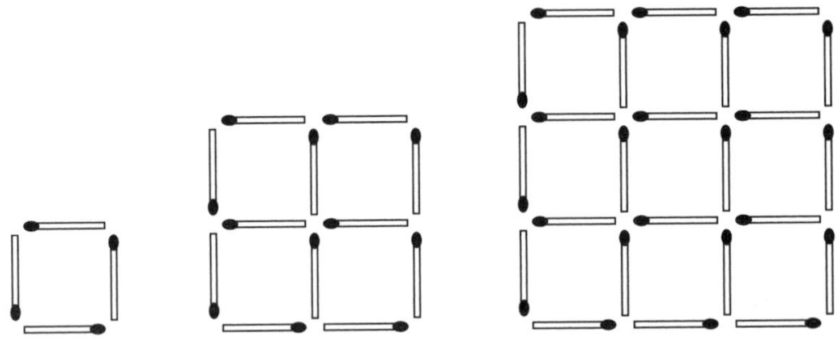

Shape number:	$n = 1$	$n = 2$	$n = 3$
Number of sticks:	4	12	24

The formula for the number of sticks in shape number n is

number of sticks $= 2n^2 + 2n$. (Note: $2n^2 = 2(n^2)$)

(a) Check that the formula gives the correct answer for $n = 1$ and for $n = 2$.

(b) Use the formula to find the number of sticks in shape number 10.

8. An estimate for the volume of a cylinder of radius r and height h is given by the formula $V = 3r^2h$.

(a) Find the value of V when $r = 10$ and $h = 2$.

(b) Find the value of V when $r = 5$ and $h = 4$.

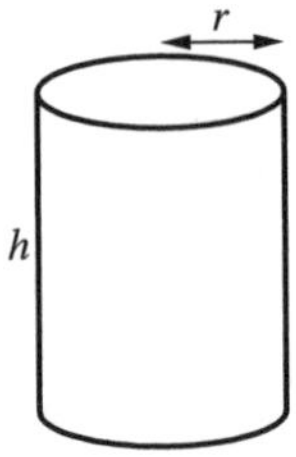

9. Find the value of c using the formulas and values given.

(a) $c = mx + 7$; $m = 5$, $x = -1$

(b) $c = 2t + t^2$; $t = 3$

(c) $c = 2pq + p^2$; $p = 3$, $q = 2$

(d) $c = (a + b^2)$; $a = 5$, $b = -2$

10. If $T = a^2 + 3a - 5$, find the values of T when

(a) $a = 3$ (b) $a = 10$ (c) $a = 1$

11. The total surface area A of the solid cuboid shown is given by the formula

$A = 2bc + 2ab + 2ac$

Find the value of A when $a = 2$, $b = 3$, $c = 4$.

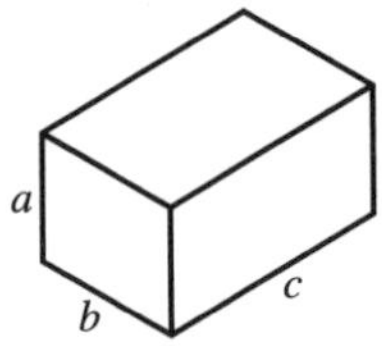

12.

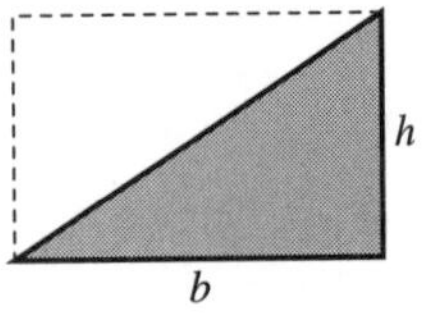

The diagram shows a rectangle with a diagonal drawn. The area of the shaded triangle is A.
Find a formula for A using b and h.

13. In the polygons below, diagonals are drawn from one vertex.

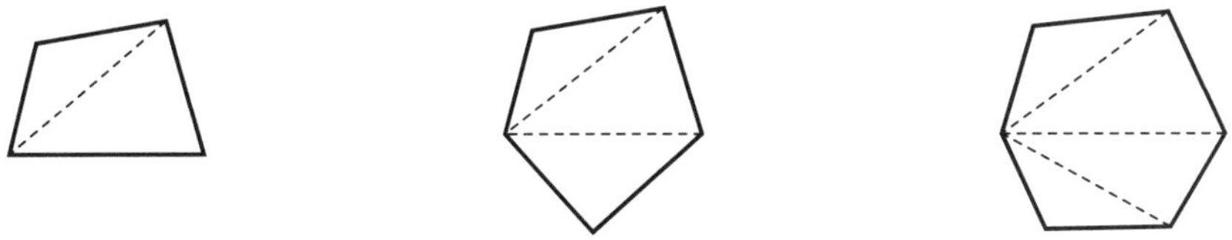

$n = 4$ sides	$n = 5$ sides	$n = 6$ sides
$d = 1$ diagonal	$d = 2$ diagonals	$d = 3$ diagonals

Find a formula connecting the number of diagonals and the number of sides. Write '$d = \ldots\ldots$'.

14. In this sequence black squares are surrounded by white squares.

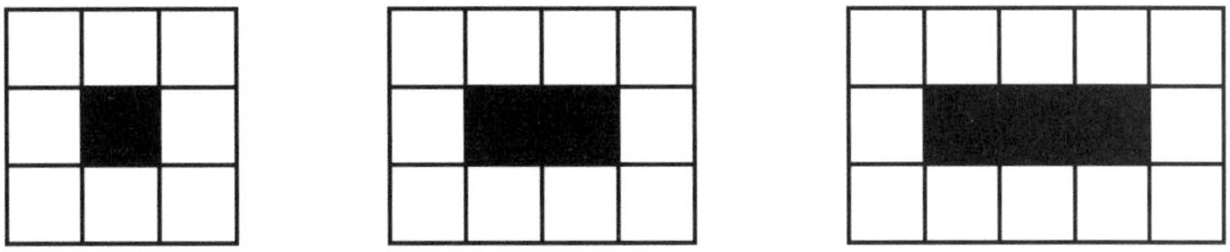

Black squares:	$b = 1$	$b = 2$	$b = 3$
White squares:	$w = 8$	$w = 10$	$w = 12$

(a) Draw the next diagram in the sequence and make a table.

black squares, b	1	2	3	4
white squares, w	8	10	12	

(b) Work out the number of white squares in the diagram which has 20 black squares.

(c) Write the formula, without words, for the number of white squares. Use b for the number of black squares and w for the number of white squares. Write '$w =$ '.

Expressions

An expression does *not* have an equals sign. For example: $3x - 7$; $2a + b$; $5y - 10$. These are all expressions.

Below are three expressions involving a, b, c and d. Find the value of each expression given that $a = 3$, $b = 2$ $c = 5$, $d = -1$

(i) $5a + 7$
$= 5 \times 3 + 7$
$= 15 + 7$
$= 22$

(ii) $2b + d$
$= 2 \times 2 + (-1)$
$= 4 - 1$
$= 3$

(iii) $ab + 5c$
$= (3 \times 2) + (5 \times 5)$
$= 6 + 25$
$= 31$

Notice that the working goes *down* the page, not across. This helps to avoid errors.

Exercise 3

In Questions **1** to **10** find the value of each expression

1. $2x + 1$ if $x = 4$

2. $3x - 1$ if $x = 2$

3. $5x - 2$ if $x = 3$

4. $4x + 3$ if $x = 3$

5. $10 + a$ if $a = 5$

6. $7 - a$ if $a = 4$

7. $12 - b$ if $b = 6$

8. $16 + b$ if $b = 3$

9. $4 + 3c$ if $c = 6$

10. $20 - 2c$ if $c = 7$

11. Find the value of these expressions when $n = 3$.
(a) $n^2 - 1$ (b) $2n^2$ (c) n^3

12. Find the value of these expressions when $a = 1{\cdot}5$.
(a) $2a + 5$ (b) $6 - a$ (c) $3(a - 1)$

13. Find the value of these expressions when $x = 2$.
(a) $\dfrac{x+2}{x}$ (b) $\dfrac{x+4}{x-1}$ (c) $\dfrac{1}{x} + 4$

14. Find the value of these expressions when $n = -2$.
(a) $n + 5$ (b) $3n$ (c) $n - 1$
(d) $5n$ (e) $n + 10$ (f) n^2

Exercise 4

In Questions **1** to **10** find the value of the expressions given that $n = 3$
$p = -1$

1. $p + 1$

2. $2(n + 1)$

3. $3(n - 1)$

4. p^2

5. $n + p$

6. $3p$

7. $n^2 - 1$

8. $2(3n - 1)$

9. $\dfrac{n+5}{n-1}$

10. $\dfrac{p+1}{p}$

In Questions **11** to **34** find the value of the expressions given that $a = 5$
$b = 4$
$c = 1$
$d = -2$

11. $5a - c$

12. $2b + a$

13. $a + d$

14. $3c - b$

15. $4b + c$

16. $2d - a$

17. $5b + 10$

18. $a + b + c$

19. $b - c$

20. $7 - 2a$

21. $25 + 5b$

22. $3a - 4d$

23. $a^2 + b^2$

24. $ac + b$

25. $6 - 2c$

26. $d^2 + 4$

27. $ab + c$

28. $5d - 2c$

29. $b^2 + cd$

30. $5a + b + d$

31. $bd + c^2$

32. $2(a - c)$

33. $3(a + d)$

34. $a(c + b)$

Race game

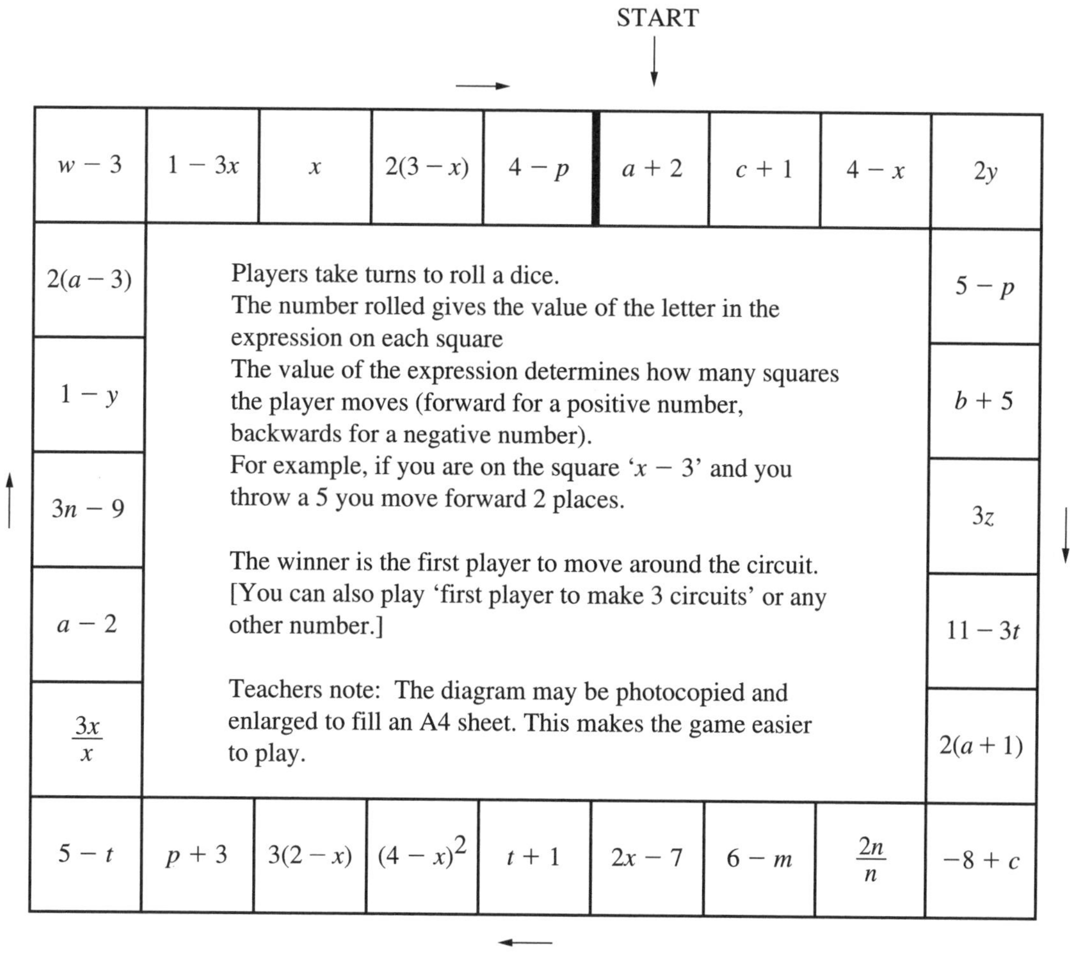

Players take turns to roll a dice.
The number rolled gives the value of the letter in the expression on each square
The value of the expression determines how many squares the player moves (forward for a positive number, backwards for a negative number).
For example, if you are on the square '$x - 3$' and you throw a 5 you move forward 2 places.

The winner is the first player to move around the circuit.
[You can also play 'first player to make 3 circuits' or any other number.]

Teachers note: The diagram may be photocopied and enlarged to fill an A4 sheet. This makes the game easier to play.

3.7 Mid book review

Review exercise 1 contains questions on Part 1 topics.
Review exercise 2 contains questions on Part 2 topics.
Review exercise 3 contains questions on Part 3 topics.
The Cross number puzzles contain questions on a wide range of topics.

Review exercise 1

1. Find the next number in each sequence.
(a) 2, 20, 200, (b) 3, 6, 12, 24, (c) 50, 49, 47, 44,
(d) 3·3, 3·2, 3·1, 3 (e) 500, 50, 5, (f) 5, 7, 11, 17, 25

2. The rule for the sequences below is '*double and add 3*'
Find the missing numbers.
(a) 1 ⟶ 5 ⟶ 13 ⟶ □
(b) 2 ⟶ □ ⟶ □
(c) □ ⟶ 9 ⟶ □

3. Write down the rule for each sequence.
(a) $1\frac{1}{2}$, 2, $2\frac{1}{2}$, 3,
(b) $3\frac{1}{2}$, 7, 14, 28,
(c) 3, 2·8, 2·6, 2·4

4. Use differences to find the next number in each of the following sequences.

(a)	(b)	(c)
3	2	7
5	4	9
9	12	17
15	26	37
23	46	75
⑦	⑦	137
		⑦

5. Here is a sequence of squares surrounded by dots.

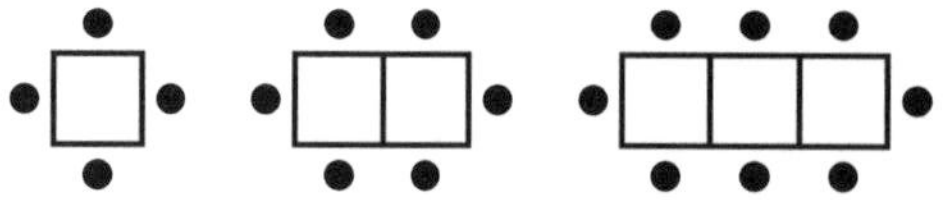

(a) How many small dots will surround the diagram with a row of 10 squares?
(b) How many squares are in the diagram which has 104 dots?

6. Work out
(a) $\frac{1}{4}+\frac{1}{8}$ (b) $\frac{1}{8}+\frac{3}{4}$ (c) $\frac{1}{10}+\frac{1}{5}$ (d) $\frac{2}{3}-\frac{1}{6}$
(e) $\frac{2}{3}$ of 60 (f) $\frac{3}{5}$ of 40 (g) $\frac{4}{7}$ of 350 (h) $\frac{1}{4}+\frac{2}{3}$

7. Work out

(a) $1 \div \frac{1}{5}$ (how many fifths are there in 1?) (b) $2 \div \frac{1}{10}$

(c) $1 \div \frac{1}{8}$ (d) $3 \div \frac{1}{3}$

8. Find the area of each shape. All lengths are in cm.

(a)

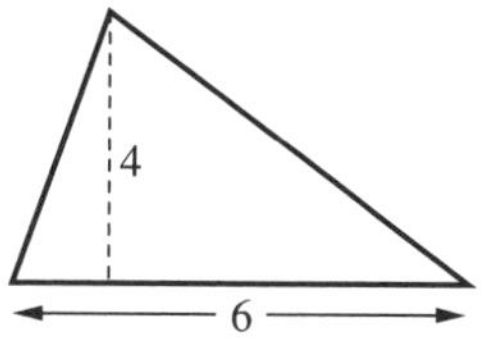

(b)

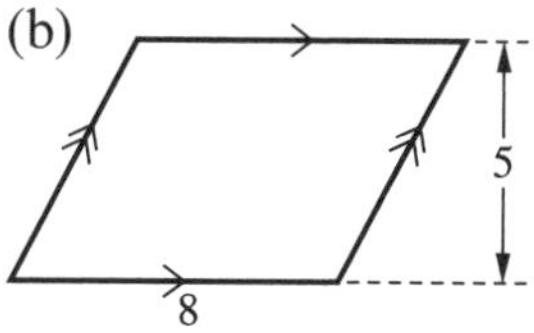

(c)

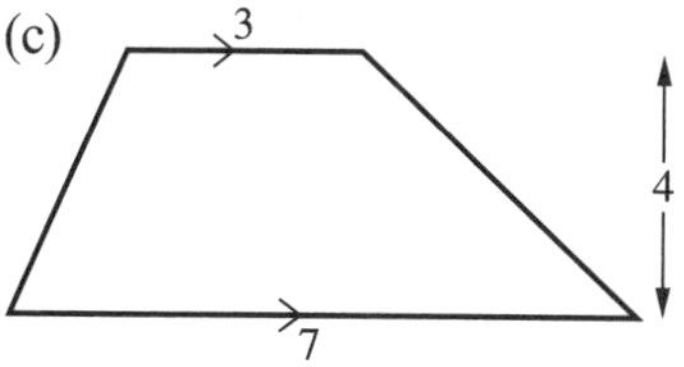

9. The perimeter of a rectangle is 24 cm. The sides of the rectangle are in the ratio 2:1. Calculate the area of the rectangle.

10. Calculate the shaded area

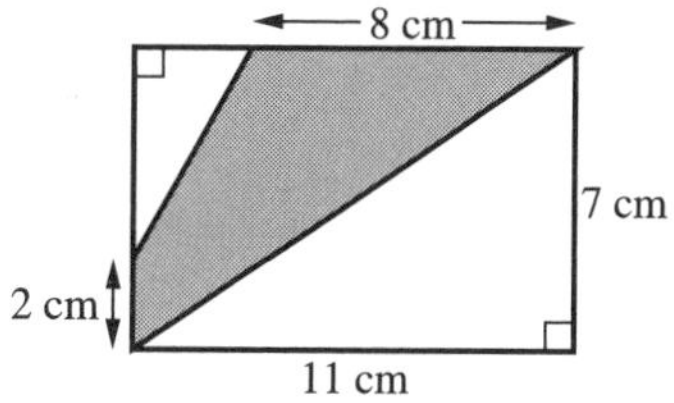

11. Work out, without a calculator:

(a) 4^2 (b) 2^3 (c) 1^5 (d) 10^3

12. Use a calculator to find the square roots, correct to 1 decimal place.

(a) $\sqrt{15}$ (b) $\sqrt{7}$ (c) $\sqrt{135}$ (d) $\sqrt{8{\cdot}21}$

13. Work out

(a) $-2-3$ (b) $6-9$ (c) -2×4 (d) $-3 \times (-2)$

(e) $-4+10$ (f) $6 \times (-2)$ (g) $-7+7$ (h) $2-20$

14. Copy and complete the magic squares

(a)

6		2
	5	
8		

(b)

−4	3	−5
	−7	0

15.

Sir, With reference to your supermarket letters, I recently decided not to buy a packet of sausages which bore the label "Thick Irish sausages", and instead chose some described as "100 per cent pork sausages (unsuitable for vegetarians; may contain meat)".

This letter appeared in 'The Times'. Estimate the amount of pork in a packet of,

(a) 'Thick Irish sausages'

(b) '100 per cent pork sausages'

(c) Ready Salted crisps

Review exercise 2

1. A CD is sold at £10·95 each. Estimate the total cost of 485 CDs.

2. Here are six calculations and six answers. Write down each calculation and insert the correct answer from the list below. Use estimation.

(a) $79{\cdot}6 \div 4$ (b) $145 \div 150$ (c) $288{\cdot}2 \div 6$
(d) $52{\cdot}2 + 47{\cdot}6$ (e) $10{\cdot}4 \div 97$ (f) $416 \div 1{\cdot}97$

Answers: 0·97, 99·8, 19·9, 0·11, 211·2, 48·0

3. Answer 'true' or 'false'

(a) $3 \times n = 3 + n$ (b) $a \times 5 = 5a$ (c) $a + b + a = 2a + b$
(d) $n + 2n = 3n$ (e) $n \div 3 = \frac{n}{3}$ (f) $n \times n = n^2$

4. (a) Find the change from 100 p for six stamps at 10 p each.
(b) Write an expression for the change from 100 p for n stamps at 10 p each.

5. Look at the sequence of square numbers.
(a) Write a similar expression for 6^2.
(b) Write a similar expression for n^2.
Use brackets and do not simplify your answer.

$2^2 = 1^2 + 2 \times 1 + 1$
$3^2 = 2^2 + 2 \times 2 + 1$
$4^2 = 3^2 + 2 \times 3 + 1$
$5^2 = 4^2 + 2 \times 4 + 1$

6. Find the angles marked with letters

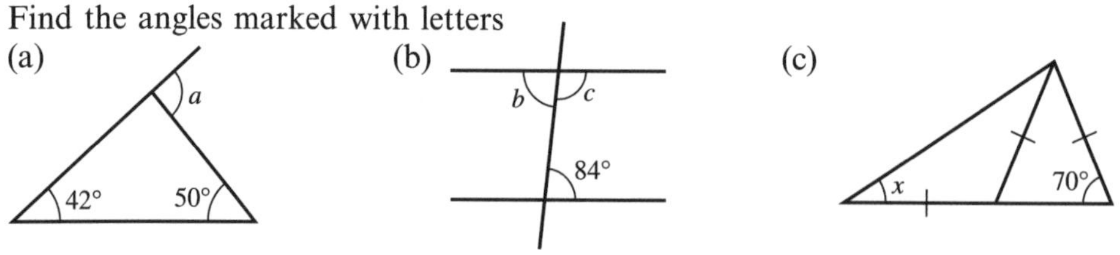

7. The outer diameter of a bicycle wheel is 95 cm.
How many complete turns does the wheel make when the bicycle travels a distance of 350 m?

8. A circle is drawn to touch the four sides of a square of side 8 cm.
Calculate the shaded area.

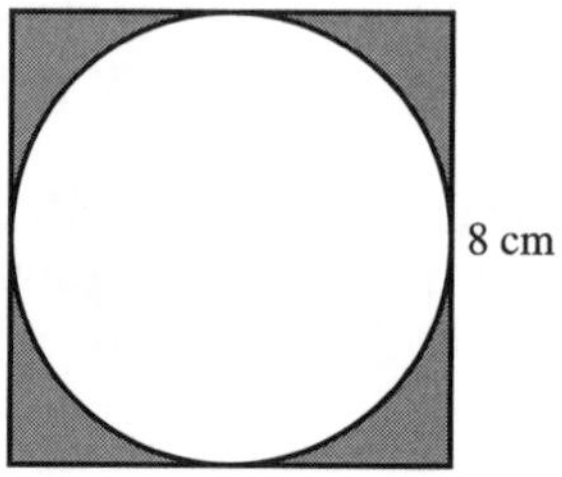

9. Calculate the area of each shape. All the arcs are semi-circles.

(a)

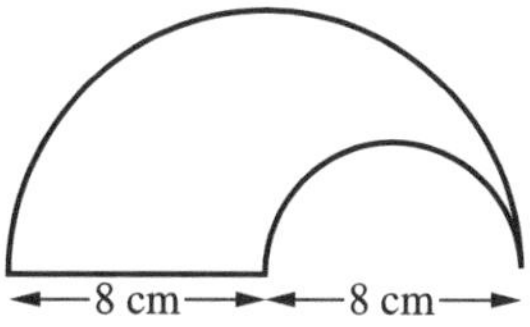

(b)

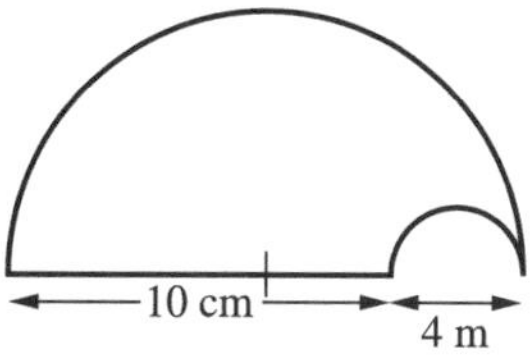

10. (a) *Construct* the perpendicular bisector of AB.

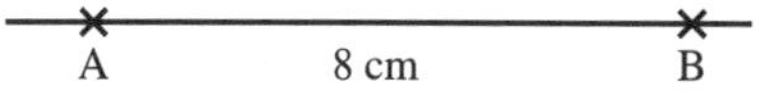

(b) *Construct* the bisector of the angle A.

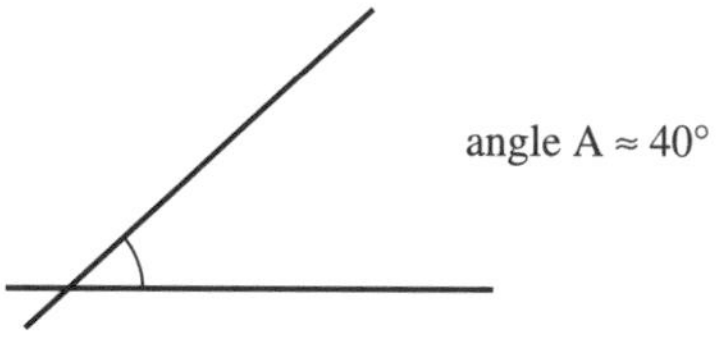

11. A spoon contains 20 ml of cough mixture. How many spoons can be filled from a one litre bottle of cough mixture?

12. Which is more:

(a) 5 metres of rope or 5 feet of rope?
(b) 6 pounds of apples or 6 kg of apples?
(c) A road 10 km long or a road 10 miles long?

13. Paul's car averages 30 miles to 1 gallon of petrol. Petrol costs £4 a gallon.
If Paul drives 27 600 miles in one year, how much does his petrol cost?

14. The time is 6.08. What was the time half an hour ago?

15. Gill and Ashni each have 15 sweets.

(a) Gill eats $\frac{2}{5}$ of her sweets. How many does she eat?
(b) Ashni eats 5 of her sweets. What *fraction* of her sweets does she eat?

16. There were 4 candidates in a class election. Mary got $\frac{1}{3}$ of the votes, George got $\frac{1}{3}$ of the votes, Henry got $\frac{1}{6}$.
What fraction did Sheena, the 4th candidate get?

17. Work out $1 + [87654321 + 12345678]$.

18. I am a 3 digit number. The product of my digits is 2.
I am an odd number, greater than 200. What number am I?

Review exercise 3

1. (a) Write in order, smallest first: £1·25, 65p, £0·8
(b) What number is mid-way between 3·4 and 3·5?
(c) True or false (i) $0{\cdot}1 > 0{\cdot}01$
(ii) $6 \times 0{\cdot}1 > 6$

2. Work out, without a calculator
(a) $7 \times 0{\cdot}1$ (b) $16 \times 0{\cdot}01$ (c) $1{\cdot}2 \times 10$
(d) $6 \div 0{\cdot}1$ (e) $4 \div 0{\cdot}01$ (f) $1{\cdot}2 \div 0{\cdot}1$

3. Work out, without a calculator
(a) $7{\cdot}56 + 4$ (b) $15 \times 0{\cdot}3$ (c) $1{\cdot}2 \times 0{\cdot}7$
(d) $8 \div 5$ (e) $8{\cdot}64 \div 0{\cdot}4$ (f) $562{\cdot}7 \div 100$

4. The stem and leaf diagram shows the marks obtained in a test.
(a) What is the median mark?
(b) What is the range?

3	1 3
4	4 4 5 7 8
5	2 2 3 4 6 9
6	3 4 7 8
7	5 6

5. The total mass of five greyhounds is 76 kg. Calculate the mean mass of the dogs.

6. The frequency table shows the scores when a dice was rolled 20 times.

score	1	2	3	4	5	6
frequency	2	5	3	4	1	5

Calculate the mean score.

7. (a) Copy the diagram.
(b) Reflect the L shape in the x axis.
(c) Reflect the L shape in the line $y = x$.

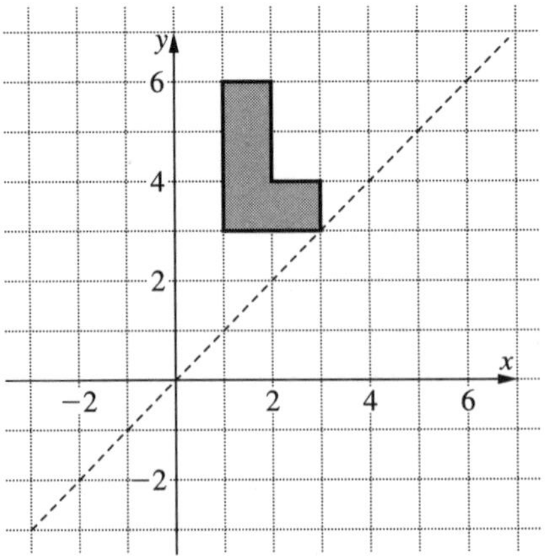

8. Work out in your head.
(a) $57 + 19$ (b) $68 - 29$ (c) $47 + 23 + 18$ (d) double 67
(e) 24×50 (f) 22×25 (g) double 136 (h) $74 + 29$

9. Draw axes with x and y from 0 to 6.
Plot A(1, 4) B(1, 1) C(3, 1)
Plot D(5, 4) E(5, 1) F(3, 1)
Write down the equation of the mirror line which reflects △ABC onto △DEF.

10. Work out the following (remember 'B I D M A S')
(a) $40 - 9 \times 2$ (b) $25 + 4^2$ (c) $(7 - 2)^2$
(d) $4 \times (3 \times 3 - 1)$ (e) $15 - 12 \div 3$ (f) $(3^2 - 5)^2$

11. Use a calculator to work out the following. Give your answers correct to 1 decimal place or as a fraction.

(a) $18{\cdot}3 - (1{\cdot}91 \times 2{\cdot}62)$ (b) $\dfrac{5{\cdot}23}{(9{\cdot}2 - 7{\cdot}63)}$ (c) $3\frac{2}{5} + \frac{1}{2}$

(d) $\dfrac{8{\cdot}91}{1{\cdot}6} + \left(\dfrac{1{\cdot}54}{0{\cdot}97}\right)$ (e) $\left(\dfrac{1{\cdot}4 + 0{\cdot}761}{1{\cdot}76}\right)^2$ (f) $2\frac{1}{4} \div \frac{3}{4}$

12. The cost of Mrs West's shopping is given by the formula $C = n^2 - 3n + 50$, where n is the number of her children staying at home.
Find C, when $n = 4$.

13. Find the value of these expressions when $n = 3$
(a) $n + 5$ (b) $4n$ (c) n^2
(d) $\dfrac{n+6}{n}$ (e) $\dfrac{5n}{n-2}$ (f) $n^2 + n$

14. Find the value of these expressions when $n = -2$
(a) $n + 8$ (b) $3n$ (c) $2n + 4$
(d) n^2 (e) $n - 10$ (f) $2(n + 2)$

15. Work out $10^5 - [1357 + 8642]$

16. I am a 3 digit number. The product of my digits is 4.
I am an odd number less than 200. What am I?

17. I am a 4 digit number. The product of my digits is 4 and the sum of my digits is 6. I am an even number less than 1200. What am I?

18. Reflect shape A in line 1 and label the image A′. Reflect A′ in line 2 and label the image A″. Describe fully the single transformation which maps A onto A″.

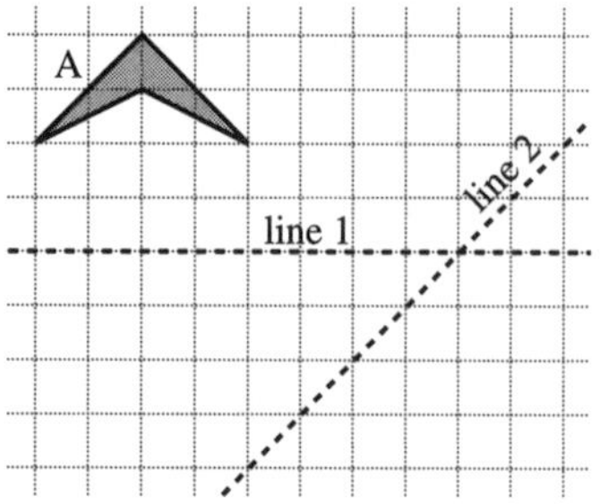

19. Draw axes with values from −6 to +6 and draw △1 with vertices at (1, 4), (1, 6), (4, 6).
(a) Reflect △1 in the line $y = x$ onto △2
(b) Reflect △2 in the x axis onto △3
(c) Reflect △3 in the line $x = 3$ onto △4
(d) Reflect △4 in the line $y = x$ onto △5
(e) Describe fully the single transformation which:
  (i) maps △1 onto △3
  (ii) maps △5 onto △1.

Review exercise 4

1. Change $\frac{27}{40}$ to a percentage
A 48%
B 148%
C $67\frac{1}{2}$%
D 27%

2. Work out $(-3) + (-7)$
A −4
B +4
C 10
D −10

3. Work out, correct to 3 significant figures,
$$\frac{4{\cdot}9}{1{\cdot}9^2 - 0{\cdot}72}$$
A 0·637
B 1·70
C 2·89
D 1·42

4. Which is the best estimate when 100 yards is converted into metres?
A 90 m
B 110 m
C 1100 m
D 0·9 m

5. On a map of scale 1 : 50 000, the length of a road is 6 cm. Find the actual length of the road on the land.
A 3 km
B 30 km
C 300 m
D 30 000 cm

6. At what point will the line $y = x$ cut the line $y = -2$?
A (−2, −2)
B (2, −2)
C (0, −2)
D (−2, 2)

Use the diagram below for questions **7** to **10**

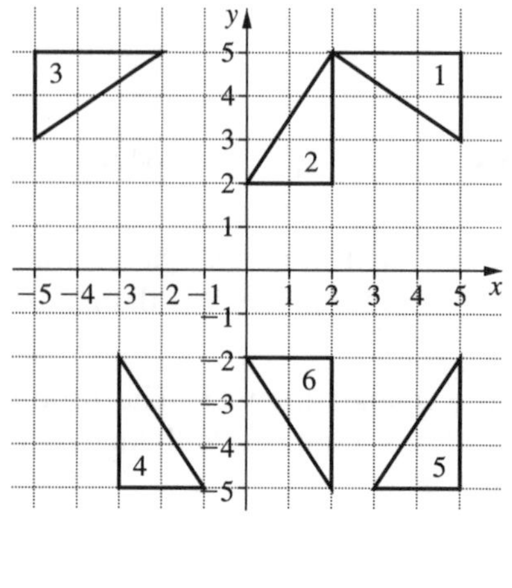

7. The image of $\triangle 3$, after reflection in the y axis, is

A $\triangle 1$
B $\triangle 2$
C $\triangle 4$
D $\triangle 5$

8. $\triangle 4$ is the image of $\triangle 5$ after reflection in the line:

A $x = 2$
B $x = 1$
C $y = 1$
D $y = 2$

9. The centre of the rotation which moves $\triangle 1$ onto $\triangle 5$ is

A (2, 5)
B (−5, 0)
C (0, 0)
D none of the above

10. The image of $\triangle 2$ after rotation through 180° about the point (0, 0) is

A $\triangle 4$
B $\triangle 1$
C $\triangle 6$
D none of the above

11. Find the next number in the sequence 5, 7, 11, 17, 25,

A 33
B 35
C 36
D 37

12. 55% of £55 is

A £1
B £55
C £30·25
D £28·50

13. Solve the equation $2x - 1 = 11$

A 6
B $\frac{1}{6}$
C 5
D $\frac{1}{5}$

14. Work out $4 - (7 \times 2) - 1$

A −11
B 11
C 9
D −9

15. When minus 5 is subtracted from 7, the answer is

A −2
B 2
C 12
D none of the above

16. Which is the odd one out?

A 20%
B 0·2
C $\frac{2}{100}$
D $\frac{1}{5}$

17. A pile of 200 cards is 1 m deep. How thick is each card?

A 2 mm
B 0·5 cm
C 0·5 mm
D 0·5 m

18. Which point does not lie on the line $y = -x$?

A (−3, −3)
B (2, −2)
C (0, 0)
D (−4, 4)

19. Find the shaded area, in cm^2.

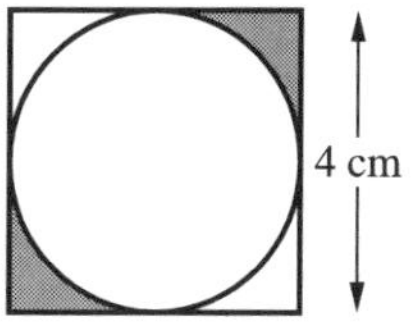

A $16 - 2\pi$
B $8 - 2\pi$
C 0·858
D 9·72

20. Which is the largest number?

A $0{\cdot}\dot{2}$
B $0{\cdot}\dot{2}\dot{1}$
C 22%
D $\frac{21}{100}$

21. Solve the equation $3(x - 1) = 2(x + 2)$

A 4
B 5
C 6
D 7

22. If $z = 3a - n$, find the value of z when $a = -2$ and $n = 5$

A 1
B 11
C −11
D none of the above

23. Find the value of $2x^2$, when $x = -1$

A 2
B −2
C 4
D −4

24. Find the ratio (shaded area) : (unshaded area)

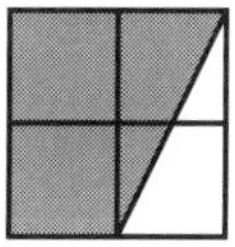

A 3 : 4
B 4 : 1
C 3 : 1
D $3\frac{1}{2} : 1\frac{1}{2}$

Part 4

4.1 Rotation and combined transformations

Rotate the triangle through 908 anticlockwise about the point O.

The diagram on the right shows how tracing paper may be used.

Notice that we need three things to describe fully a rotation:

(a) the angle,
(b) the direction, (clockwise or anticlockwise)
(c) the centre of rotation.

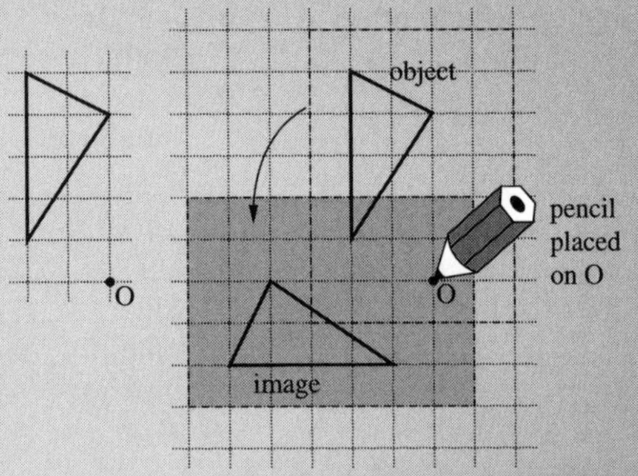

Exercise 1

In Questions **1** to **6** draw the object and its image under the rotation given. Take O as the centre of rotation in each case.

1.

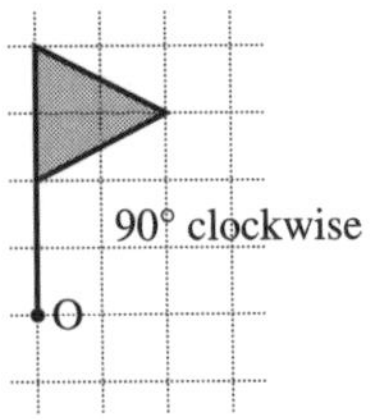

2.

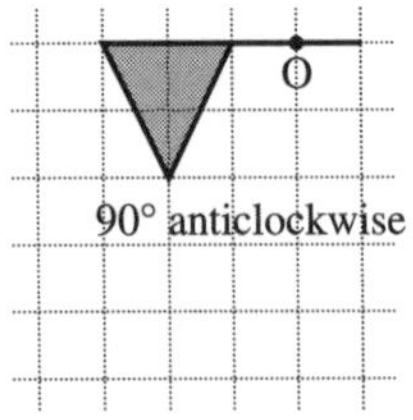

3.

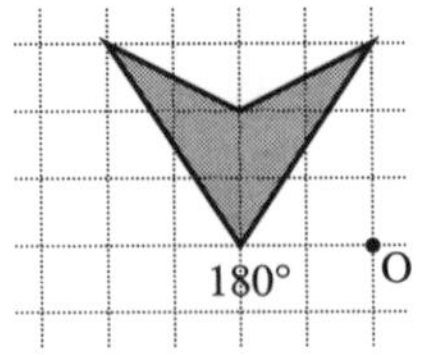

4.

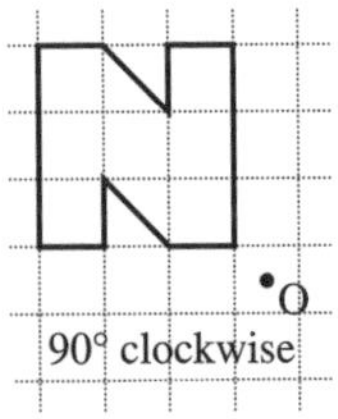

5.

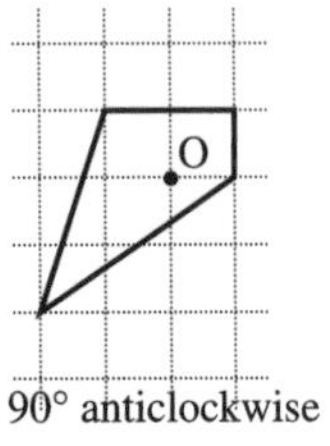

6.

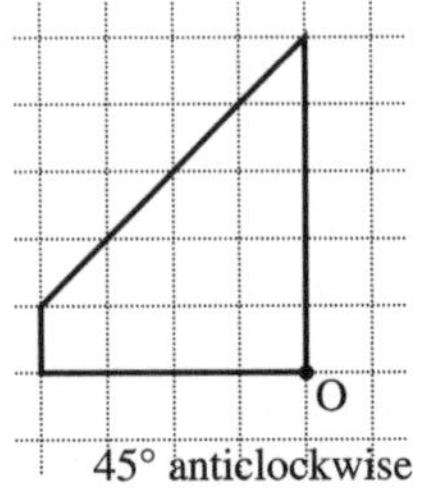

7. Copy the diagram shown, using axes from −6 to 6.
   (a) Rotate △1 90° clockwise about (0, 0) onto △A.
   (b) Rotate △2 180° about (0, 0) onto △B.
   (c) Rotate shape 3 90° anticlockwise about (2, 2) onto shape C.

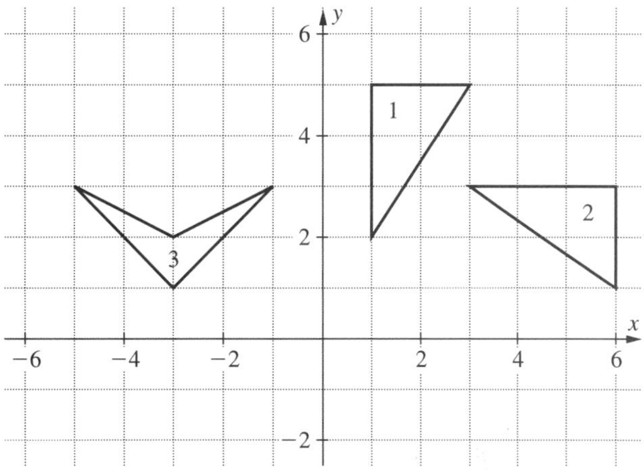

8. Copy the diagram shown.
   (a) Rotate shape 1 90° anticlockwise about (−3, −4) onto shape A.
   (b) Rotate △2 90° clockwise about (1, 0) onto △B.
   (c) Rotate shape 3 90° clockwise about (2, 1) onto shape C.
   (d) Rotate shape 3 180° about (−2, 3) onto shape D.

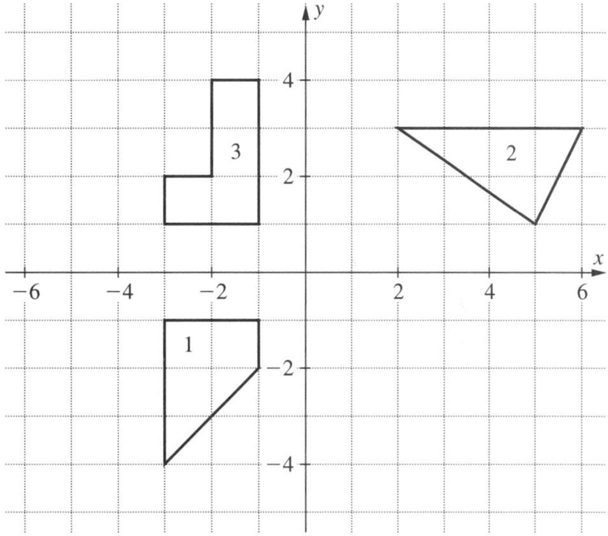

9. (a) Draw axes with values from −6 to 6 and draw △1 with vertices at (2, 6), (6, 6), (6, 4).
   (b) Rotate △1 90° clockwise about (2, 6) onto △2.
   (c) Rotate △2 180° about (2, 0) onto △3.
   (d) Rotate △3 90° clockwise about (1, 0) onto △4.
   (e) Rotate △4 90° anticlockwise about (−1, 4) onto △5.
   (f) If △5 is in the correct position you can now easily rotate △5 onto △1. Give the angle, direction and centre for this rotation.

10. (a) Draw axes with values from −6 to 6 and draw △1 with vertices at (−5, 2), (−5, 6), (−3, 5).
   (b) Rotate △1 90° clockwise about (−4, −2) onto △2.
   (c) Rotate △2 90° clockwise about (6, 0) onto △3.
   (d) Rotate △3 180° about (1, 1) onto △4.
   (e) Rotate △4 90° anticlockwise about (−5, 1) onto △5.
   (f) Describe fully the rotation which moves △5 onto △1.

Finding the centre of a rotation

Exercise 2

In Questions **1** to **4** copy each diagram. Draw the shaded shape on tracing paper. Place the tip of a pencil on different points until the shape can be rotated onto the other shape. Mark the centre of rotation with a dot.

1.

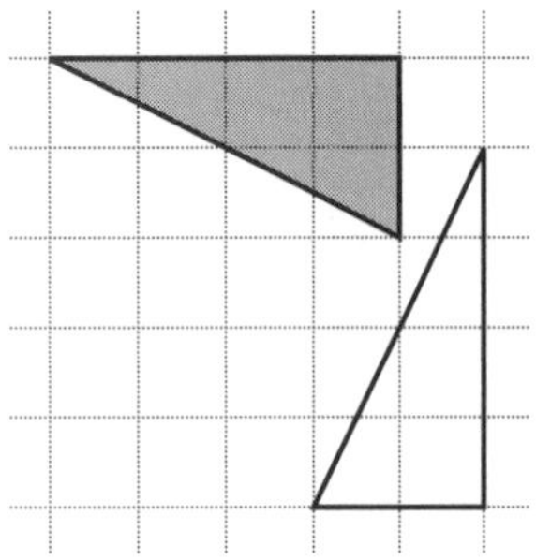

2.

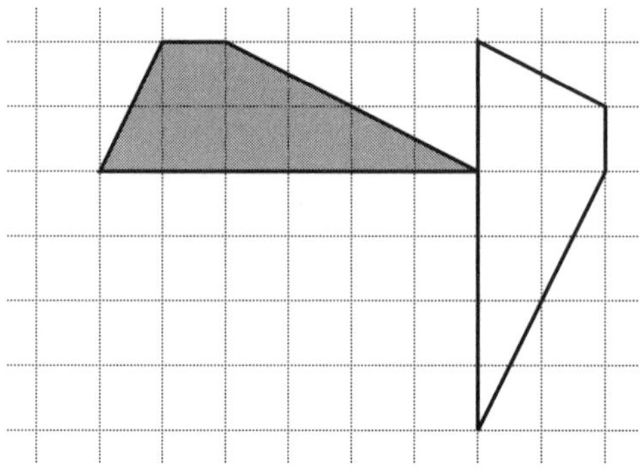

3.

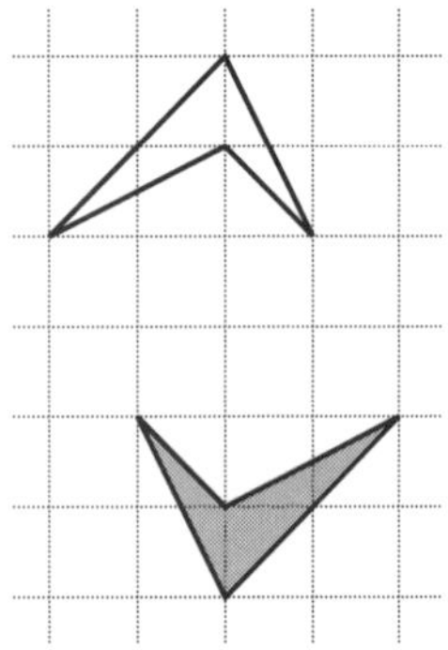

4.

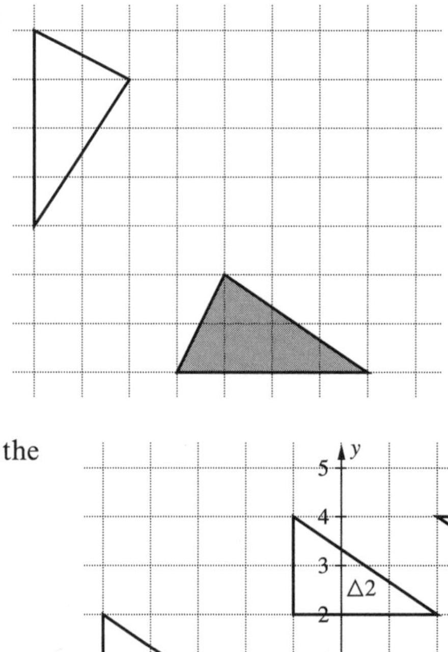

5. Find the coordinates of the centres of the following rotations:
(a) △1 → △2
(b) △1 → △3
(c) △1 → △4
(d) △3 → △5

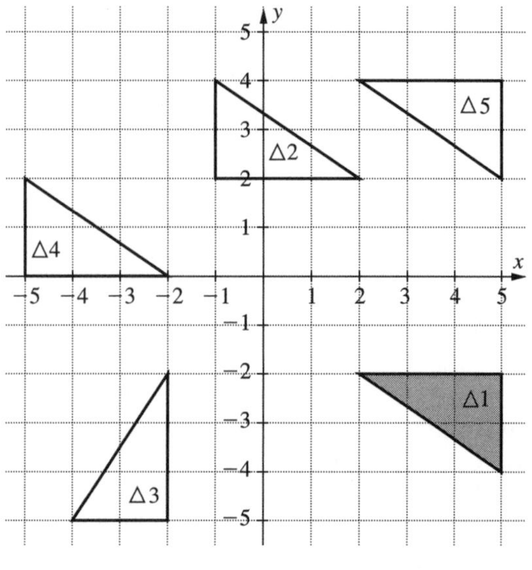

6. Copy the two squares carefully. It is possible to rotate the shaded square onto the unshaded square using three different centres of rotation. Find and mark these three points.

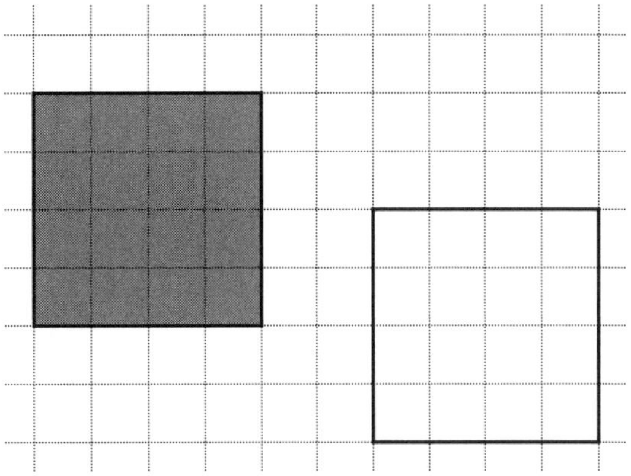

Questions **7** and **8** involve both rotations and reflections.

7. Draw axes with values from -7 to $+7$ and draw triangles with the following vertices:

$\triangle 1$:	$(-6, -6)$	$(-2, -6)$	$(-2, -4)$
$\triangle 2$:	$(-6, -6)$	$(-6, -2)$	$(-4, -2)$
$\triangle 3$:	$(6, 2)$	$(2, 2)$	$(2, 0)$
$\triangle 4$:	$(-6, 2)$	$(-2, 2)$	$(-2, 0)$
$\triangle 5$:	$(6, 3)$	$(6, 7)$	$(4, 7)$

Describe fully the following rotations or reflections. For rotations, give the angle, direction and centre. For reflections, give the equation of the mirror line.

(a) $\triangle 1 \to \triangle 2$
(b) $\triangle 1 \to \triangle 3$
(c) $\triangle 1 \to \triangle 4$
(d) $\triangle 1 \to \triangle 5$

8. Draw axes with values from -7 to $+7$ and draw triangles with the following vertices:

$\triangle 1$:	$(3, 1)$	$(7, 1)$	$(7, 3)$
$\triangle 2$:	$(1, 3)$	$(1, 7)$	$(3, 7)$
$\triangle 3$:	$(7, -1)$	$(3, -1)$	$(3, -3)$
$\triangle 4$:	$(-1, -7)$	$(-3, -7)$	$(-3, -3)$
$\triangle 5$:	$(-2, 2)$	$(-6, 2)$	$(-6, 0)$
$\triangle 6$:	$(3, -4)$	$(3, -6)$	$(7, -6)$

Describe fully the following rotations or reflections:

(a) $\triangle 1 \to \triangle 2$
(b) $\triangle 1 \to \triangle 3$
(c) $\triangle 1 \to \triangle 4$
(d) $\triangle 1 \to \triangle 5$
(e) $\triangle 3 \to \triangle 6$

Combinations of two transformations

Reflection, rotation, translation and enlargement are all transformations. Sometimes we need a combination of transformations to move a shape where we want to.

Exercise 3

1. 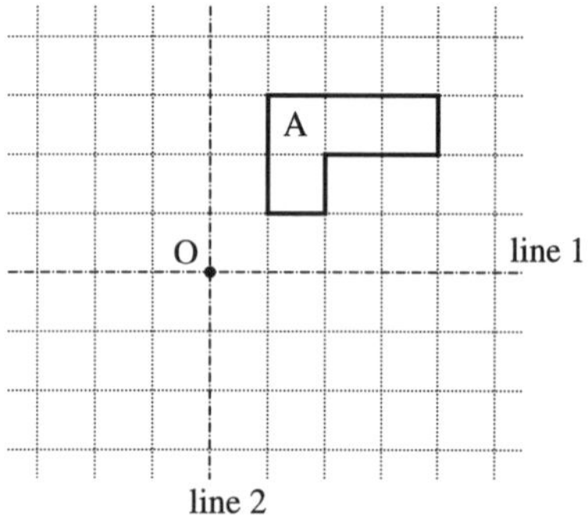

(a) Reflect shape A in line 1 onto shape B.
(b) Reflect shape B in line 2 onto shape C.
(c) What single transformation will move shape A onto shape C?

2. (a) Rotate △D 90° clockwise about (0, 0). Label the image △E.
(b) Rotate △E 90° clockwise about (0, 0). Label the image △F.
(c) What single transformation will move △D onto △F?

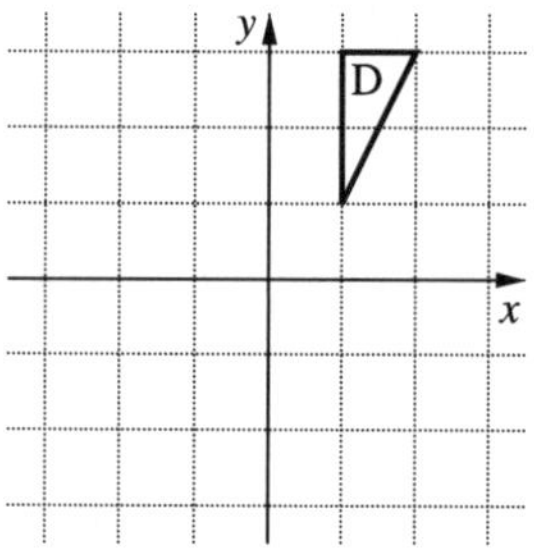

3. 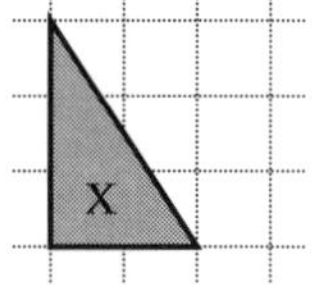

(a) Draw △X.
(b) Translate △X 4 units right onto △Y.
(c) Translate △Y 1 unit right and 2 units up onto △Z.
(d) What single translation will move △X onto △Z?

4. Describe the transformations below. Mark any points and lines necessary to write the answers.
(a) △A → △B in one move.
(b) △B → △C in one move.
(c) △D → △C in one move.
(d) △A → △C in two moves.

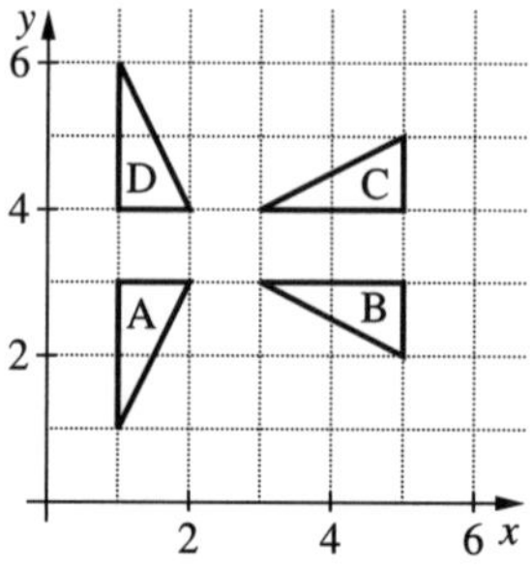

5. Describe fully the following transformations
(a) $\triangle A \to \triangle B$
(b) $\triangle B \to \triangle C$
(c) $\triangle A \to \triangle D$
(d) $\triangle C \to \triangle E$
(e) $\triangle A \to \triangle C$ (in two transformations)
(f) $\triangle A \to \triangle E$ (in two or three transformations).

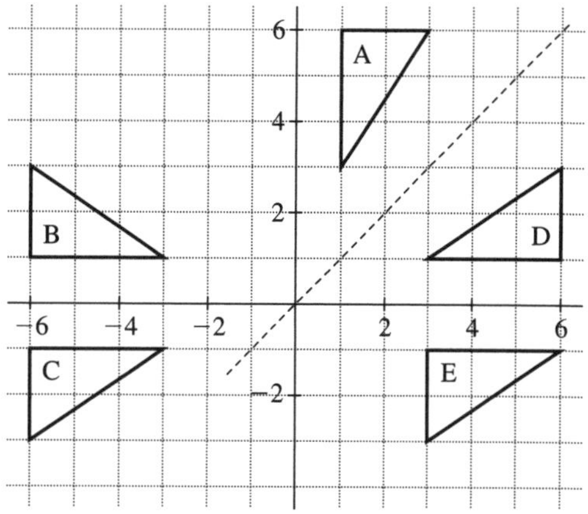

6. Make three copies of the diagram below, but leave out the dotted lines.

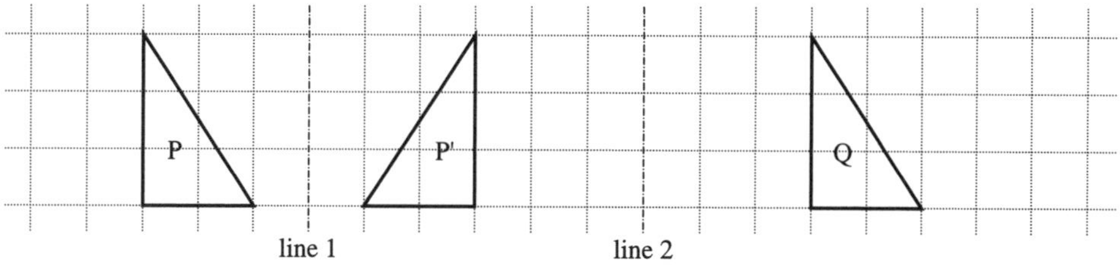

Triangle P is reflected in line 1 onto triangle P′.
Then triangle P′ is reflected in line 2 onto triangle Q.
(a) Show that P can be reflected onto Q using two different mirror lines.
Do this three times.
(b) What do you notice each time? (How far apart are your two lines?)
(c) Do you obtain the same connection if one of the mirror lines is to the left of triangle P?

7. Show that $\triangle B$ can be transformed onto $\triangle A$ by a combination of a translation and a reflection. Describe the translation and the reflection.
Find another way of doing this.

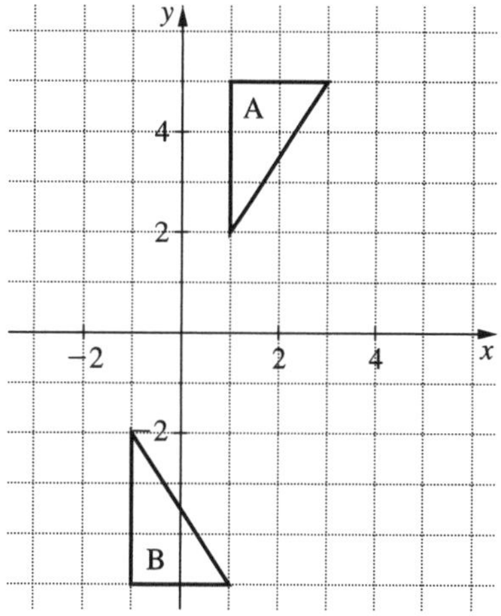

In Questions **8** to **11** the transformations used are:

A: reflection in $y = 1$
B: rotation 90° clockwise, centre (0, 2)
C: translation $\begin{pmatrix} -4 \\ 2 \end{pmatrix}$

[4 units left and 2 units up]

E: reflection in $y = x$
F: translation $\begin{pmatrix} 3 \\ -3 \end{pmatrix}$

[3 units right and 3 units down]

For each question draw a set of axes for x and y from -8 to $+8$

8. Plot and label L(−2, −2), M(−2, −4), N(−1, −4).

Draw and label the image △LMN after the transformations:
(a) E followed by A
(b) B followed by F
(c) A followed by F
(d) F followed by C

Write down the coordinates of the image of the point L in each case.

9. Plot and label X(−4, 0), Y(−4, −4), Z(−2, −4).

Draw the label the image of △XYZ after:
(a) B followed by F
(b) A followed by C
(c) B followed by F followed by E.

Write down the coordinates of the image of point X in each case.

10. (a) Plot and label L(1, 5), M(1, 1), N(3, 1).
(b) Draw and label the image of △LMN after:
(i) B followed by C
(ii) F followed by B
(c) Describe the equivalent *single* transformation in each case.

11. (a) Plot and label P(0, 4), Q(−2, 0), R(0, 0).
(b) Draw and label the image of △PQR after:
(i) E followed by A
(ii) C followed by B
(iii) E followed by F
(c) Describe the equivalent single transformation in each part.

4.2 Real-life graphs

Exercise 1

1. The graph shows a return journey from A.
   (a) When is the car halfway between A and C on the outward journey?
   (b) Between what times does the car stop at B?
   (c) When is the car halfway between C and B on the return journey?
   (d) Find the speed of the car
      (i) From A to C
      (ii) From C back to B
      (iii) From B back to A

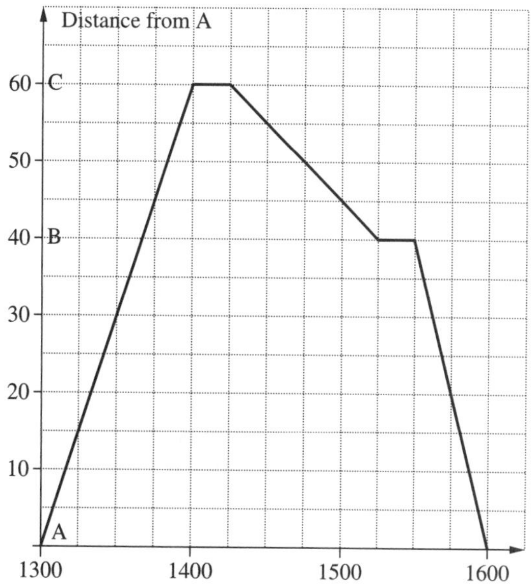

2. The petrol consumption of a car depends on the speed, as shown below.
   (a) What is the petrol consumption at a speed of
      (i) 30 km per hour
      (ii) 100 km per hour
      (iii) 180 km per hour?
   (b) At what speed is the petrol consumption
      (i) 8 km per litre
      (ii) 12 km per litre
      (iii) 9 km per litre?
   (c) At what speed should the car be driven in order to use the least amount of petrol?
   (d) A car is driven at 160 km per hour. How far can it travel on 20 litres of petrol?

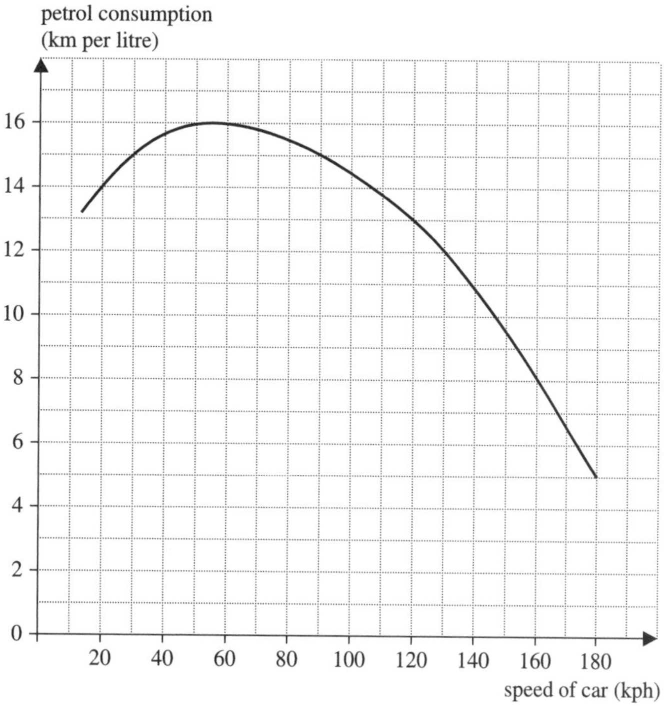

3. Water is poured at a constant rate into each of the containers A, B and C.
The graphs X, Y and Z shows how the water level rises.
Decide which graph fits each container.
State your reasons.

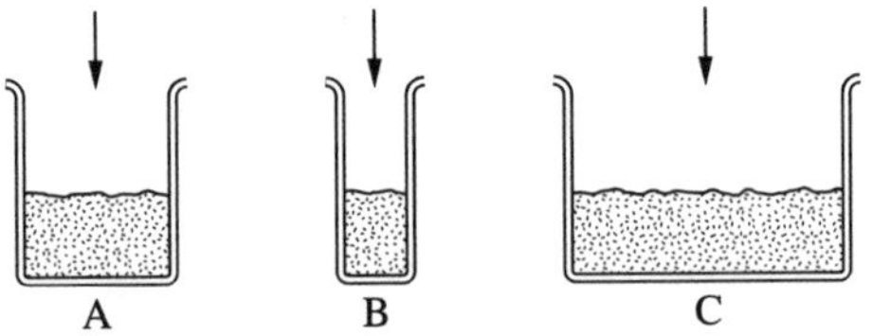

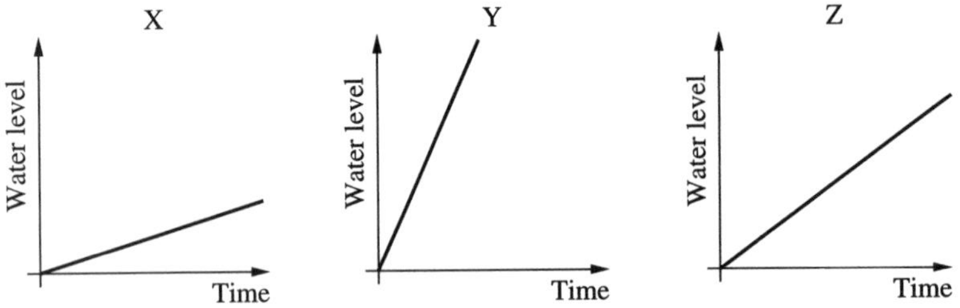

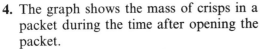

4. The graph shows the mass of crisps in a packet during the time after opening the packet.
(a) Were all the crisps eaten?
(b) What is the mass of a full packet of crisps?
(c) Explain the shape of the graph. Why are some vertical lines on the graph longer than others?

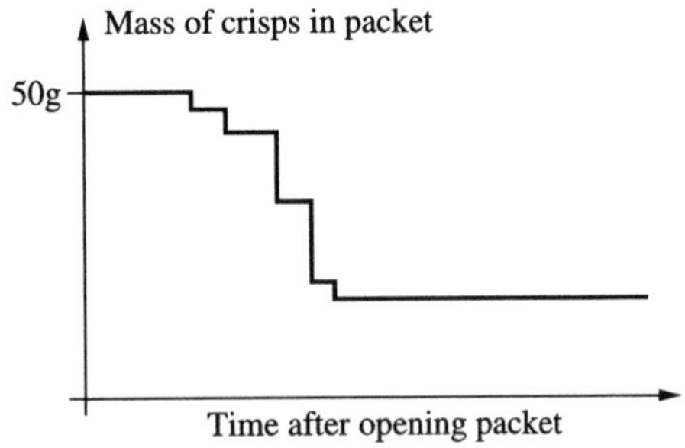

5. A packet of frozen fish is taken out of a freezer and left on a kitchen table for 4 hours. The fish is then heated in a frying pan. Sketch a graph to show the temperature of the fish after it is taken from the freezer.

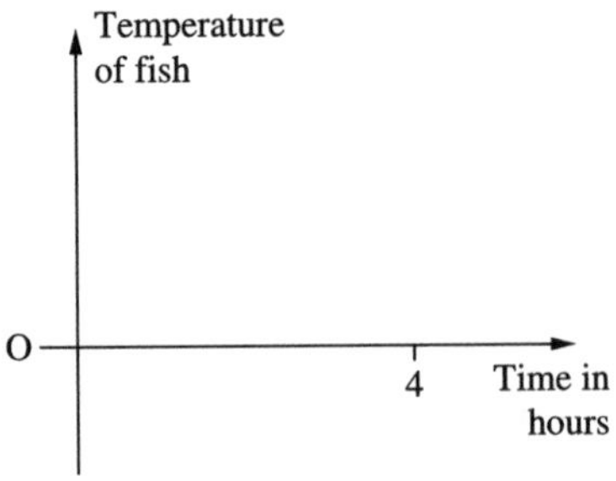

6.

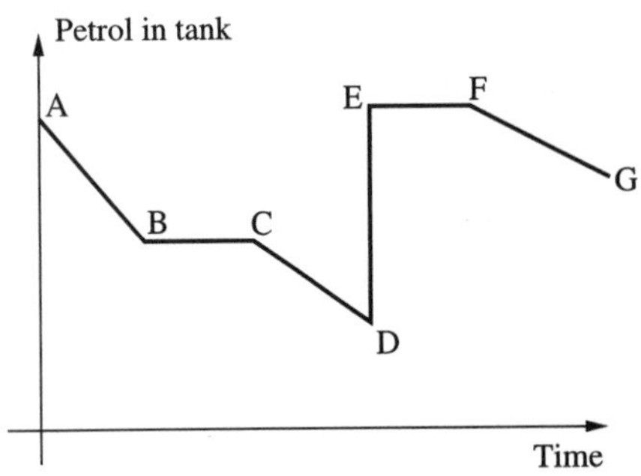

The graph shows the amount of petrol in the tank of a car.
Explain briefly what you think is happening in each section of the graph:
AB, BC, CD, DE, EF, FG.

7.

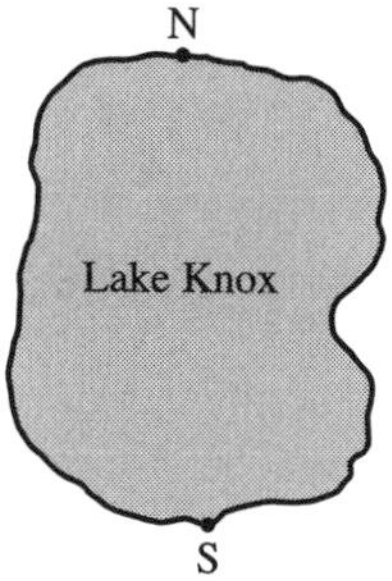

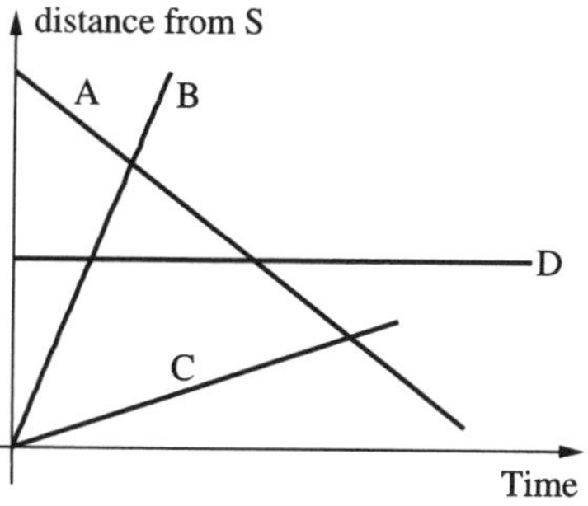

Points S and N are on the banks of Lake Knox.
A, B, C, D are travel graphs for different people/objects.
Decide which graph fits with each description.
(a) A man swimming from S to N.
(b) A motor boat travelling from S to N.
(c) A marker buoy on the lake.
(d) A rowing boat going from N to S.

8. Which of the graphs **A** to **D** best fits each of the following statements?
(a) 'The price of petrol was steady for several years but has fallen recently.'
(b) 'The cost of air flights was falling slowly until 2002, but is now rising
(c) 'The birthrate in Italy has fallen steadily over the the last decade.'
(d) 'The weight of the bird increased steadily after hatching,'

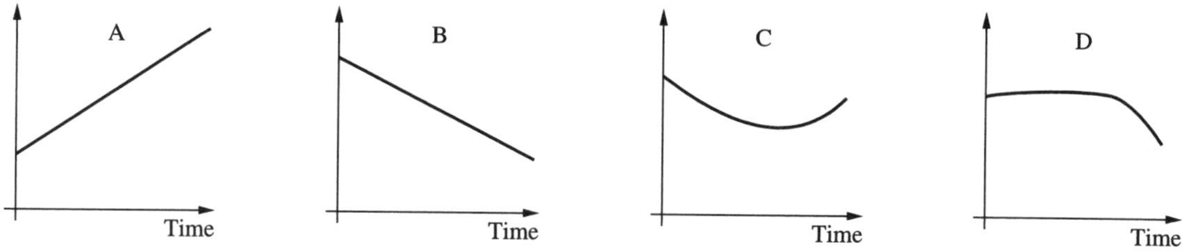

9. Sketch a graph to show how a man's height changes from birth until the age of 30 years.

10. Sketch the locus of a sailing boat as it 'tacks' against a headwind.

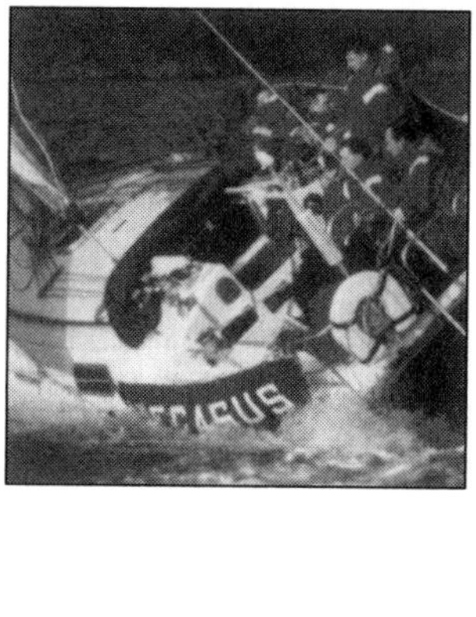

4.3 Brackets and equations

The area of the whole rectangle shown can be found by multiplying its length by its width.

Area $= 4(x+2)$

Alternatively the area can be found by adding together the areas of the two smaller rectangles.

Area $= 4x + 4 \times 2$

We see that $4(x+2) = 4x + 4 \times 2$

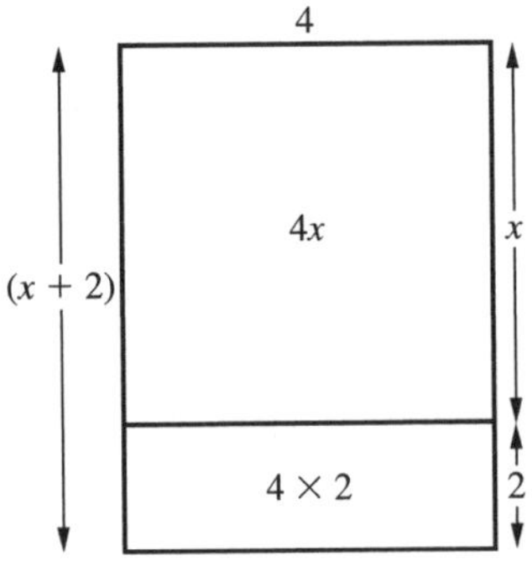

In general a number or symbol outside a pair of brackets multiplies each of the numbers or symbols inside the brackets.

$5(x+2) = 5x + 10$ $\quad$ $3(x-2) = 3x - 6$

$4(2x+1) = 8x + 4$ $\quad$ $2(1+3x) = 2 + 6x$

$a(x+b) = ax + ab$ $\quad$ $n(a+b+c) = na + nb + nc$

Remove the brackets and simplify.

(a) $3(x+2) + 2(x+1)$
$= 3x + 6 + 2x + 2$
$= 5x + 8$

(b) $4(x+1) + 2(2x+3)$
$= 4x + 4 + 4x + 6$
$= 8x + 10$

Note the method: First remove the brackets.
Second add the x terms and the number terms separately.

(c) Find expressions for the area and the perimeter of the photo

Area $= 7(x+5)$
$= 7x + 35$

Perimeter $= x + 5 + x + 5 + 7 + 7$
$= 2x + 24$

7

$x + 5$

Exercise 1

In Questions **1** to **15** remove the brackets.

1. $3(x+4)$ **2.** $5(x+3)$ **3.** $4(x-2)$

4. $6(x-2)$ **5.** $2(2x+1)$ **6.** $3(2x+3)$

7. $4(3x+1)$ **8.** $3(4x+5)$ **9.** $9(2-x)$

10. $2(4x-5)$ **11.** $7(3x-1)$ **12.** $10(2x+5)$

13. $5(3x-5)$ **14.** $2(3-2x)$ **15.** $3(x+y)$

In Questions **16** to **35** remove the brackets and simplify.

16. $2(x+1)+3(x+3)$ **17.** $3(x+4)+2(x+1)$

18. $4(x+2)+2(x+2)$ **19.** $5(x+1)+3(x+2)$

20. $2(4x+3)+4(3x+4)$ **21.** $3(4x+5)+2(x+5)$

22. $5(x+1)+3(x-2)$ **23.** $6(2x+1)+3(1+2x)$

24. $4(3x+1)+(2x-1)$ **25.** $2(4+x)+(5x-2)$

26. $3(2x+4)+2(x+1)$ **27.** $5(3+2x)+10x$

28. $7(2x-1)-4x$ **29.** $4x+5(2x+1)$

30. $6x+3(2x+3)$ **31.** $9+3(3x-1)$

32. $5(3x-1)+6(2x+1)$ **33.** $8(1+2x)-5$

34. $x+6(3x+2)$ **35.** $4(3x-2)-10x$

36.

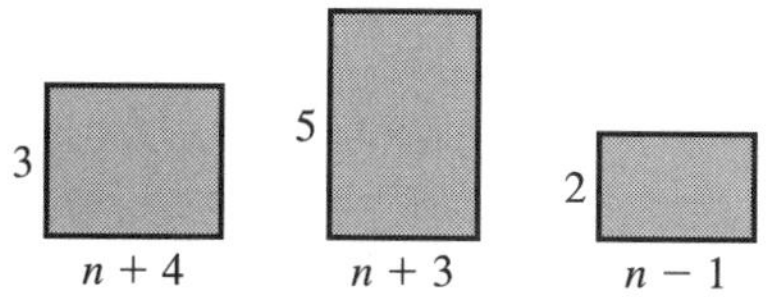

Find an expression for the total area of the three rectangles. Simplify your answer.

37. (a) Write an expression for the area of the picture.
(b) Write an expression for the perimeter of the picture.

Remove the brackets and simplify. Be careful with negative numbers.

(a) $3(n+3) - 2(n+1)$
$= 3n + 9 - 2n - 2$
$= n + 7$

(b) $2(a+1) - (a-2)$
↑
[put a '1' here]
$= 2(a+1) - 1(a-2)$
$= 2a + 2 - a + 2$
$= a + 4$

(c) $3(a+b) - 2(a+2b)$
$= 3a + 3b - 2a - 4b$
$= a - b$

(d) $5(a+b) - (2a+b)$
$= 5(a+b) - 1(2a+b)$
$= 5a + 5b - 2a - b$
$= 3a + 4b$

Exercise 2

Remove the brackets and simplify

1. $3(n+2) + (n-2)$
2. $4(n+3) - 2(n+1)$
3. $8(a+1) - 3(a+2)$
4. $7(a+3) - 2(a-1)$
5. $5(m+2) - (m+3)$
6. $6(m+1) - (m-2)$
7. $3(a+b) + 5(2a+b)$
8. $3(3a+b) - 2(a+b)$
9. $4(2a+b) - 2(a-b)$
10. $5(a+3b) - (2a+b)$
11. $5(a-b) - 3(a-2b)$
12. $4(2a+b) - (3a-b)$

Write in a more simple form.

13. $a^2 + a^2$
14. $2n^2 - n^2$
15. $m^3 + 2m^3$
16. $a^2 + 2a + a^2$
17. $n + 2n^2 + 5n$
18. $2a^2 - a - a^2$
19. $n \times n^2$
20. $n \times n \times n \times n$
21. $n^3 \div n$
22. In number walls each brick is made by adding the two bricks underneath it.

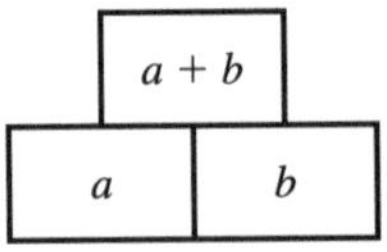

Draw the walls below and fill in the missing expressions.

(a)

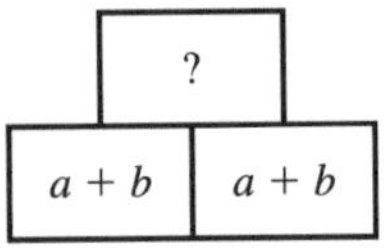

(b)

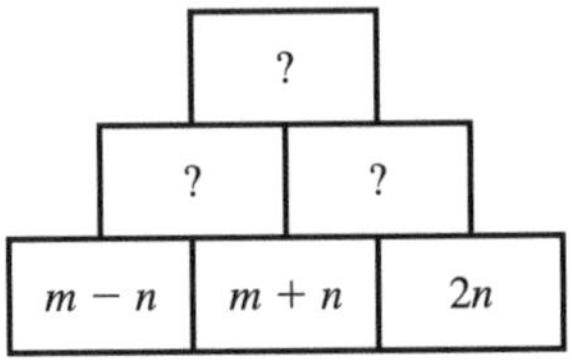

(c)

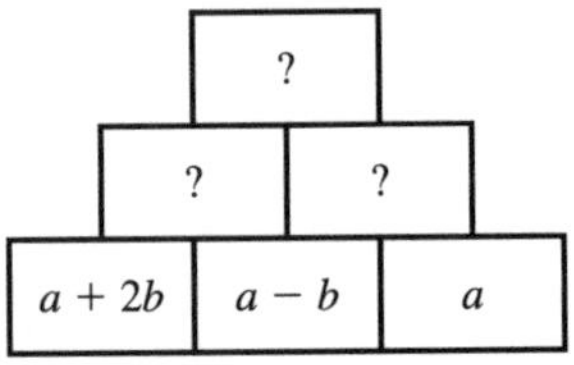

23. Draw the walls and fill in the missing expressions.

(a)

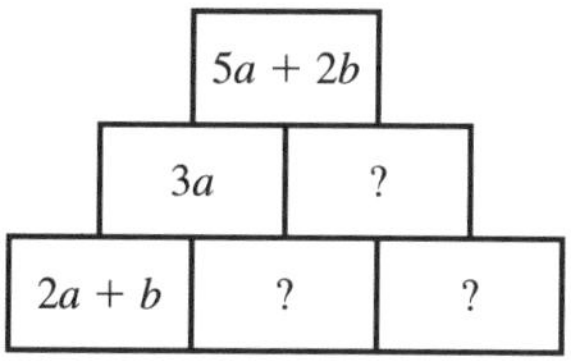

(b)

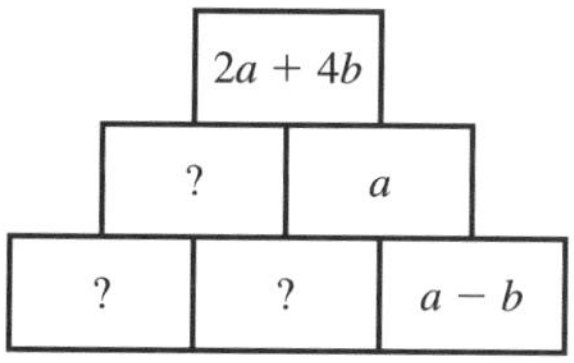

(c)

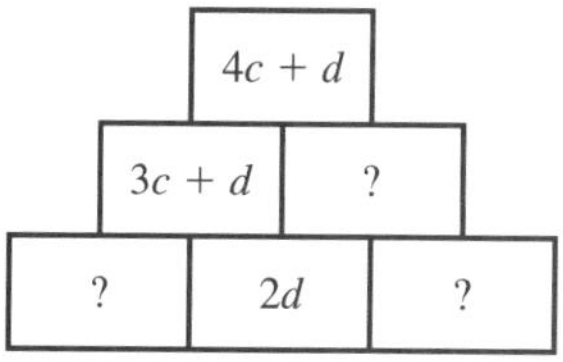

(d)

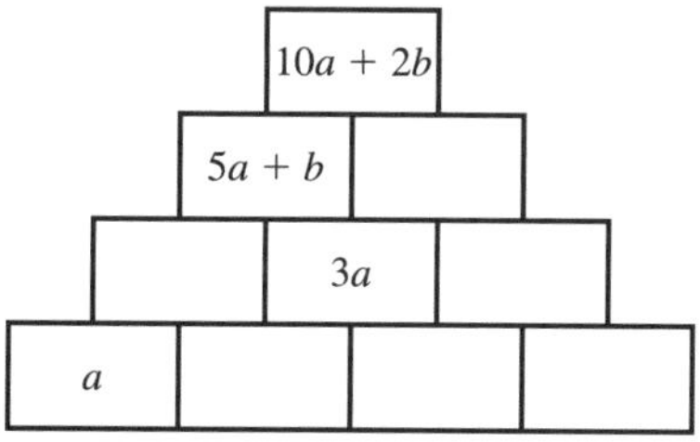

(e)

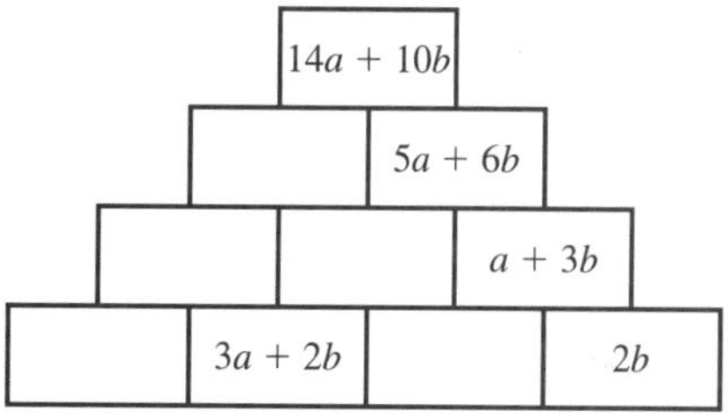

Rules for solving equations

Equations are solved in the same way as we solve the weighing scale problems. The main rule when solving equations is

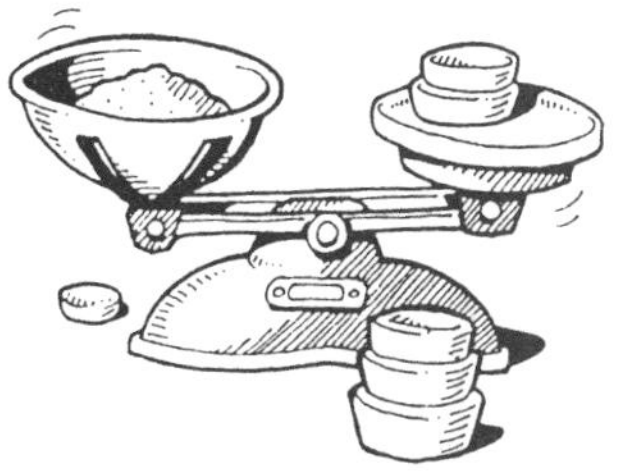

'Do the same thing to both sides'

You may *add* the same thing to both sides.
You may *subtract* the same thing from both sides.
You may *multiply* both sides by the same thing.
You may *divide* both sides by the same thing.

Solve the equations. The operations circled are performed on both sides

(a) $n + 5 = 12$

$\textcircled{-5}\ \textcircled{-5}$

$n = 7$

(b) $n - 7 = 11$

$\textcircled{+7}\ \textcircled{+7}$

$n = 18$

(c) $2n + 3 = 15$

$\textcircled{-3}\ \textcircled{-3}$

$2n = 12$

$\textcircled{\div 2}\ \textcircled{\div 2}$

$n = 6$

(d) $3n - 5 = 16$

$\textcircled{+5}\ \textcircled{+5}$

$3n = 21$

$\textcircled{\div 3}\ \textcircled{\div 3}$

$n = 7$

Exercise 3

Solve the equations.

1. $n + 7 = 11$ **2.** $n + 3 = 15$ **3.** $n - 7 = 7$
4. $n - 5 = 25$ **5.** $6 + n = 100$ **6.** $8 + n = 28$
7. $11 = n + 2$ **8.** $7 = n - 52$ **9.** $0 = n - 3$
10. $6 + n = 6$ **11.** $n - 11 = 11$ **12.** $14 = 5 + n$

Questions **13** to **24** involve different operations.

13. $3a = 18$ **14.** $2a = 60$ **15.** $5a = 40$

16. $8 = 2a$ **17.** $6 = 2a$ **18.** $2a = 1$

19. $2a + 1 = 7$ **20.** $3a + 2 = 14$ **21.** $4a + 7 = 19$

22. $3a + 2 = 17$ **23.** $4a + 6 = 50$ **24.** $6a + 5 = 41$

Questions **25** to **36** are more difficult

25. $5x - 3 = 7$ **26.** $3x - 4 = 11$ **27.** $7x + 3 = 24$

28. $6x + 5 = 6$ **29.** $9x + 1 = 100$ **30.** $3x - 5 = 10$

31. $3 + 2x = 15$ **32.** $5 + 3x = 11$ **33.** $8 + 4x = 8$

34. $14 = 3x - 1$ **35.** $31 = 7x + 3$ **36.** $100 = 5x - 5$

Equations involving brackets

(a) $3(2x + 1) = 15$
$6x + 3 = 15$
(−3) (−3)
$6x = 12$
(÷6) (÷6)
$x = 2$

(b) $4(3x - 1) = 8$
$12x - 4 = 8$
(+4) (+4)
$12x = 12$
(÷12) (÷12)
$x = 1$

Notice that in both examples we began by *removing the brackets.*

Exercise 4

Solve the equations for x.

1. $2(x + 1) = 10$ **2.** $2(x + 3) = 12$ **3.** $3(x + 4) = 21$

4. $3(x - 2) = 12$ **5.** $3(2x + 1) = 9$ **6.** $4(x - 2) = 8$

7. $5(x + 1) = 5$ **8.** $2(3x - 1) = 10$ **9.** $2(3x + 2) = 10$

10. $2(x + 3) = 7$ **11.** $4(x + 1) = 5$ **12.** $6(x + 2) = 13$

Questions **13** to **24** involve different unknowns.

13. $5(a + 1) = 20$ **14.** $3(t - 1) = 18$ **15.** $4(b + 3) = 20$

16. $3(2y + 3) = 10$ **17.** $14 = 2(3a + 1)$ **18.** $16 = 4(n - 2)$

19. $18 = 2(2m + 3)$ **20.** $5(2x + 2) = 10$ **21.** $3(2n - 7) = 3$

22. $8(2 + x) = 24$ **23.** $10(3 + x) = 100$ **24.** $5(1 + 2x) = 20$

Using equations to solve problems

Mike is thinking of a number. He tells us that when he doubles it and adds 5, the answer is 12. What number is Mike thinking of?

Suppose that Mike is thinking of the number x.

He tells us that	$2x + 5 = 12$
Subtract 5 from both sides	$2x = 7$
Divide both sides by 2	$x = \frac{7}{2}$
	$x = 3\frac{1}{2}$

So Mike is thinking of the number $3\frac{1}{2}$

Exercise 5

In each question I am thinking of a number. Use the information to form an equation and then solve it to find the number.

1. If we multiply the number by 3 and then add 1, the answer is 25.

2. If we multiply the number by 10 and then subtract 3, the answer is 19.

3. If we multiply the number by 5 and then add 8, the answer is 11.

4. If we multiply the number by 4 and then subtract 3, the answer is 297.

5. If we double the number and add 7, the answer is 20.

6. If we treble the number and subtract 7, the answer is 0.

7. If we double the number and subtract 20, the answer is 9.

In Question **8** to **13** form an equation with brackets

8. If we add 3 to the number and then double the result, the answer is 140.

9. If we subtract 5 from the number and then treble the result, the answer is 15.

10. If we add 7 to the number and then multiply the result by 3, the answer is 22.

11. If we subtract 4 from the number and then multiply the result by 5, the answer is 15.

12. If we double the number, add 3 and then multiply the result by 4, the answer is 16.

13. If we double the number, subtract 5 and then multiply the result by 7, the answer is 7.

Equations with the unknown on both sides

(a) $2n + 3 = n + 7$

$(-n)$ $(-n)$

$n + 3 = 7$

(-3) (-3)

$n = 4$

(b) $5n - 3 = 2n + 9$

$(-2n)$ $(-2n)$

$3n - 3 = 9$

$(+3)$ $(+3)$

$3n = 12$

$n = 4$

Exercise 6

Solve the equations.

1. $5n = 3n + 10$
2. $7n = n + 12$
3. $3n = n + 2$
4. $4n = n + 30$
5. $4n = n + 15$
6. $12n = n + 66$
7. $13n = 7n + 24$
8. $10n = 3n + 21$
9. $5n = 8 + n$
10. $2n = 7 + n$
11. $4n + 3 = n + 9$
12. $7n + 1 = 6n + 8$
13. $3n + 7 = n + 15$
14. $6n - 1 = 3n + 8$
15. $5n - 4 = 2n + 5$
16. $1 + 3n = n + 2$
17. $4n - 11 = 2n + 11$
18. $1 + 5n = 3n + 13$
19. $6n = 3n + 24$
20. $5n - 4 = n$

Questions **21** to **30** involve brackets.

21. $3(x + 2) = 2(x + 5)$
22. $4(x + 1) = 3(x + 3)$
23. $2(x + 5) = x + 13$
24. $6x - 10 = 2(x + 7)$
25. $3(x - 1) = 2(x + 6)$
26. $5(x - 2) = 3(x + 2)$
27. $6(2x + 1) = 10x + 4$
28. $2(2x - 3) = 3(x + 7)$
29. $7(2x - 1) = 7$
30. $5(5x + 2) = 2(3x + 5)$

Exercise 7

Solve the equations for x.

1. $3(x - 1) = 2x - 2$
2. $4(x + 2) = 3x + 10$
3. $2(2x - 1) = x + 4$
4. $3(x - 1) = 2(x + 1) - 2$
5. $4(2x - 1) = 3(x + 1) - 2$
6. $5 + 2(x + 1) = 5(x - 1)$
7. $6 + 3(x + 2) = 2(x + 5) + 4$
8. $5(x + 1) = 2x + 3 + x$
9. $4(2x - 2) = 5x - 17$
10. $x + 2(x + 4) = -4$
11. $3x + 2(x + 1) = 3x + 12$
12. $4x - 2(x + 4) = x + 1$

Questions **13** to **18** involve different unknowns.

13. $5(2a + 1) - 5 = 3(a + 1)$
14. $3(4a - 1) - 3 = a + 1$
15. $2(a - 10) = 4 - 3a$
16. $7(n - 3) = 10 - n$
17. $3(n + 1) = 2(n + 3) - 6$
18. $5(2n - 1) = 9(n + 1) - 8$

Exercise 7

1. The length of a rectangle is twice its width.
   The perimeter is 30 cm. Find the width.

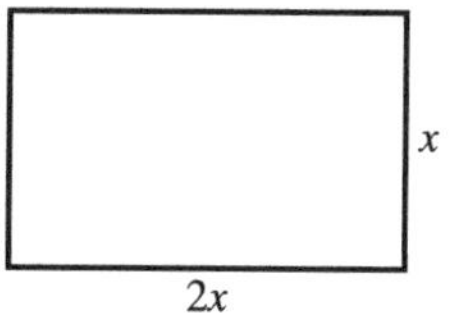

2. The length of a rectangle is three times its width.
   If the perimeter is 32 cm, find its width. [Hint: Let the width be x.]

3. The length of a rectangle is five times its width.
   If the perimeter is 60 cm, find its width.

4. Form equations to find x.

(a)

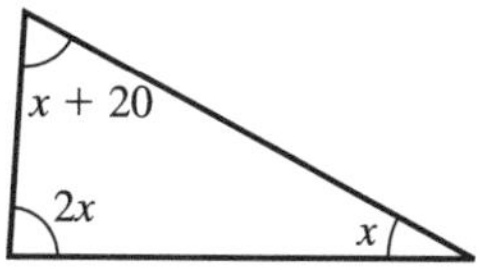

(b)

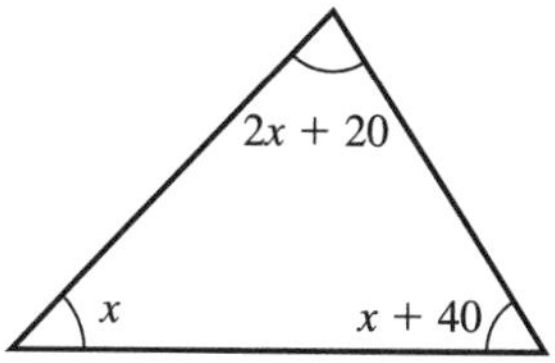

5.

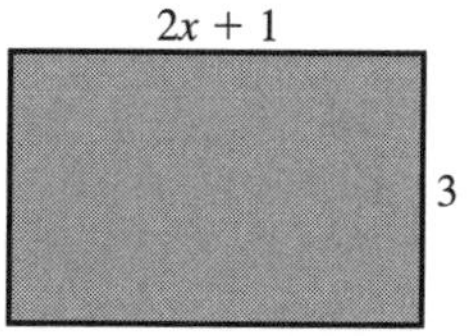

The rectangle has an area of 27 square units. Form an equation and solve it to find x.

6. In the triangle, BC is twice as long as AB.
   AC is 9 cm long.
   If the perimeter is 24 cm, form an equation and solve it to find x.

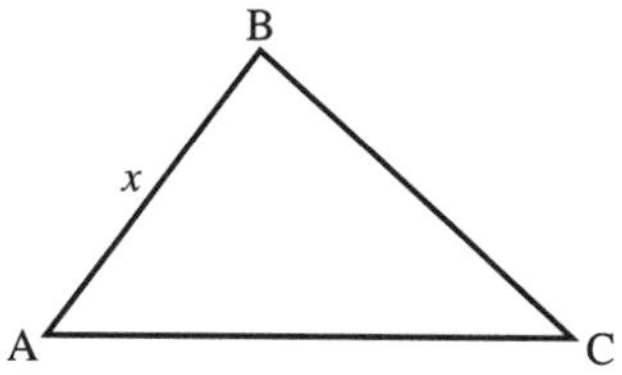

7. The total mass of three stones A, B and C is 60 kg. Stone B is twice as heavy as stone A.
   Stone C is 30 kg heavier than stone A.
   Find the mass of stone A. [Call it x kg.]

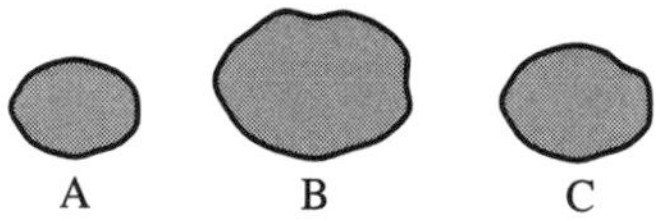

8. An equilateral triangle has sides of length $3x + 1$, $2x + 3$ and $2x + 3$. Find x.

9. The perimeter, P, of a rectangle is given by the formula $P = 2(a + b)$.
   If $P = 19$ and $b = 7$, find the value of a.

10. The volume of a cuboid is given by the formula $V = \ell b h$.
    If $V = 30$, $\ell = 2$ and $b = 6$, find the value of h.

11. In an arithmagon, the number in a square is the sum of the numbers in the two circles either side of it.
    (a) Explain why the number in circle B is $20 - x$.
    (b) Explain why the number in circle C is $15 - x$.
    (c) Form an equation across the lowest side of the triangle. Solve the equation to find x.

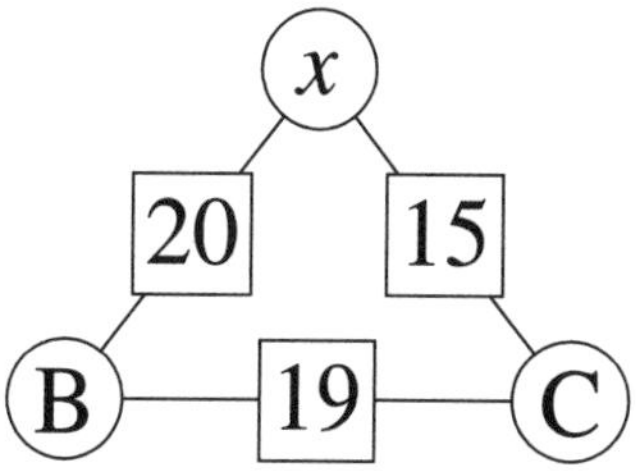

12. Use the method above to find x in these arithmagons.

(a)

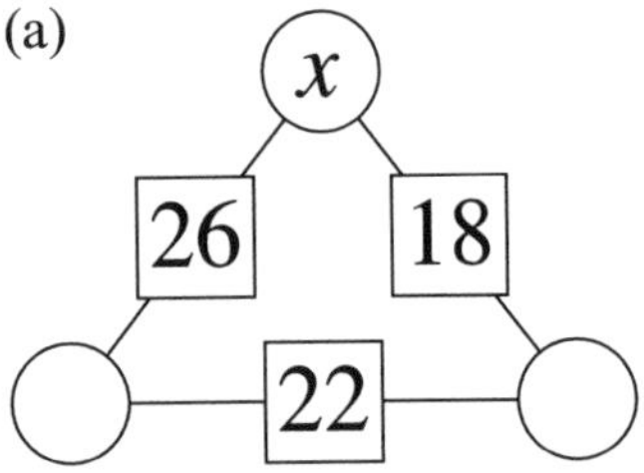

(b)

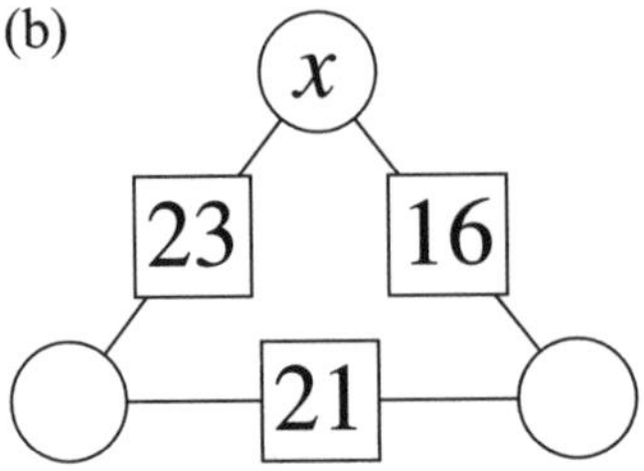

(c)

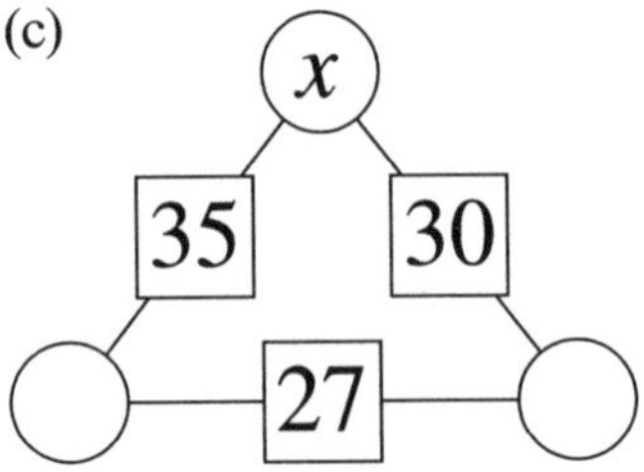

13. The diagram shows a road from A to E.
A to B is 5 km more than D to E.
C to D is twice the distance from A to B.
C is midway between B and D.
If the total distance from A to E is 91 km, find the distance from D to E.

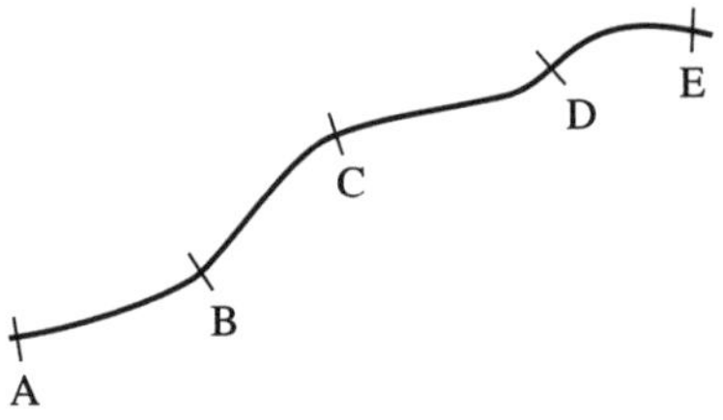

14. The sum of four consecutive whole numbers is 98. Let the first number be x and write down the other three numbers in terms of x. Find the four numbers.

15. The sum of four consecutive *odd* numbers is 216. Find the numbers.

16. The triangle and the rectangle have the same area. Find x.

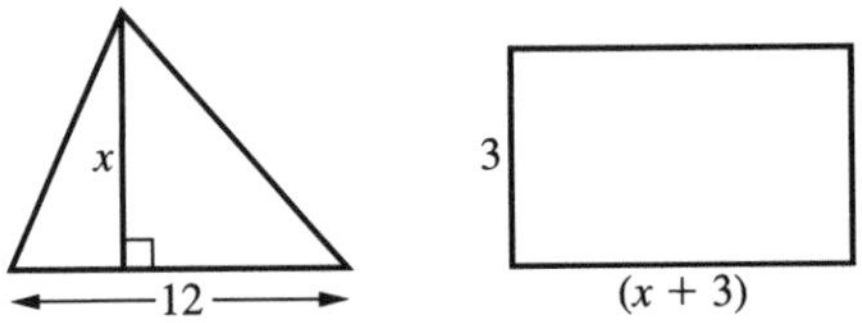

17. (a) The area of rectangle P is five times the area of rectangle Q. Find x.
(b) The value of x is changed and the areas of the unshaded rectangles become equal. Find the new value of x.

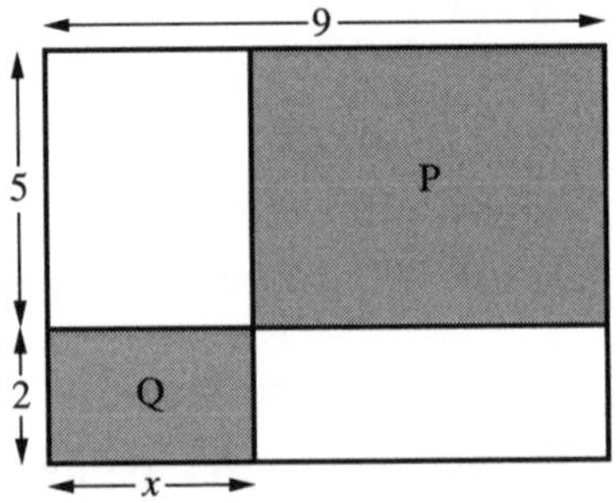

18. My daughter asked how old I am. I answered 'In 20 years, I'll be twice as old as I was 12 years ago.' How old am I?

19. You have three consecutive even numbers so that the sum of twice the smallest number plus three times the middle number is four times the largest number. Find the three numbers.

'L' puzzles

(a) This is an 'L' puzzle.

$3 + 9 = 12$
$3 + 1 = 4$

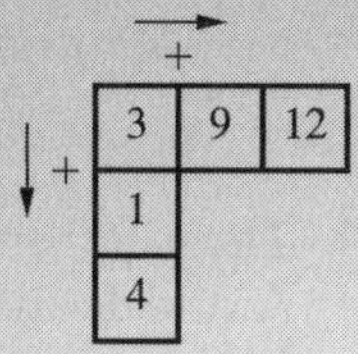

(b) Here is another.

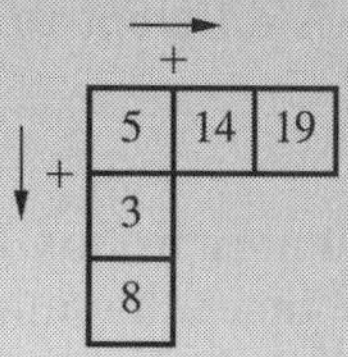

(c) Find all the numbers in this puzzle given that the number in box B is twice the number in box A.

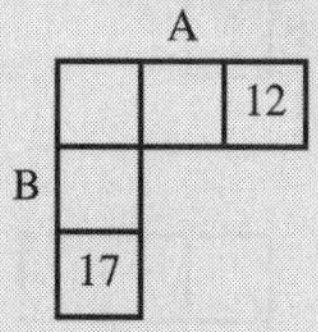

Let the number in box A be x.
Then the number in box B is $2x$.
Write ? for the corner number.

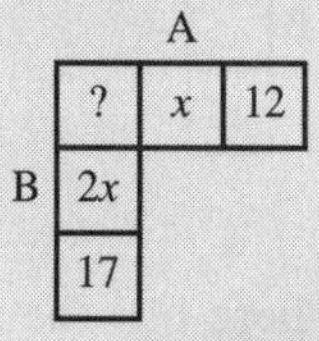

Across the top row: $? + x = 12$
so $? = 12 - x$

Using this value in the left hand column,

$12 - x + 2x = 17$
$x = 5$

The puzzle can now be completed:

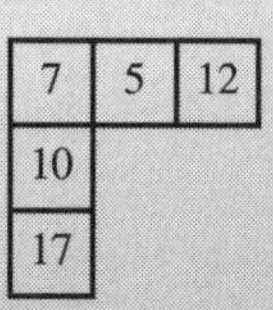

Exercise 8

1. Copy and complete the following puzzles. You do not need an equation.

(a)

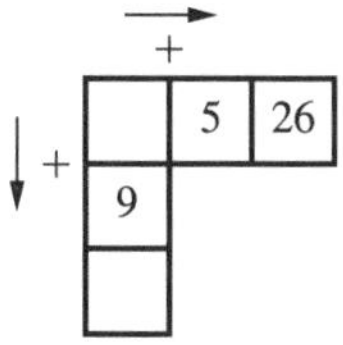

(b)

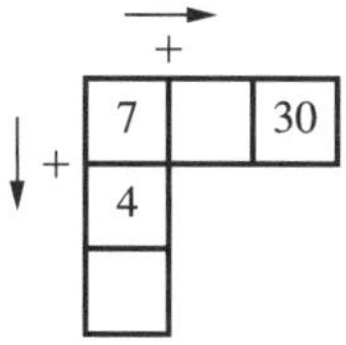

(c)

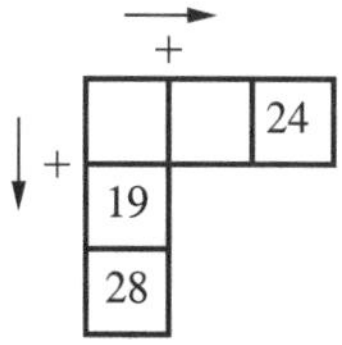

In question **2** onwards use the method shown in the above example to form an equation and then solve it to find the missing numbers.

2. The number in box B is twice the number in box A. Start by letting x be the number in box A.

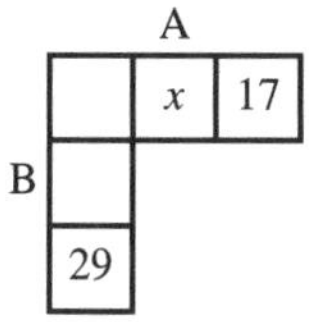

3. The number in box B is four times the number in box A.

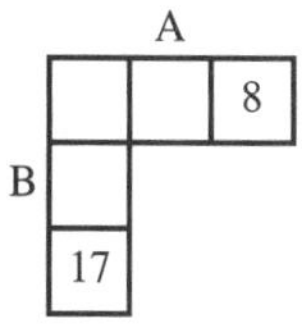

4. The number in box B is twice the number in box A. [Notice that box B is different to Qu. 3].

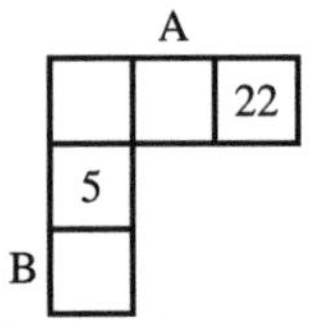

5. The number in box B is three times the number in box A.

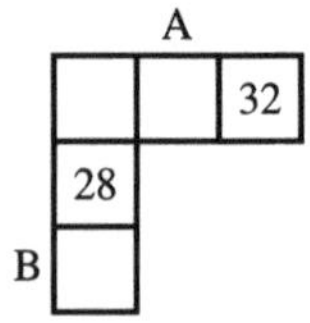

6. The number in box B is four times the number in box A.

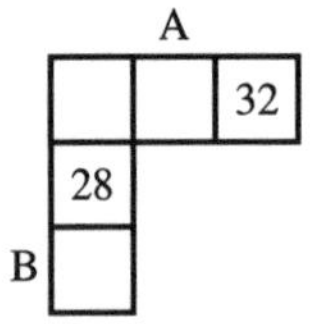

7. The numbers in boxes A and B add up to 20. Let the number in box A be x.

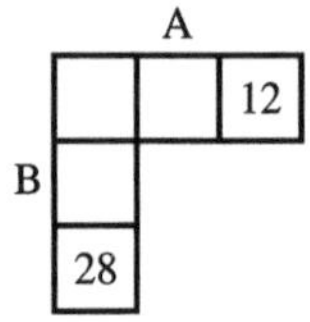

8. The numbers in boxes A and B add up to 20.

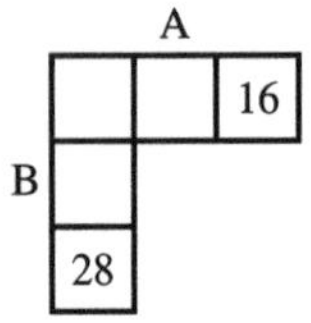

9. The number in box B is 5 *less* than the number in box A.

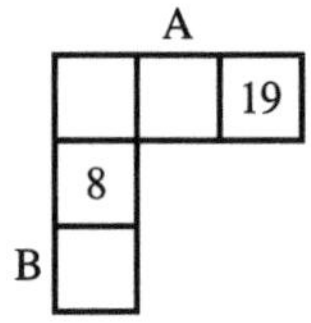

10. The diagram has changed here but the principle is similar to the above.
$9+5=14$; $9+7=16$; $14+4=18$; $16+2=18$.

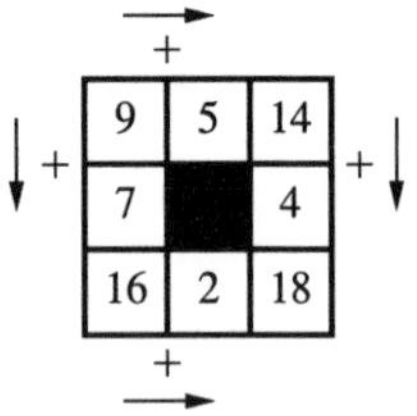

Find all the missing numbers given that:
(a) the number in box B is four times the number in box A.
(b) the number in box C is nine times the number in box A.

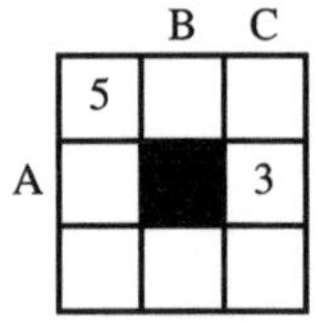

11. Find all the missing numbers given that:
(a) the number in box B is one less than the number in box A.
(b) the number in box C is one third of the number in box A.

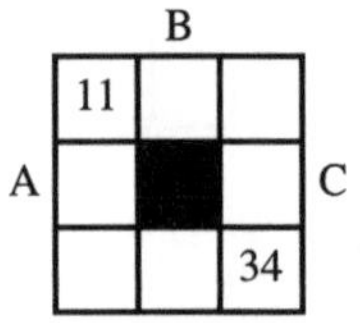

12. This one is more difficult.
Find all the missing numbers given that:
(a) the number in box A is three times the number in box C.
(b) the number in box B is two more than the number in box A.
(c) the number in box D is one more than twice the number in box B.

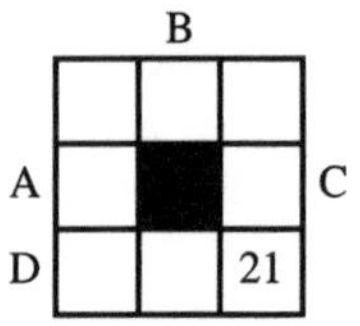

4.4 Handling data

Scatter graphs

Sometimes it is important to discover if there is a connection or relationship between two sets of data.
Examples

- Do tall people weigh more than short people?
- If you spend longer revising for a test, will you get a higher mark?
- Do tall parents have tall children?
- Do older people have higher pulse rates?

If there is a relationship, it will be easy to spot if your data is plotted on a scatter diagram – that is a graph in which one set of data is plotted on the horizontal axis and the other on the vertical axis

- Here is a scatter graph showing the test marks of some pupils in a maths test and a science test.
- We can see a connection: the pupils who got a high mark in science generally got a high mark in maths.

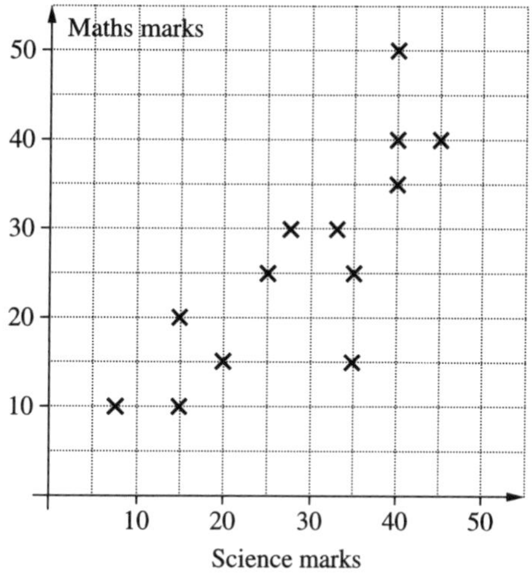

Exercise 1

1. Here are the heights and masses of 9 people. Draw the axes shown and complete the scatter graph.

Name	Mass (kg)	Height (cm)
Alice	45	115
Fred	60	160
Jack	65	155
John	55	125
Percy	75	160
Hugh	75	170
Mabel	65	140
Diana	85	180
Cyril	52	146

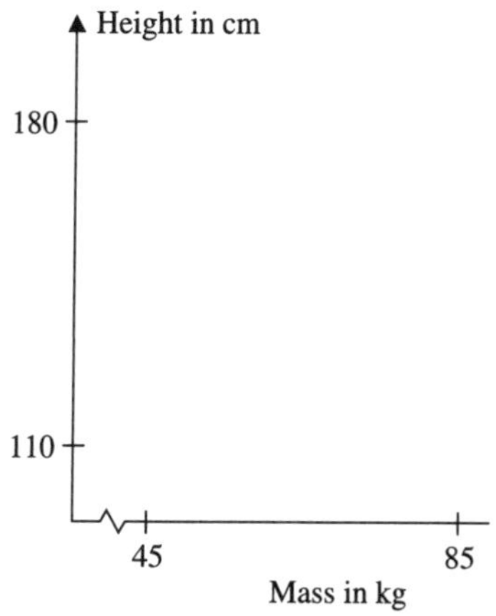

2. The scatter graph shows the number of hot drinks sold by a cafe and the outside temperature.
(a) On how many days was it less than 12°C?
(b) How many hot drinks were sold when it was 35°C?
(c) On how many days were 40 or more hot drinks sold?
(d) Fill the blank with either 'increases' or 'decreases': As temperature *increases* the number of drinks sold ________.

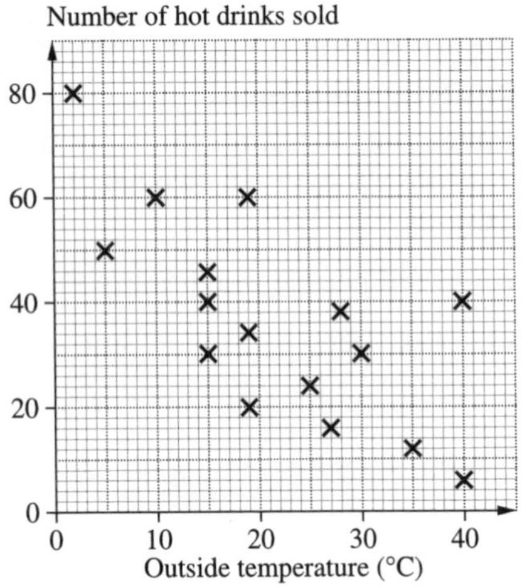

3. The graph shows the scores in a spelling test and the shoe sizes of 14 children.
(a) How many take size 6 or less?
(b) The pass mark is 4 or more. How many people failed?
(c) Is there a connection between a person's shoe size and test score?

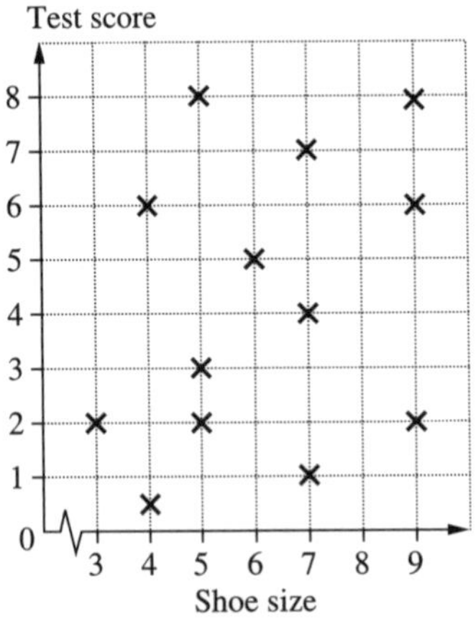

Correlation

The word correlation describes how things *co-relate*. There is correlation between two sets of data if there is a connection or relationship.

The correlation between two sets of data can be positive or negative and it can be strong or weak as indicated by the scatter graphs below.

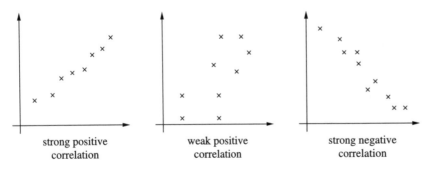

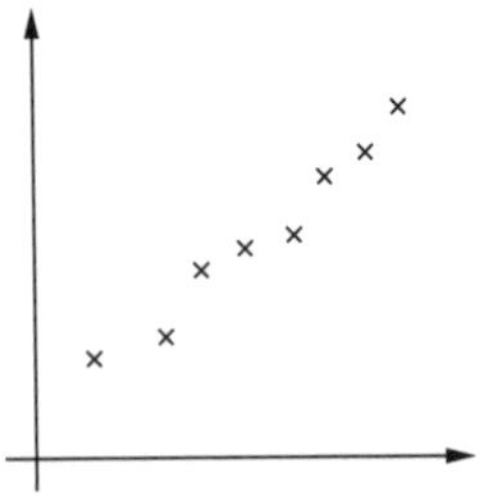
strong positive correlation

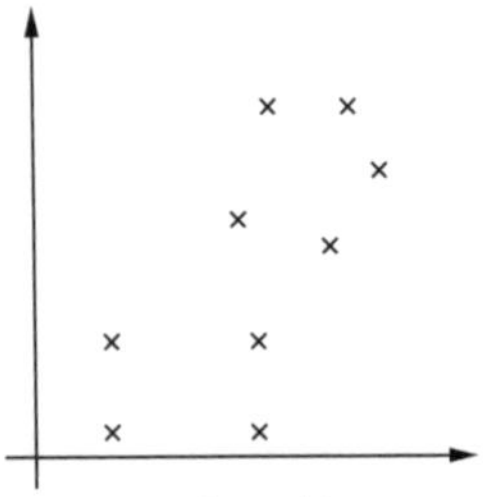
weak positive correlation

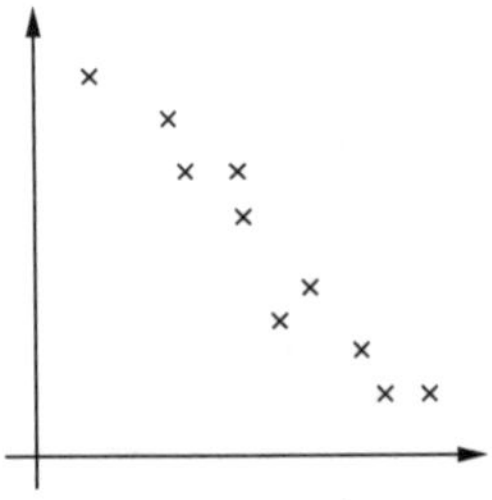
strong negative correlation

When the correlation is positive the points are around a line which slopes upwards to the right. When the correlation is negative the 'line' slopes downwards to the right.
When the correlation is strong the points are bunched close to a line through their midst. When the correlation is weak the points are more scattered.

It is important to realise that often there is *no* correlation between two sets of data.
If, for example, we take a group of students and plot their maths test results against their time to run 800 m, the graph might look like the one on the right. A common mistake in this topic is to 'see' a correlation on a scatter graph where none exists.

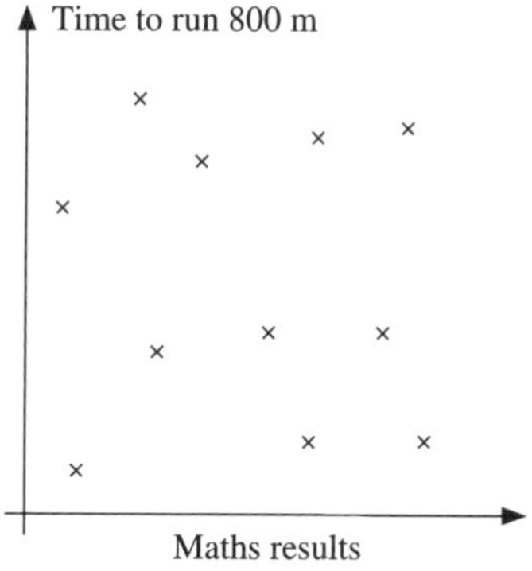

There is also *no* correlation in these two scatter graphs.

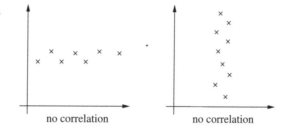

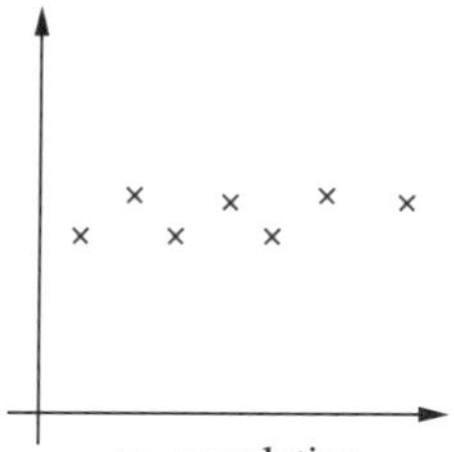
no correlation

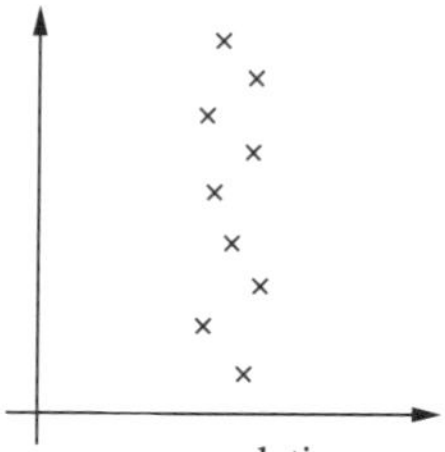
no correlation

Exercise 2

1. Make the following measurements for everyone in your class:

height	(nearest cm)
armspan	(nearest cm)
head circumference	(nearest cm)
hand span	(nearest cm)
pulse rate	(beats/minute)

For greater consistency of measuring, one person (or perhaps 2 people) should do all the measurements of one kind (except on themselves!)

Enter all the measurements in a table, either on the board or on a sheet of paper.

Name	Height	Armspan	Head
Roger	161	165	56 cm
Liz	150	148	49 cm
Gill			

(a) Draw the scatter graphs shown below

(i)

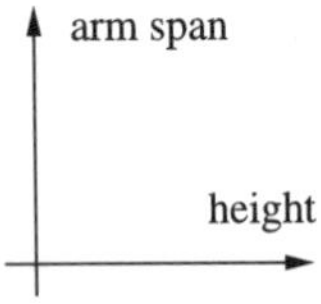

(ii)

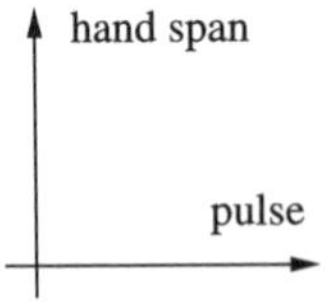

(b) Describe the correlation, if any, in the scatter graphs you drew in part (a).

(c) (i) Draw a scatter graph of two measurements where you think there might be positive correlation.

(ii) Was there indeed a positive correlation?

2. Plot the points given on a scatter graph, with s across the page and p up the page. Draw axes with values from 0 to 20. Describe the correlation, if any, between the values of s and p. [i.e. 'strong negative', 'weak positive' etc.]

(a)

s	7	16	4	12	18	6	20	4	10	13
p	8	15	6	12	17	9	18	7	10	14

(b)

s	3	8	12	15	16	5	6	17	9
p	4	2	10	17	5	10	17	11	15

(c)

s	11	1	16	7	2	19	8	4	13	18
p	5	12	7	14	17	1	11	8	11	5

3. Describe the correlation; if any, in these scatter graphs.

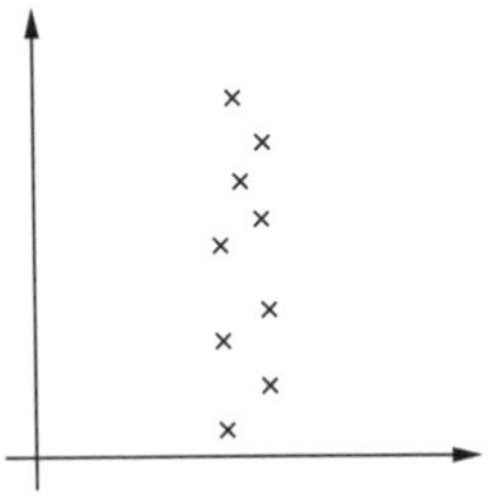

(a)

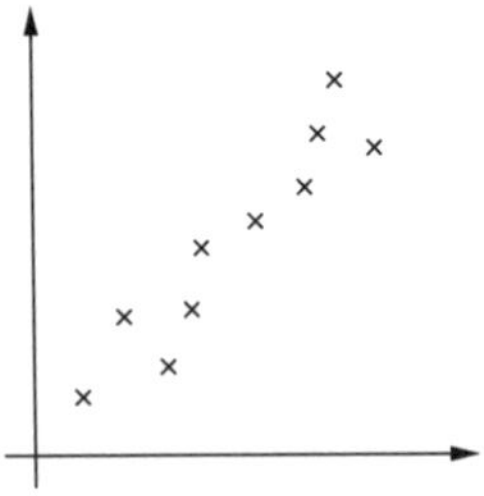

(b)

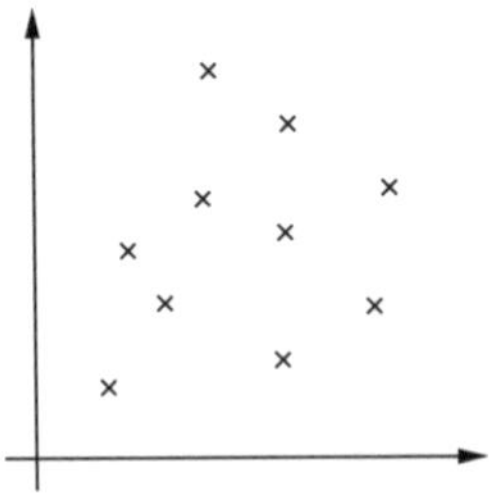

(c)

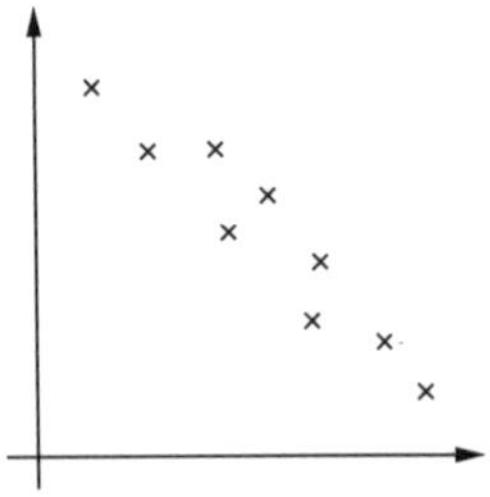

(d)

4. The table shows the marks of 7 students in the two papers of a science examination.

Paper 1	35	10	60	17	43	55	49
Paper 2	26	15	40	15	30	34	35

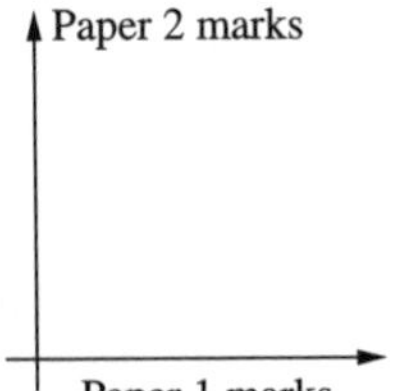

(a) Plot the marks on a scatter diagram, using a scale of 1 cm to 5 marks.

(b) A student got a mark of 25 on paper 1 but missed paper 2. What would you expect her to get on paper 2?

5. The table shows the mean weight of the apples from a certain apple tree together with the latitude of the farm where the tree was growing

Latitude (N)	37	50	32	45	36	30	44
Mean weight of apples (g)	100	70	115	75	110	120	80

(a) Draw a scatter graph, using a scale of 1 cm to 5 g across the page and 2 cm to 5 up the page.

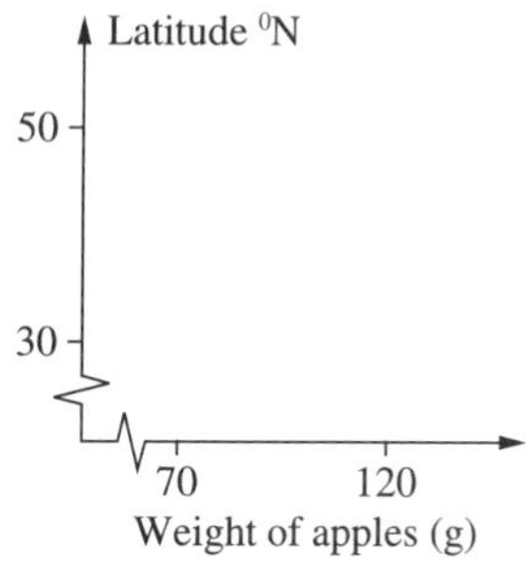

(b) What would you expect the mean weight of the apples to be on a farm at latitude 42N?

6. Suppose scatter graphs were drawn, with the quantities below on the two axes. What sort of correlation, if any, would you expect to see in each case?

(a) height of a man; height of the man's father
(b) a person's pulse rate; a person's reaction time
(c) outside temperature; consumption of energy for heating a home
(d) value of a car; mileage of the car [for the same kind of car]
(e) price of goods in U.K; price of similar goods in Germany
(f) number of ice creams sold; outside temperature
(g) exposure to sun; degree of sunburn
(h) use of a calculator; ability to do mental arithmetic
(i) length of time sleeping; rate of growth of fingernails

7. The table below show details of the number of rooms and the number of occupants of 11 houses in a street.

Number of rooms	2	3	7	11	7	5	5	11	5	6	4
Number of occupants	2	8	5	2	6	2	7	7	4	0	1

(a) Draw a scatter graph
(b) Can you estimate the likely number of people living in a house with 9 rooms? If so, what is the number?
Explain your answer.

Bar charts and pie charts

Exercise 3

1. The bar chart shows age groups on three different holidays.

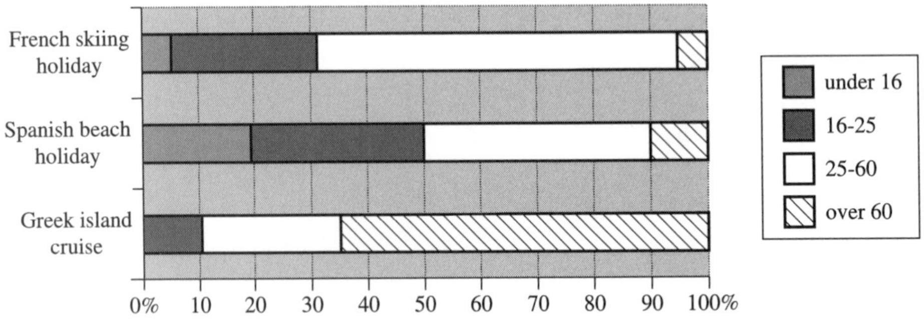

(a) What percentage of holiday makers are:
   (i) between 25 and 60 on the Spanish beach holiday,
   (ii) under 25 on the Greek island cruise,
   (iii) over 25 on the French skiing holiday?

(b) Describe the main difference between the top and bottom charts. Why are they so different?

2. A drug company claims that its new nutrient pill helps people to improve their memory.
As an experiment two randomly selected groups of people were given the same memory test. Group A took the new pills for a month while group B took no pills. Here are the results of the tests: (A high score indicates a good memory).

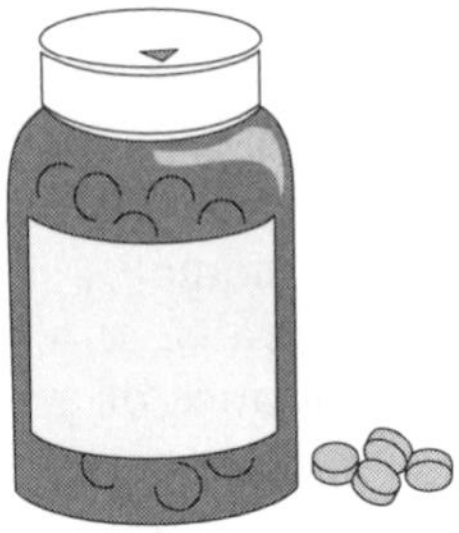

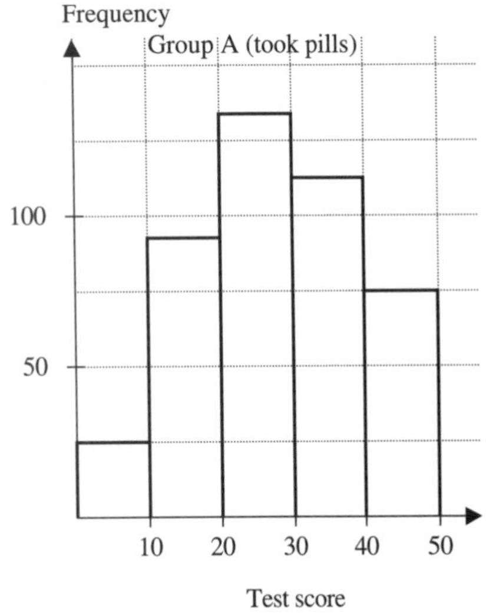

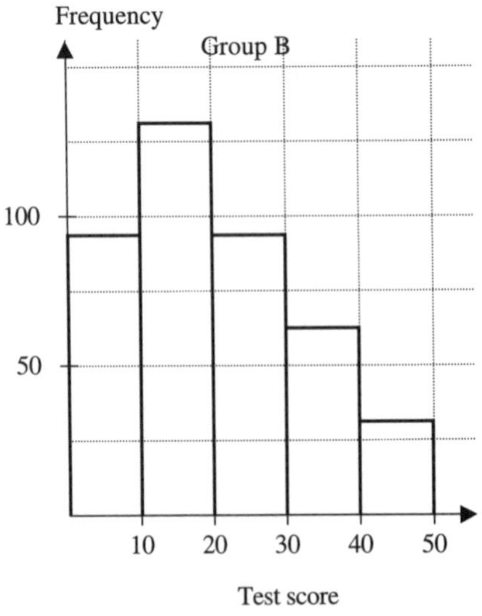

Does it appear that the new pills did in fact help to improve memory?

3. The pie charts show how much money two shopkeepers get from selling different products.

Mr. Brown

Mrs. Evans

(a) Mr Brown gets £180 from selling ice cream. Estimate how much he gets from selling sweets.

(b) From all sales: Mr Brown gets a total of £800 and Mrs Evans gets a total of £1200.
Estimate how much each shopkeeper gets from selling magazines.

4. The table shows the number of periods for different subjects on a school timetable.
Work out the angle for each sector and then draw a pie chart.

Subject	Frequency
Maths	5
English	5
Science	6
Humanities	4
Arts	4
Others	16

5. Eurostar did a survey of over a thousand passengers on one of their trains. Here are their nationalities:

British 30% French 20%
German 15% Dutch 35%

On a pie chart, the angle for British passengers is found by working out 30% of 360°. Find the angle on a pie chart representing

(a) French passengers (b) Dutch passengers.

6. The pie chart illustrates the sales of four brands of crisps.

(a) What percentage of total sales does KP have?

(b) If Walkers accounts for 35% of total sales, calculate the angles x and y.

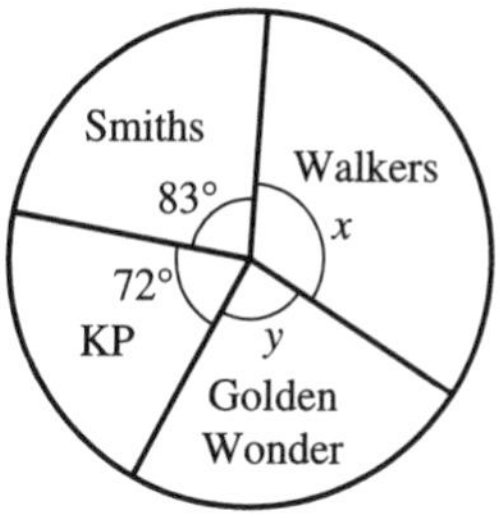

Pie charts and bar charts using a spreadsheet on a computer

Teacher's note: There is an introduction to using spreadsheets in section 4.7.

Example: Display the data about the activities in one day.

Enter the headings: Sleep in A1, School in B1 etc. [Use the *tab* key to move across the page.]

Enter the data: 8 in A2, 7 in B2 etc.

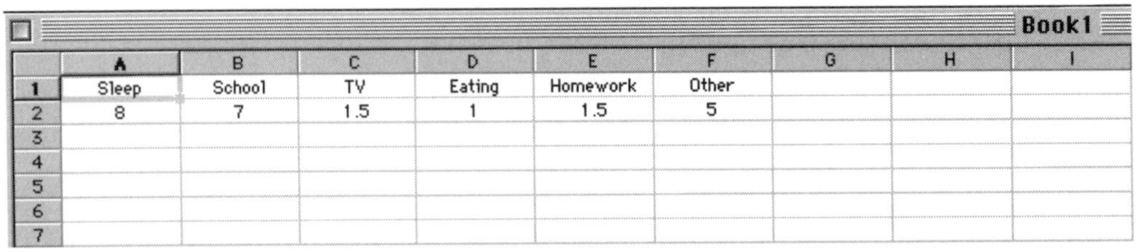

	A	B	C	D	E	F	G	H	I
1	Sleep	School	TV	Eating	Homework	Other			
2	8	7	1.5	1	1.5	5			
3									
4									
5									
6									
7									

Now highlight all the cells from A1 to F2. [Click on A1 and drag across to F2.]

Click on the () Chart wizard on the tool bar.

Select 'pie' and then choose one of the examples displayed. Follow the on-screen prompts.

Alternatively, for a bar chart, select 'charts' after clicking on the chart wizard. Proceed as above.

You will be able to display your charts with various '3D' effects, possibly in colour. This approach is recommended when you are presenting data that you have collected as part of an investigation.

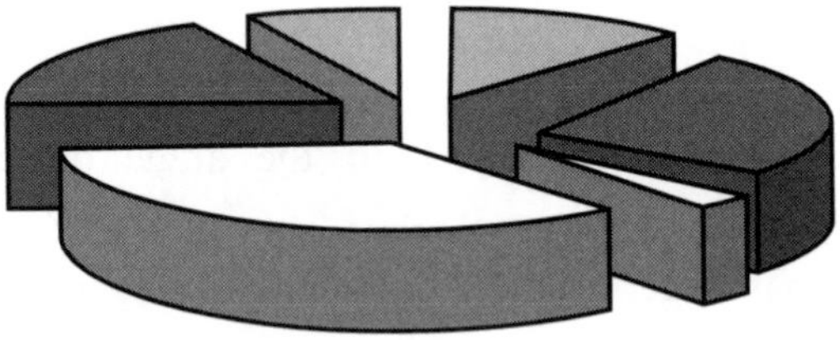

Scatter graphs on a computer

Example: Plot a scatter graph showing the marks of 10 students in Maths and Science.

Enter the headings: *Maths* in A1, *Science* in B1
Enter the data as shown.

	A	B
1	Maths	Science
2	23	30
3	45	41
4	73	67
5	35	74
6	67	77
7	44	50
8	32	41
9	66	55
10	84	70
11	36	32

Now highlight all the cells from A2 to B11.
[Click on A1 and drag across and down to B11.]

Click on the  Chart wizard on the toolbar.

Select XY (Scatter) and select the picture which looks like a scatter graph.

Follow the on-screen prompts.

On 'Titles' enter: Chart title: Maths/Science results
Value (X) axis: Maths
Value (Y) axis: Science

Experiment with 'Axes', 'Gridlines', 'Legend' and 'Data Labels'.

Task 1 Enter the data on a spreadsheet and print a scatter graph. What does each scatter graph show?

(a)

Height	Armspan
162	160
155	151
158	157
142	144
146	148
165	163
171	167
148	150
150	147

(b)

Temperature	Sales
23	7
18	14
7	23
20	9
4	30
12	19
15	15
18	15
10	20

4.5 Fractions, decimals, percentages

Changing fractions to decimals

(a) In Book 7 we changed fractions to decimals using known equivalents.

Eg. $\frac{3}{12} = \frac{1}{4} = 0{\cdot}25 \qquad \frac{11}{20} = \frac{55}{100} = 0{\cdot}55 \qquad \frac{12}{25} = \frac{48}{100} = 0{\cdot}48$

(b) We can think of the fraction $\frac{3}{5}$ as $3 \div 5$. When we perform the division, we obtain the decimal which is equivalent to $\frac{3}{5}$.

$$\begin{array}{r} 0{\cdot}\,6 \\ 5\overline{)3{\cdot}{}^{3}0} \end{array}$$

Answer: $\frac{3}{5} = 0{\cdot}6$

(c) $\frac{5}{8}$ can be thought of as $5 \div 8$.

$$\begin{array}{r} 0{\cdot}\,6\;2\;5 \\ 8\overline{)5{\cdot}{}^{5}0{}^{2}0{}^{4}0} \end{array}$$

Answer: $\frac{5}{8} = 0{\cdot}625$

Exercise 1

Without using a calculator, change the following fractions to decimals. Afterwards use your calculator to check your answer.

1. $\frac{2}{5}$ **2.** $\frac{1}{4}$ **3.** $\frac{3}{8}$ **4.** $\frac{1}{5}$ **5.** $\frac{9}{10}$

6. $\frac{3}{4}$ **7.** $\frac{3}{5}$ **8.** $\frac{4}{8}$ **9.** $\frac{3}{10}$ **10.** $\frac{7}{8}$

Change these mixed numbers to decimals.

11. $1\frac{2}{5}$ **12.** $4\frac{3}{4}$ **13.** $3\frac{1}{2}$ **14.** $1\frac{7}{8}$ **15.** $5\frac{1}{100}$

Use a calculator, to convert the fractions to decimals. Write in order of size, smallest first.

16. $\frac{7}{8}$, 0·85, $\frac{9}{10}$

17. $\frac{13}{20}$, 0·645, $\frac{31}{50}$

18. $\frac{3}{4}$, 0·715, $\frac{29}{40}$

19. $\frac{3}{16}$, 0·18, $\frac{1}{5}$

20. What fraction of each shape is shaded?

(a)

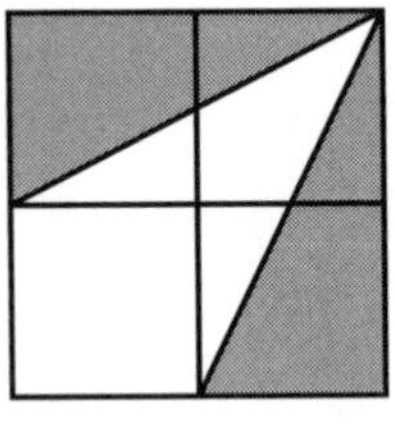

(b)

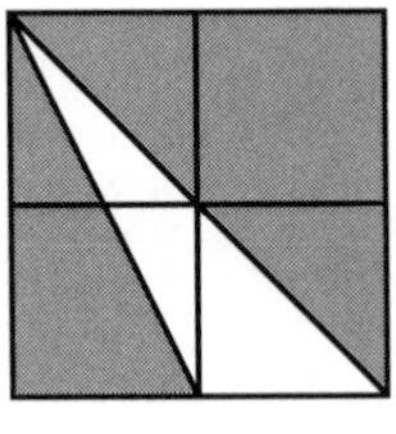

(c)

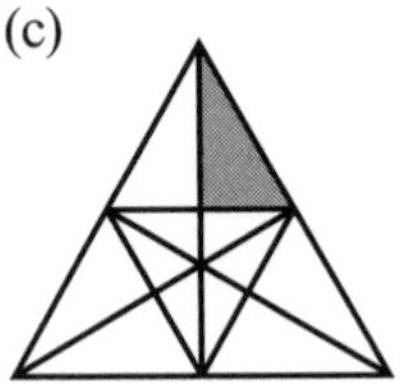

Recurring decimals

Some fractions give rise to decimals which repeat themselves forever. We call these recurring decimals, and use the notation below to save us from writing out the number until our ink runs out!

(a) $0{\cdot}555\ldots$ — We write $0{\cdot}\dot{5}$
(b) $0{\cdot}434343\ldots$ — We write $0{\cdot}\dot{4}\dot{3}$
(c) $0{\cdot}5265265\ldots$ — We write $0{\cdot}\dot{5}2\dot{6}$

(a) Change $\frac{1}{3}$ to a decimal

$$\begin{array}{r} 0{\cdot}\ 3\ 3\ 3\ 3\ 3\ldots \\ 3\overline{)1{\cdot}{}^{1}0{}^{1}0{}^{1}010{}^{1}0\ldots} \end{array}$$

The calculation is never going to end.

We write $\frac{1}{3} = 0{\cdot}\dot{3}$. We say 'nought point three recurring'.

(b) Change $\frac{3}{11}$ to a decimal.

$$\begin{array}{r} 0{\cdot}\ 2\ 7\ 2\ 7\ 2\ 2\ldots \\ 11\overline{)3{\cdot}{}^{3}0{}^{8}0{}^{3}0{}^{8}0{}^{3}0{}^{8}0\ldots} \end{array}$$

This time a *pair* of figures recurs.

We write $\frac{3}{11} = 0{\cdot}\dot{2}\dot{7}$

(c) Change $\frac{1}{7}$ to a decimal.

$$\begin{array}{r} 0{\cdot}\ 1\ 4\ 2\ 8\ 5\ 7\ 1\ 42\ldots \\ 7\overline{)1{\cdot}{}^{1}0{}^{3}0{}^{2}0{}^{6}0{}^{4}0{}^{5}0{}^{1}0{}^{3}00\ldots} \end{array}$$

The sequence '142857' recurs.

We write $\frac{1}{7} = 0{\cdot}\dot{1}4285\dot{7}$

Exercise 2

Change the following fractions to decimals.

1. $\frac{2}{3}$	**2.** $\frac{2}{9}$	**3.** $\frac{7}{9}$	**4.** $\frac{1}{6}$	**5.** $\frac{2}{7}$
6. $\frac{3}{7}$	**7.** $\frac{5}{6}$	**8.** $\frac{6}{7}$	**9.** $\frac{2}{11}$	**10.** $\frac{5}{11}$

Changing decimals to fractions

- $0{\cdot}8 = \frac{8}{10} = \frac{4}{5}$ $0{\cdot}21 = \frac{21}{100}$

  $0{\cdot}35 = \frac{35}{100} = \frac{7}{20}$ $0{\cdot}08 = \frac{8}{100} = \frac{2}{25}$

Simplify the answer if possible

Exercise 3

Change the following decimals to fractions in their most simple form.

1. $0{\cdot}4$	**2.** $0{\cdot}7$	**3.** $0{\cdot}03$	**4.** $0{\cdot}05$	**5.** $0{\cdot}007$
6. $0{\cdot}006$	**7.** $0{\cdot}08$	**8.** $0{\cdot}12$	**9.** $0{\cdot}38$	**10.** $0{\cdot}015$
11. $0{\cdot}25$	**12.** $0{\cdot}45$	**13.** $0{\cdot}37$	**14.** $0{\cdot}025$	**15.** $0{\cdot}125$

Changing to a percentage and vice versa

To change a fraction or a decimal to a percentage, multiply by 100

(a) To change $\frac{2}{5}$ to a percentage, multiply by 100.

$\frac{2}{5} \times \frac{100}{1} = \frac{200}{5}$

$= 40\%$

(b) To change $\frac{1}{8}$ to a percentage, multiply by 100.

$\frac{1}{8} \times \frac{100}{1} = \frac{100}{8}$

$= 12\frac{1}{2}\%$

(c) To change $\frac{3}{7}$ to a percentage, multiply by 100.

$\frac{3}{7} \times \frac{100}{1} = \frac{300}{7}$

$= 42{\cdot}857\ldots\%$

$= 43\%$, to the nearest whole number.

(d) To change 0·37 to a percentage, multiply by 100.

$0{\cdot}37 \times 100 = 37\%$

Exercise 3

Change these fractions to percentages.

1. $\frac{1}{2}$ 2. $\frac{3}{4}$ 3. $\frac{2}{5}$ 4. $\frac{7}{10}$ 5. $\frac{13}{20}$

6. $\frac{1}{8}$ 7. $\frac{5}{8}$ 8. $\frac{1}{4}$ 9. $\frac{7}{20}$ 10. $\frac{71}{100}$

11. Here are some examination results. Change them to percentages.
(a) $\frac{14}{25}$ (b) $\frac{33}{40}$ (c) $\frac{42}{60}$ (d) $\frac{66}{120}$

12. Class 8P and class 8W were each set a maths test. The average mark for 8P was $\frac{25}{40}$ and the average mark for 8W was $\frac{15}{25}$.
Which class had the higher average percentage result?

13. Change these decimals to percentages.
(a) 0·32 (b) 0·14 (c) 0·03 (d) 0·815 (e) 1·4

14. Change these fractions to percentages, rounding to the nearest whole number.
(a) $\frac{5}{6}$ (b) $\frac{7}{12}$ (c) $\frac{4}{9}$ (d) $\frac{6}{11}$ (e) $\frac{2}{3}$

15. The chart opposite shows the way that 40 people travel to work. What percentage travel
(a) By car
(b) By train
(c) By bus
(d) By some other method

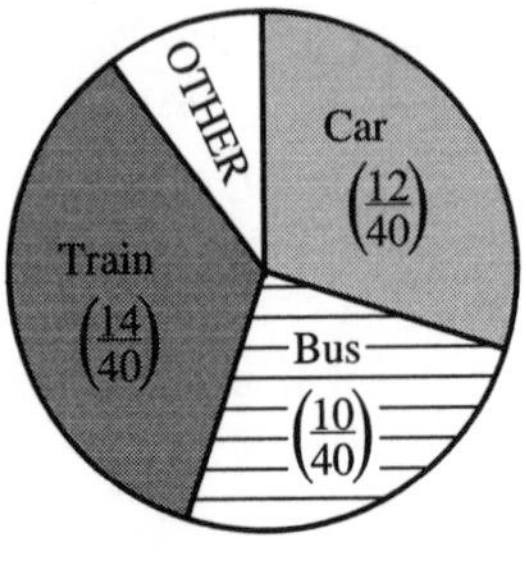

Exercise 4

1. The letters shown on the right are each given a number as either a fraction, a decimal or a percentage.

In (a), (b), (c) below the numbers 1, 2, 3, ... give the positions of the letters in a sentence. So 1 is the first letter, 2 is the second letter and so on.

Find the letter whose value is the same as the number given, and write it in the correct position.

A	24%	N	0·9
E	0·05	O	0·625
F	0·32	R	0·6
G	$\frac{3}{20}$	S	$\frac{7}{20}$
H	0·36	T	0·02
I	3%	U	$\frac{3}{25}$
L	0·49	V	0·1%
M	$\frac{3}{4}$	Y	99%

For example in part (a) number 1 is $\frac{3}{5}$.
Since $\frac{3}{5} = 0{\cdot}6$, letter R goes in the first box.
Find the sentence in each part.

(a)

1	2	3	4	5	6	7	8	9	10	11	12
R											

1. $\frac{3}{5}$ 2. 0·24 3. 2% 4. 0·03 5. $\frac{5}{8}$ 6. 0·35
7. $\frac{6}{25}$ 8. 60% 9. $\frac{1}{20}$ 10. 32% 11. 0·12 12. $\frac{9}{10}$

(b) 1. 15% 2. $62\frac{1}{2}\%$ 3. 49% 4. $\frac{8}{25}$ 5. $\frac{3}{100}$ 6. 35%
7. 0·75 8. 0·99 9. 0·15 10. 0·24 11. 75% 12. 5%

(c) 1. $(0{\cdot}6)^2$ 2. $0{\cdot}2 + 0{\cdot}04$ 3. $\frac{1}{2}$ of 0·98 4. 32% 5. $\frac{5}{8}$ 6. $\frac{8}{25}$
7. $0{\cdot}2 \div 10$ 8. 5% 9. 90% 10. $\frac{15}{500}$ 11. 50% of $\frac{7}{10}$ 12. $\frac{64}{200}$
13. $3 \div 100$ 14. $\frac{1}{1000}$ 15. $(0{\cdot}2)^2 + (0{\cdot}1)^2$

2. Make up a sentence of your own using the letters given in Question **1**. Write clues and try it out on a friend.

3. 24% of the grid below is shaded (Of the 100 squares on the grid exactly 24 are shaded).

Draw a grid like this one and draw a number of your own choice. For example if you chose '16' make sure you shade in 16 out of the 100 squares. Try to make both figures the same size!

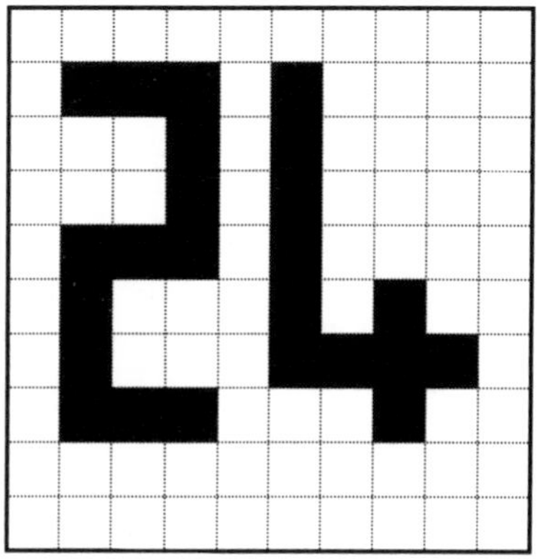

4.6 Puzzles and problems

Cross numbers

Make three copies of the pattern below and complete the puzzles using the clues given. To avoid confusion it is better not to write the small reference numbers 1, 2, ... 19 on your patterns. Write any decimal points on the lines between squares.

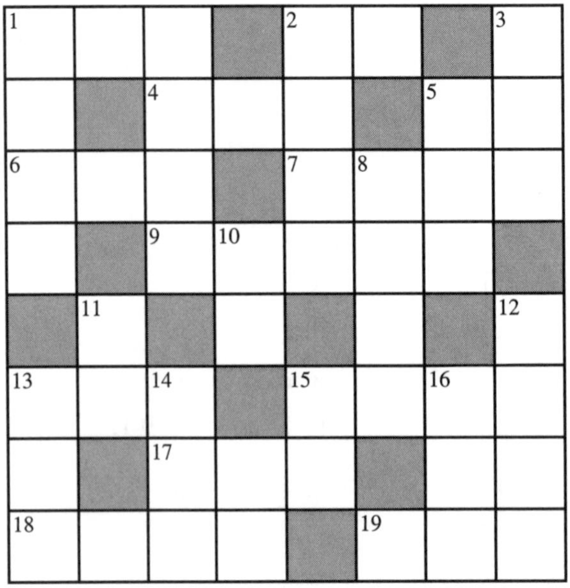

Part A

Across

1. 15% of 23
2. Next prime number after 23
4. One-third of 2409
5. Solve the equation $\frac{x}{5} = 3{\cdot}8$
6. Area of a circle of diameter 30 cm (to 3 s.f.)
7. $(71{\cdot}6)^2 - (\frac{1}{2} + \frac{3}{50})$
9. $245^2 - (3^3 \times 2^2)$
13. $7 + 7^2 + 7^3$
15. $\frac{1}{4} + 3 \times 13$
17. Last 3 digits of (567×7)
18. 50 m written in cm
19. $75 \div 6$

Down

1. Volume of a cube of side 15 cm
2. One minute to midnight on the 24 hour clock
3. $\frac{5{\cdot}2}{0{\cdot}21} + \frac{17}{0{\cdot}31}$ to 1 d.p.
5. $(11\frac{1}{4})^2$ to the nearest whole number
8. $12 - \frac{1}{100}$
10. Prime number
11. $2^5 - 3$
12. $\frac{3}{7}$ of 3675
13. North-west as a bearing
14. $\frac{3}{4}$ of 11% of 12 000
16. Number of minutes between 1313 and 1745.

Check: There should be 5 decimal points in the puzzle.

Part B

Across

1. $\left(0{\cdot}5 \div \frac{1}{2}\right) \times 123$
2. $1001 \div 77$
4. $200 - (4 \div 0{\cdot}5)$
5. $(2^3 - 1)^2$
6. $33\frac{1}{3}\%$ of 2802
7. $8{\cdot}14 - (1{\cdot}96 \times 0{\cdot}011)$ to 3 d.p.
9. 7391×11
13. $1^1 + 2^2 + 3^3 + 4^4$
15. $10^4 - [2 \times 20^2 + 9 \times 7]$
17. Number of minutes between 0340 and 1310.
18. $80^2 + 9^2 + 1^2$
19. $19 + \frac{3}{20} + \frac{1}{4}$

Down

1. (1 across) × (2 across)
2. $\frac{1}{2} + \frac{1}{3} + \frac{1}{4} + \frac{1}{5}$ to 3 d.p.
3. $20^2 - \sqrt{4}$
5. $42{\cdot}2 - (8{\cdot}1 \times 0{\cdot}13)$ to 1 d.p.
8. 143×7
10. Inches in a foot.
11. $(2^3 \times 3^2) + 2^2 + 2$
12. Number of hours in a leap year.
13. 13% of £22·80, to the nearest penny
14. Next in the sequence 0·858, 8·58, 85·8, ...
16. $113 \times 0{\cdot}3$

Check: There should be 6 decimal points in the puzzle.

Part C

Across

1. South-west as a bearing.
2. Inches in a yard
4. Last three digits of $(11^2 + 2^2)^2$
5. 4 score plus ten
6. $\left(26\frac{1}{2}\right)^2$, to the nearest whole number
7. $\dfrac{24{\cdot}3}{1{\cdot}9} + \dfrac{357}{24} + \dfrac{87{\cdot}04}{3{\cdot}7}$, correct to 2 d.p.
9. $(13 \text{ across})^2 + (5 \text{ across})^2 + 103$
13. $800 - 694$
15. Last three digits of $(407 \times 21 \times 11)$
17. $\frac{2}{3} + \frac{3}{4} + \frac{4}{5} + \frac{5}{6}$
18. $\dfrac{392{\cdot}2}{(4{\cdot}97 + 2{\cdot}66)}$, correct to 2 d.p.
19. Next in the sequence 3, 5, 9, 17, 33, 65

Down

1. Solve the equation $\dfrac{555}{x} = 2$
2. 11% of £323·11, to the nearest penny
3. $\dfrac{1{\cdot}23}{1{\cdot}4 - 0{\cdot}271}$, correct to 2 d.p.
5. $30 \times 31 - 11$
8. Area, in cm^2, of a rectangle measuring 1·2 m by 11 cm
10. (A square number) − 1
11. 80% of 50
12. $\sqrt{(4 \text{ across})} \times (13 \text{ across}) + (10 \text{ down})$
13. Angle in degrees between the hands of a clock at 2·30
14. A quarter share of a third share of a half share of £152·16
16. $76{\cdot}8 \div 0{\cdot}4$

Check: There should be 7 decimal points in the puzzle.

Hidden words

(a) Start in the top left box.
(b) Work out the answer to the calculation in the box.
(c) Find the answer in the top corner of another box.
(d) Write down the letter in that box.
(e) Repeat steps (b), (c) and (d) until you arrive back at the top left box. What is the message?

1.

$\frac{1}{2}$ 25% of 84	613 S $\frac{1}{2}$ of $\frac{3}{4}$	0·56 T 29·2 ÷ 8	0·01 G $0{\cdot}5 \times 10^3$	6 E 10 000 ÷ 200
20 S 5·6 × 0·1	21 H 0·4 − 0·04	50 D $\frac{2}{3}$ of 162	3·5 O 1234 + 4321	3·65 I 1% of 55
500 L $\frac{7}{8} - \frac{1}{4}$	15 E 295 + 318	0 K $\frac{5}{6} - \frac{1}{3}$	0·55 C $2^4 - 4^2$	0·36 I 22·82 ÷ 7
3·26 S $(0{\cdot}1)^2$	$\frac{3}{8}$ N 7% of 50	5555 T 2 ÷ 0·1	$\frac{5}{8}$ U 5 + 5 ÷ 5	108 O $2^4 - 1$

2.

612 $\frac{6}{1{\cdot}5} + \frac{9}{1{\cdot}5}$	0·8 T 5% of 400	0·77 W $\frac{5}{0{\cdot}1} - 2$	0·2 V 15 × 23	0·62 T 20% of 65
32 C 50 000 ÷ 200	10 B $\frac{2}{5}$ of 450	13 R 0·6 × 2·6	18 E 5 − (7 − 2)	250 U $0{\cdot}9^2 - 0{\cdot}1^2$
1·56 E $\frac{3}{8}$ of 48	0·6 R $\frac{1}{4} - 0{\cdot}1$	180 E $(0{\cdot}2)^2$	0·15 S 6·4 ÷ 0·2	0 S 18 × 34
0·04 A 10% of 2	0·27 O $\frac{1}{10}(5{\cdot}5 + 2{\cdot}2)$	20 D 0·3 − 0·03	48 N $\frac{3}{5} + 0{\cdot}02$	345 E $\frac{3}{4}$ of $\frac{4}{5}$

3.

4 $(-6) \times 5$	−5 L $12 \div (-1)^3$	−19 N $\frac{1}{2} - 0{\cdot}6$	−4 E $17 + (-25)$	0 S $24 \times (-3)$
30 N $(-5)^2 \times 10$	−30 S $8 - (-4)$	36 R $0{\cdot}1 - 0{\cdot}3$	−0·1 C $-3 + 10 - 4$	10 I $(-60) \times \left(-\frac{1}{2}\right)$
−6 U $(-2 - 6) \times (-2)$	−0·2 E $81 - 100$	3 H $(7 - 9)^2$	250 F $(-6) \times (-6)$	12 O $(-2)^2 + (-1)^2$
5 L $(-12) \div 3$	−8 I $-6 - 7 + 8$	16 N $-7 + 17$	−12 I $3 - 8 + 5$	−72 S $-2\frac{1}{2} - 3\frac{1}{2}$

4.

$-\frac{1}{2}$ $16 - 200$	19 H $(3 - 9)^2$	−2 C $[(-9) \times (-3)] + 20$	−80 A $15 + (-16)$	18 S $800 \div (-2)^3$
$4\frac{1}{2}$ M $27 - 270$	$2\frac{1}{2}$ E $(8 - 14) \times (-3)$	0·05 L $8 - (-4) - (+6)$	47 E $4 \times \left(-\frac{1}{8}\right)$	$-4\frac{1}{2}$ Y $(-10)^3$
−1 T $0{\cdot}4 \times \left(-\frac{1}{2}\right)$	−100 O $(-0{\cdot}1) \times (-0{\cdot}1)$	−184 M $-8\frac{1}{2} + 4$	16 S $(-20) \div (-8)$	−243 I $(-8) \div (-2)^2$
−1000 C $-35 - 45$	36 A $8 - 12 + 20$	6 Y $-1\frac{1}{2} + 6$	0·01 N $\frac{1}{4} - 0{\cdot}2$	−0·2 C $17 + (-2) - (-4)$

Forestry problem

The owner of a forestry company in Norway has to decide which kind of trees to plant so as to make the maximum profit in years ahead. Whatever trees are planted, they have to be thinned out after 10 years and again after 15 years to allow the trees to grow to their optimum size.
The owner has the following data for the three kinds of trees which are most suitable for the climate and soil conditions:

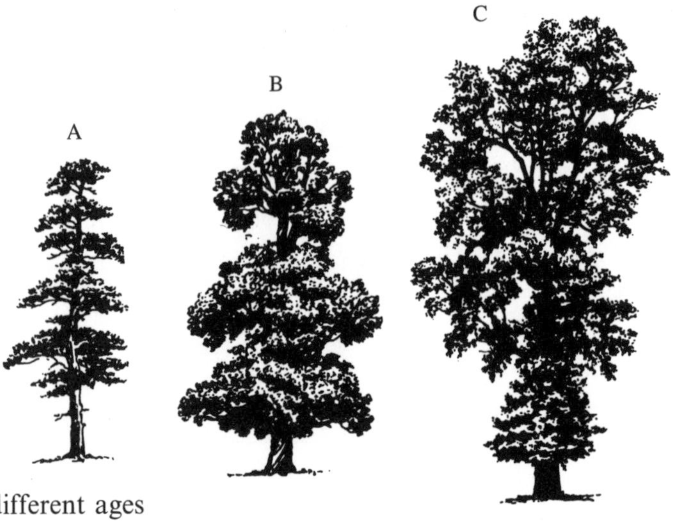

(a) planting costs
(b) profits from thinning
(c) weight of the trees per hectare at different ages
(d) value of the wood at different ages.

All figures are given 'per hectare'

	Type A	Type B	Type C
Planting cost	£250 000	£140 000	£135 000
Profit from thinning after 10 years	£20 000	£42 000	£18 000
Profit from thinning after 15 years	£25 000	£80 000	£30 000

	Type A		Type B		Type C	
	Weight of trees (tonne)	Value of wood £/tonne	Weight of trees (tonne)	Value of wood £/tonne	Weight of trees (tonne)	Value of wood £/tonne
After 20 years	27 000	22	29 000	30	28 400	27
30	39 000	36	40 200	45	39 200	40
40	48 500	51	52 300	40	51 000	51
50	60 800	57	61 600	33	62 300	57
60	70 200	60	67 500	31	69 500	52
70	77 600	66	71 000	26	75 000	45

As an example, one hectare of type A would cost £250 000 to plant. The total thinning profits would be £20 000 + £25 000. After 50 years the weight of the trees in one hectare would be 60 800 tonnes. The value of the wood after 50 years would be £(60 800 × 57), which is £3 465 600.

- Decide which kind of trees should be planted to give the highest profit after 30 years. [Don't forget to include the profit from thinning.]
- Which trees should be planted to give the highest profit after
  (a) 50 years?
  (b) 70 years?

4.7 Using a spreadsheet on a computer

This section is written for use with Microsoft Excel. Other spreadsheet programs work in a similar way.

Select Microsoft Excel from the desk top.

A spreadsheet appears on your screen as a grid with rows numbered 1, 2, 3, 4,...... and the columns lettered A, B, C, D, ...
The result should be a window like the one below.

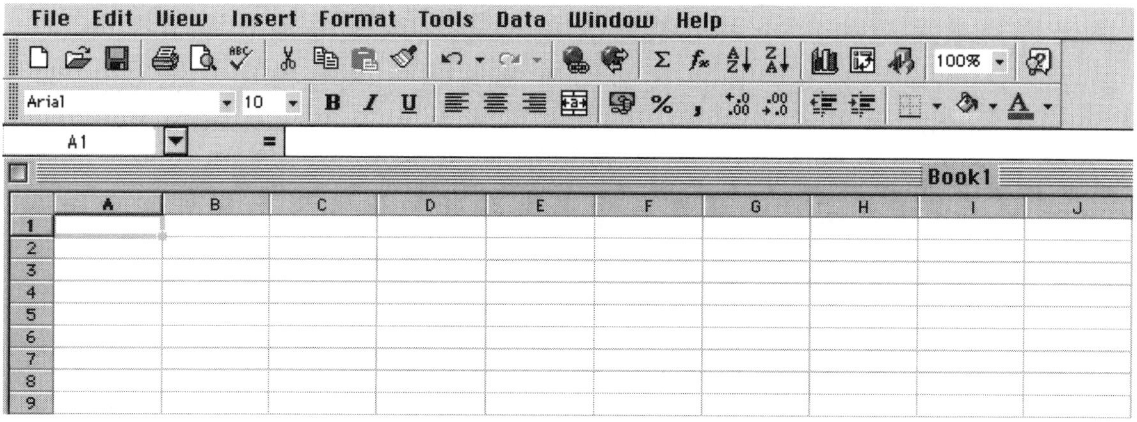

Cell The spaces on the spreadsheet are called cells. Individual cells are referred to as A1, B3, F9, like grid references. Cells may contain *labels*, *values* or *formulas*. The current cell has a black border.

Label Any words, headings or messages used to help the layout and organisation of the spreadsheet.

Value A number placed in a cell. It may be used as input to a calculation.

Tasks 1, 2 and 3 are written for you to become familiar with how the main functions of a spreadsheet program work. Afterwards there are sections on different topics where spreadsheets can be used.

Task 1. To generate the whole numbers from 1 to 10 in column A.

(a) In cell A1 type '1' and press *Return*. This will automatically take you to the cell below. (NOTE that you must use the *Return* button and not the arrow keys to move down the column.)

(b) In cell A2 type the formula ' = A1 + 1' and press *Return*. [NOTE that the = sign is needed before any formula.]

(c) We now want to copy the formula in A2 down column A as far as A10. Click on A2 again and put the arrow in the bottom right corner of cell A2 (a + sign will appear) and drag down to A10.

Task 2. To generate the odd numbers in column B.

(a) In B1 type '1' (press *Return*).

(b) In B2 type the formula ' = B1 + 2' (press *Return*).

(c) Click in B2 and copy the formula down column B as far as B10.

Task 3. To generate the first 15 square numbers.

(a) As before generate the numbers from 1 to 15 in cells A1 to A15.

(b) In B1 put the formula ' = A1 * A1' and press *Return*.

(c) Click in B1 and copy the formula down as far as B15.

Part 5

5.1 Ratio and proportion

- We use ratio to compare parts of a whole.
  In a mixed class of 30 children, 13 are girls.
  Since there are 30 children altogether, there are 17 boys.
  The ratio girls : boys is 13 : 17
- Ratios can sometimes be written in a simpler form:
  The ratios 4 : 10 and 2 : 5 are the same. [divide by 2]
  The ratios 10 : 20 : 25 and 2 : 4 : 5 are the same [divide by 5]

Exercise 1

In Questions **1** to **4**, make sure that your answers are in their simplest form.

1. In a hall there are 36 chairs and 9 tables.
Find the ratio of chairs to tables.

2. In a room there are 14 women and 12 men.
Find the ratio of women to men.

3. In a mixed class of 20 children, 8 are boys
Write down the ratio boys : girls.

4. In an office there are twice as many men as women.
Write down the ratio men : women.

5. Write these ratios in a more simple form.

(a) 9 : 6 (b) 15 : 25 (c) 10 : 40
(d) 48 :44 (e) 18 : 24 (f) 40 : 25

6. In a box, the ratio of rulers to pencils is 1 : 3. If there are 5 rulers, how many pencils are there?

7. In a classroom the ratio of girls to boys is 3 : 2.
If there are 14 boys, how many girls are there?

8. In a greengrocer's shop, the ratio of apples to pears is 5 : 2. If there are 200 pears, how many apples are there?

9. A factory produces mainly cars but also the occasional washing machine! The ratio of cars to washing machines is 5 : 1. One day 400 cars were made. How many washing machines were produced?

10. Write these ratios in a more simple form.

(a) 9 : 6 : 12 (b) 40 : 5 : 15 (c) 12 : 10 : 8
(d) 18 : 12 : 18 (e) 70 : 10 : 50 (f) 14 : 7 : 35

11. In a box, the ratio of apples to peaches to bananas is 3 : 1 : 2. If there are 24 apples, how many peaches are there and how many bananas are there?

12. On a Saturday the football results gave a ratio of home wins to away wins to draws of 6 : 2 : 1. If there were 10 away wins, how many home wins were there and how many draws were there?

13. On a farm, the ratio of cows to sheep to pigs is 3 : 4 : 5. If there are 35 pigs, how many sheep are there and how many cows are there?

14. Find the ratio (shaded area) : (unshaded area) for each diagram.

(a)
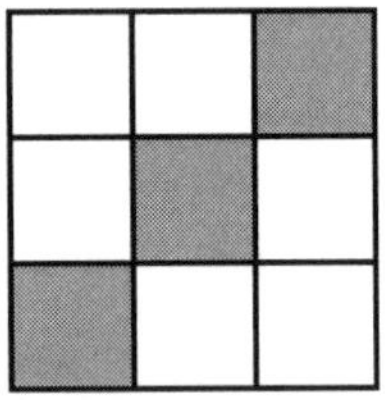
(b)
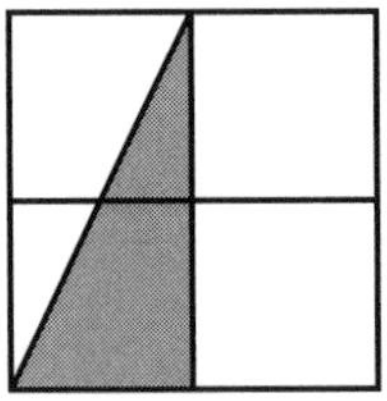
(c)
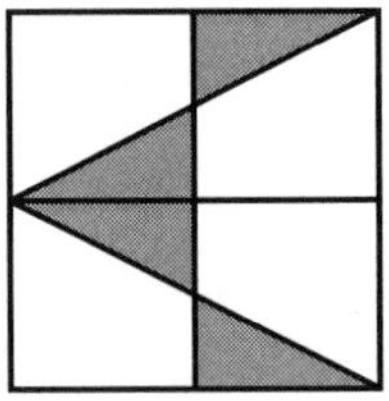

15. If $\frac{2}{5}$ of the children in a school are girls, what is the ratio of girls to boys?

Ratio and sharing

- Share 30 apples between Ken and Denise in the ratio 2 : 3

Ken : Denise
= 2 : 3
Total of **5** shares

Each share = 30 ÷ **5**
= 6 apples
So Ken's share is 2 × 6 = 12 apples
Denise's share is 3 × 6 = 18 apples

[Check: 12 + 18 = 30 ✓]

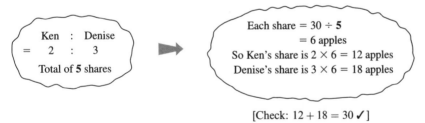

- Share a prize of £63 between Ann, Ben and Carol in the ratio 2 : 3 : 4.

Ann : Ben : Carol
= 2 : 3 : 4
Total of **9** shares

Each share = £63 ÷ **9**
= £7
So Ann gets 2 × 7 = £14
Ben gets 3 × 7 = £21
Carol gets 4 × 7 = £28

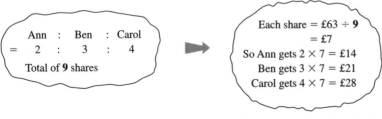

[Check: 14 + 21 + 28 = 63 ✓]

Exercise 2

1. Alex and Debbie share a bag of 30 sweets in the ratio 3 : 2. How many sweets does each person get?

2. A mother and her son share a prize of £60 in the ratio 3 : 1. How much does each person receive?

3. Share each quantity in the ratio given.

(a) 54 cm, 4 : 5 (b) £99, 4 : 7 (c) 132 km, 6 : 5
(d) £36, 2 : 3 : 4 (e) 200 kg, 5 : 2 : 3 (f) £2000, 1 : 9

4. Three starving dogs share a meal weighing 660 g in the ratio 2 : 5 : 3. Find the largest share.

5. To make concrete you can mix 3 parts sand to 1 part cement. How much sand do you need to make 8 tonnes of concrete?

6. To make grey paint you can mix 3 parts black paint with 7 parts white paint. How much of each colour paint do you need to make 20 litres of grey paint?

7. Two squares are shown with their perimeters.
(a) Write down the ratio of the lengths of their sides.
(b) Work out the ratio of their areas.

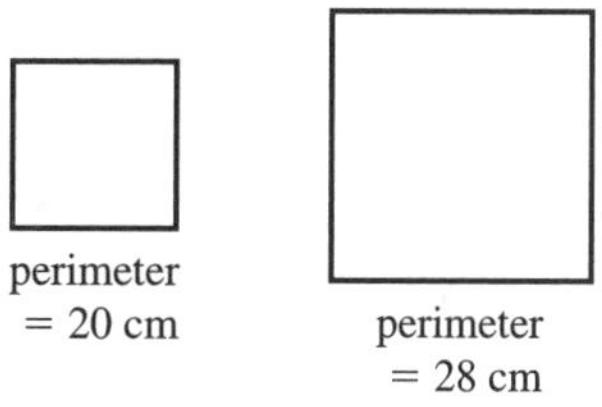

8. An alloy weighing 210 g consists of copper, zinc and iron. There is three times as much copper as zinc and one and a half times as much zinc as iron. How much zinc is there?

In Questions **9** to **16** write the ratios in a more simple form.

9. 20 cm : 1 m **10.** 20 mm : 5 cm

11. 400 g : 2 kg **12.** 250 m : 1 km

13. 200 ml : 2 litres **14.** 50 cm : 4 m

15. 0·5 m : 60 cm : 3 m **16.** 300 g : 0·7 kg : 3 kg

17. The angles in a triangle are in the ratio 3 : 1 : 2. Find the sizes of the three angles.

18. The angles in a quadrilateral are in the ratio 2 : 2 : 3 : 2. Find the largest angle in the quadrilateral.

19. The sides of a rectangle are in the ratio 3 : 1. The area of the rectangle is 48 cm^2. Find the sides of the rectangle.

20. A pond contains carp and trout. If $\frac{5}{9}$ of the fish are carp, what is the ratio of carp to trout?

21. The ratio of Lucy's age to Helen's age is 3 : 4. How old is Helen if she is 7 years older than Lucy?

22. The sum of two numbers p and q is 66 and p is 6 less than q. Find the ratio $p:q$.

23. The ratio $x:y = 1:2$ and the ratio $y:z = 4:5$
What is the ratio $x:z$?

24. In the diagram, $\frac{4}{5}$ of the circle is shaded and $\frac{2}{3}$ of the triangle is shaded.
What is the ratio of the area of the circle to the area of the triangle?

25. In a Fibonacci sequence, each successive term is obtained by adding the two previous terms. A Fibonacci sequence starts

1, 1, 2, 3, 5, 8, 13, 21, 34, 55, . . .

(a) Write down the next four numbers in the sequence.

(b) The ratio of successive pairs of terms can be found:
$\frac{1}{1} = 1$, $\frac{2}{1} = 2$; $\frac{3}{2} = 1{\cdot}5$ etc.
Find the next ten ratios of successive pairs of terms. [ie $\frac{5}{3}$, $\frac{8}{5}$, $\frac{13}{8}$ etc]

What do you notice?

Map scales

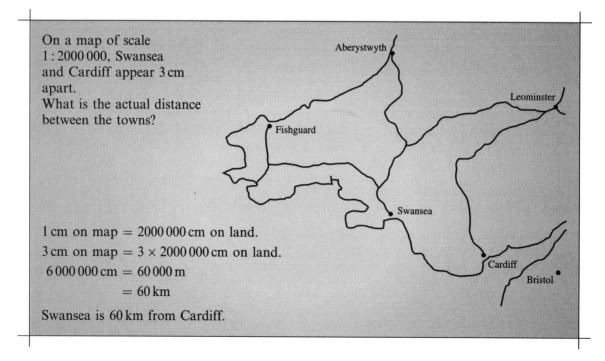

On a map of scale 1 : 2000 000, Swansea and Cardiff appear 3 cm apart.
What is the actual distance between the towns?

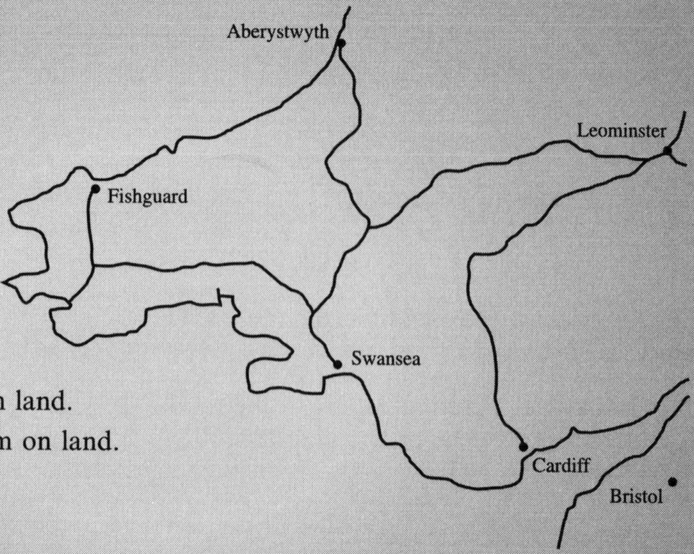

1 cm on map = 2000 000 cm on land.

3 cm on map = 3 × 2000 000 cm on land.

6 000 000 cm = 60 000 m

= 60 km

Swansea is 60 km from Cardiff.

Exercise 3

1. On a map whose scale is 1:1000, the distance between two houses is 3 cm. Find the actual distance between the two houses, giving your answer in metres.

2. The distance on a map between two points is 8 cm. Find the actual distance in metres between the two points, given that the scale of the map is 1:100.

3. The scale of a certain map is 1:10 000. What is the actual distance in metres between two churches which are 4 cm apart on the map?

4. On a map whose scale is 1:100 000, the distance between two villages is 7 cm. What is the actual distance in kilometres between the two villages?

5. The distance on a map between two towns is 9 cm. Find the actual distance in kilometres between the two towns, given that the scale of the map is 1:1 000 000.

6. Find the actual distance in metres between two towers which are 5 cm apart on a map whose scale is 1:10 000.

7. A river is 5 cm long on a map whose scale is 1:20 000. Find the actual length of the river.

8. Andrew finds that the distance between two cities on a map whose scale is 1:1 000 000 is 12 cm. What is the actual distance in kilometres between the two cities?

9. The distance between two points is 30 km. How far apart will they be on a map of scale 1 : 50 000?

10. The length of a section of motorway is 15 km. How long will it be on a map of scale 1 : 100 000?

11. The scale of a map is 1:200 000. What is the actual distance between two villages given that they are 8·5 cm apart on the map?

12. If two towns are 5·4 cm apart on a map and the scale of the map is 1:3 000 000, what is the actual distance between the two towns?

13. A world map is drawn to a scale of 1 : 80 000 000, while a map of Great Britain is drawn to a scale of 1 : 3 000 000. On the map of Great Britain, the distance from Land's End to John o'Groats is 36 cm. How far apart are the two places on the world map?

14. The scale used in a motoring atlas is '1 inch to 3 miles'. Write this in the form $1 : n$. [1 mile = 1760 yards]

5.2 Enlargement

- The original picture here has been enlarged by a scale factor of 2

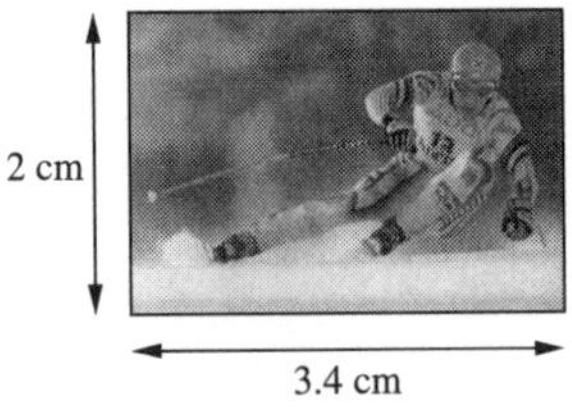

Notice that both the height *and* the width have been doubled.

- For an enlargement the original and the enlargement must be exactly the same shape. All angles in both shapes are preserved.

- 

Length of A = 2 × length of B
Width of A = 2 × width of B
∴ A *is* an enlargement of B

Exercise 1

Look at each pair of diagrams and decide whether or not one diagram is an enlargement of the other. For each question write the scale factor of the enlargement or write 'not an enlargement'.

1. 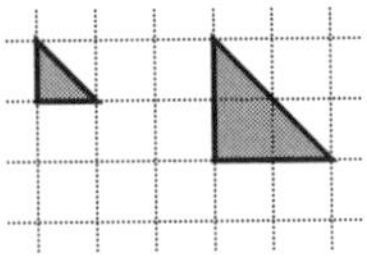

2. 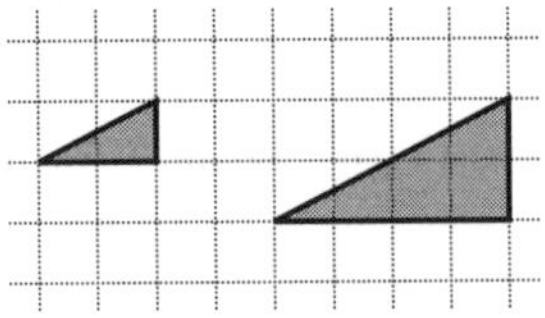

3. 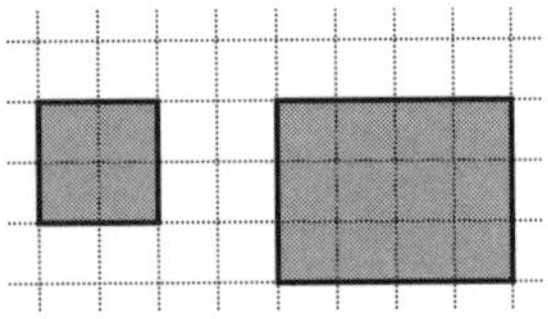

4. 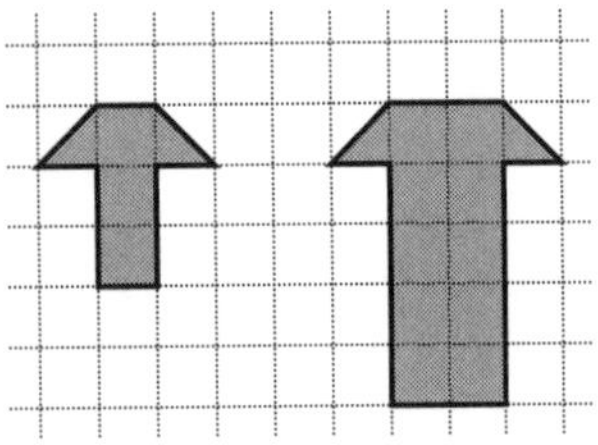

5. 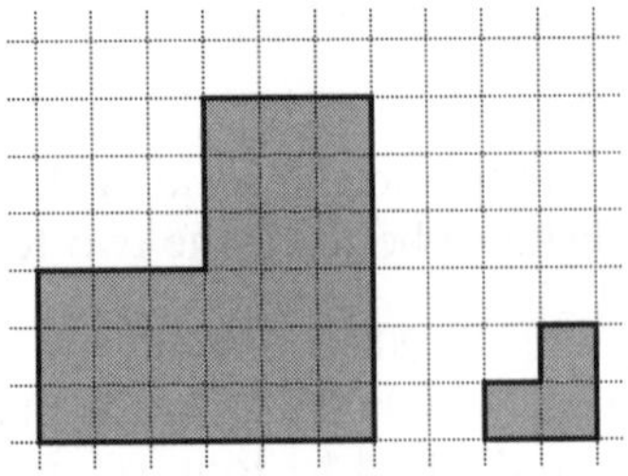

6. 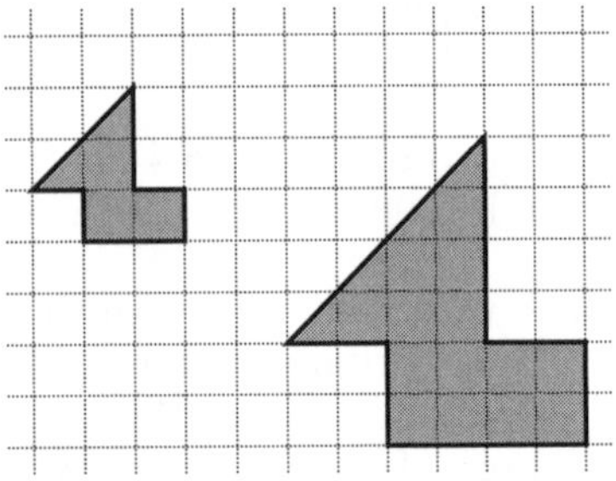

Exercise 2

Enlarge the following shapes by the scale factor given. Make sure you leave room on your page for the enlargement!

1.

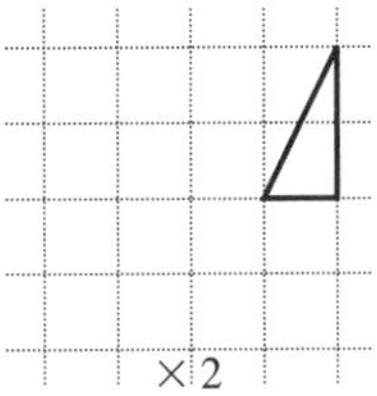

2.

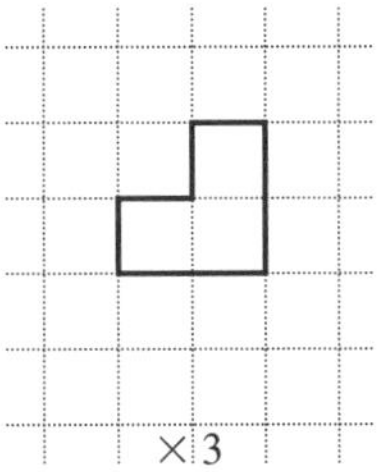

3.

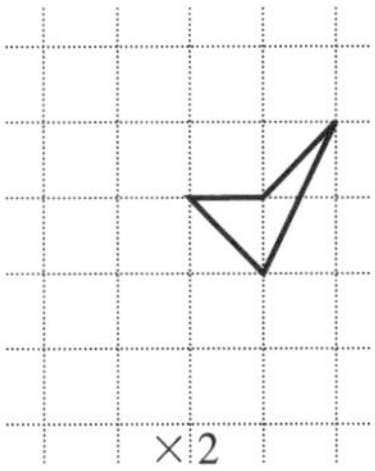

4.

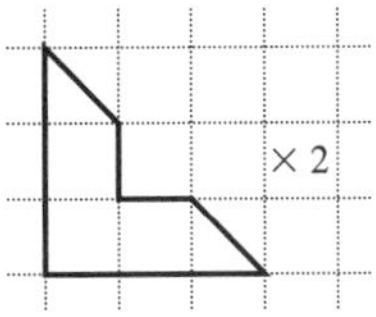

5.

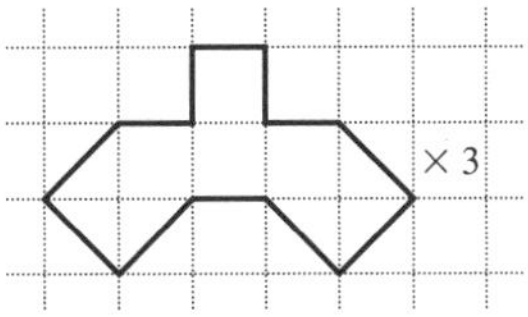

6.

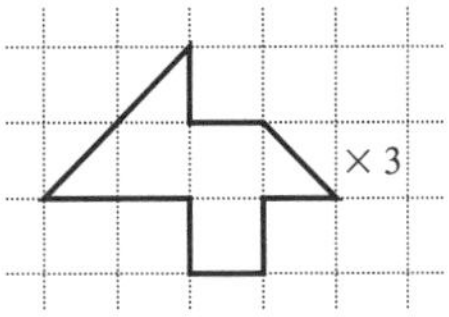

7. Here are some letters of the alphabet.
(a) Enlarge them by a scale factor of 2.
(b) Draw your own initials and enlarge them by a scale factor of 2.

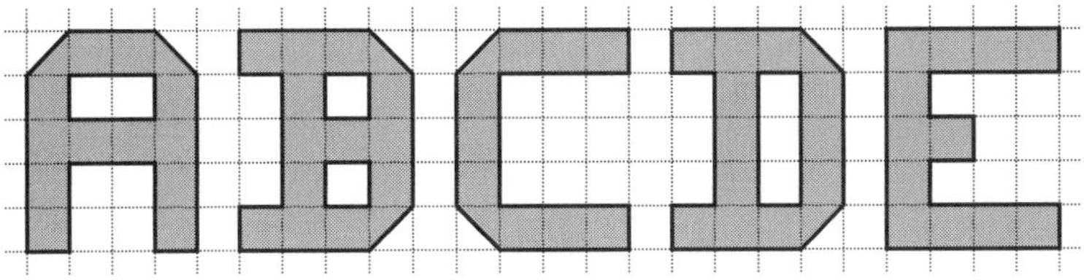

8. This picture is to be enlarged to fit the frame. Find the height of the frame.

60 mm

40 mm

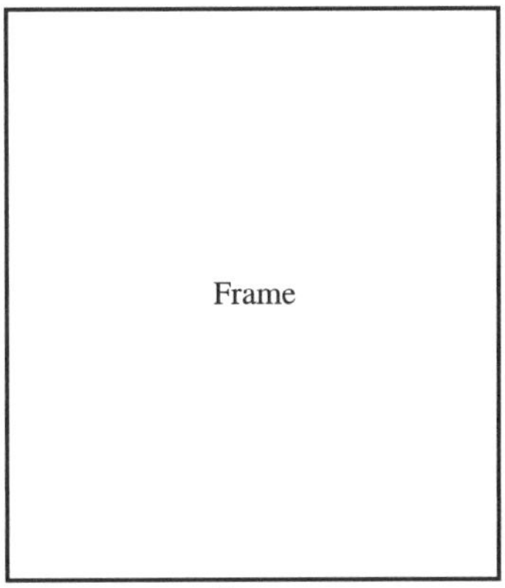

?

80 mm

9. A photograph measuring 5 cm by 3·5 cm is enlarged so that it fits exactly into a frame measuring 20 cm by x cm. Calculate the value of x.

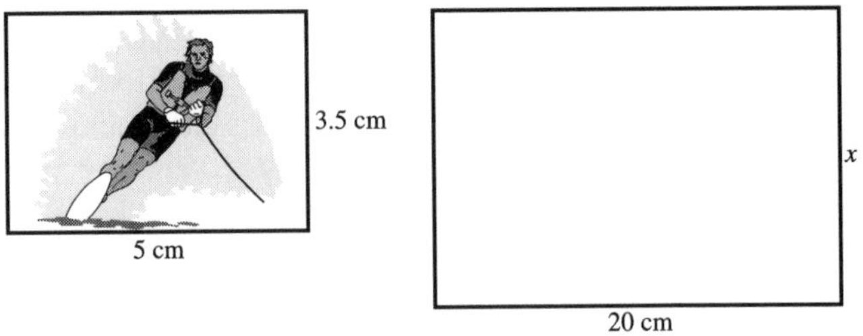

10. A photograph measuring 6 cm by 4 cm is reduced to fit frame A and another copy of the photograph is enlarged to fit frame B.

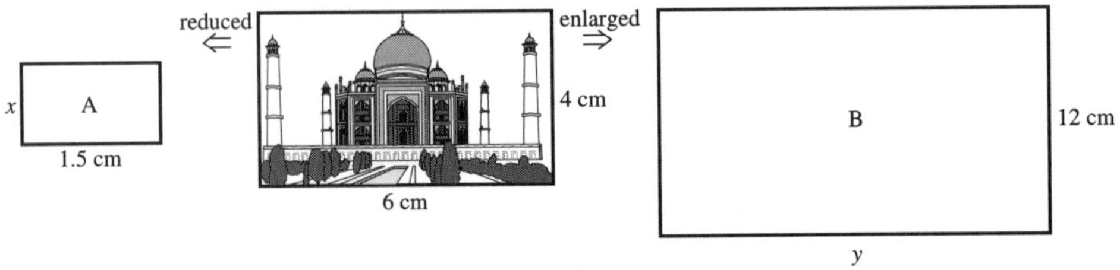

Calculate the value of x and the value of y.

Centre of enlargement

A mathematical enlargement always has a *centre of enlargement* as well as a scale factor. The centre of enlargement is found by drawing lines through corresponding points on the object and image and finding where they intersect. For greater accuracy it is better to count squares between points because it is difficult to draw construction lines accurately over a long distance.

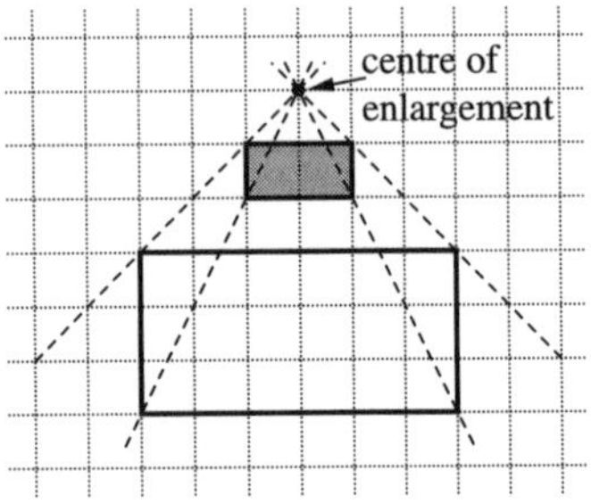

In the second diagram, A′B′C′ is an enlargement of ABC with scale factor 2 and centre O.

Observe that OA′ = 2 × OA
OB′ = 2 × OB
OC′ = 2 × OC

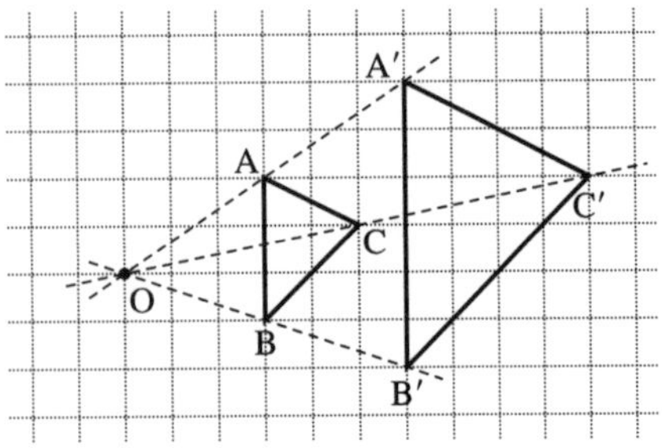

Always measure distances from the centre of enlargement.

Exercise 3

Draw the shapes and then draw lines through corresponding points to find the centre of enlargement. Don't draw the shapes too near the edge of the page!

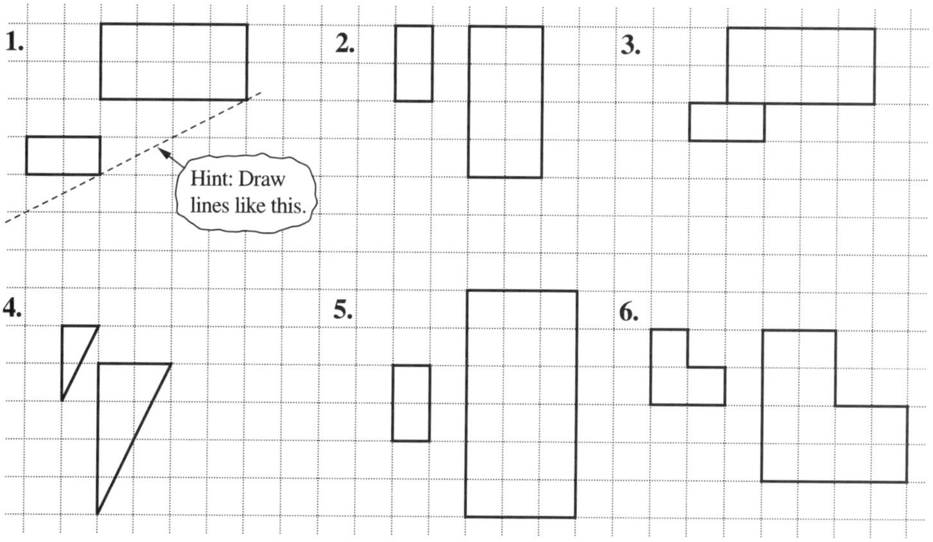

To fully describe an enlargement we need two things: the scale factor and the centre of enlargement.

(a) Draw an enlargement of $\triangle 1$ with scale factor 3 and centre O.

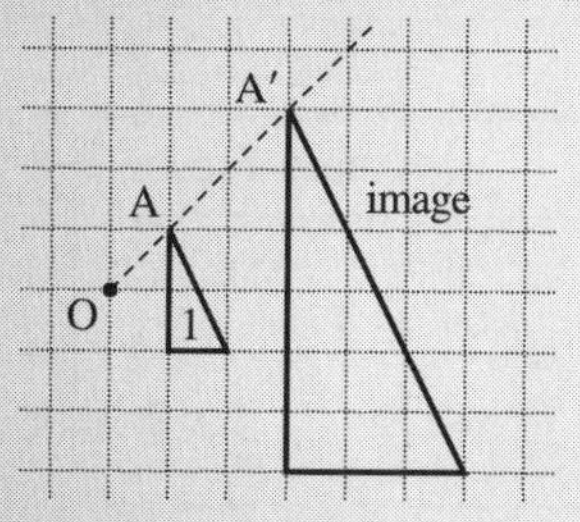

Notice that $OA' = 3 \times OA$.

(b) Draw an enlargement of shape P with scale factor 2 and centre O.

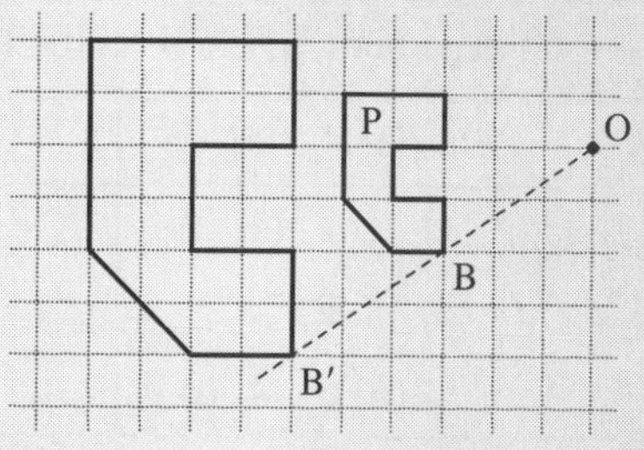

Notice that $OB' = 2 \times OB$.

In both diagrams, just one point on the image has been found by using a construction line or by counting squares. When one point is known the rest of the diagram can easily be drawn, since the size and shape of the image is known.

Exercise 4

In questions **1** to **6** copy the diagram and then draw an enlargement using the scale factor and centre of enlargement given.
Leave room for enlargement!

1.

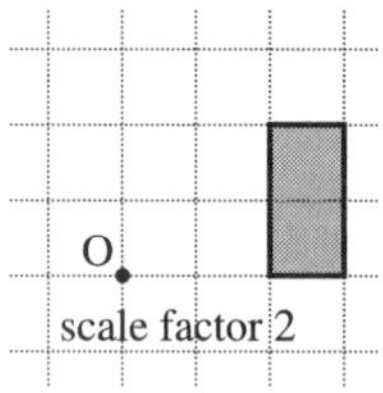

2.

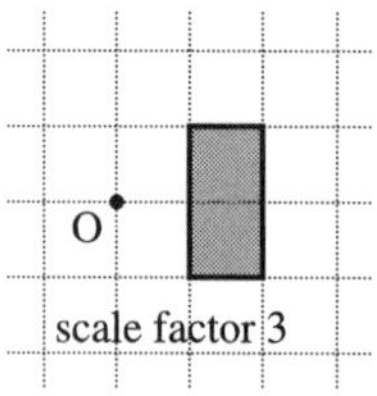

3.

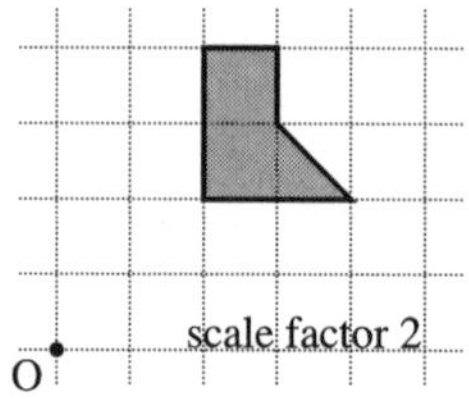

4.

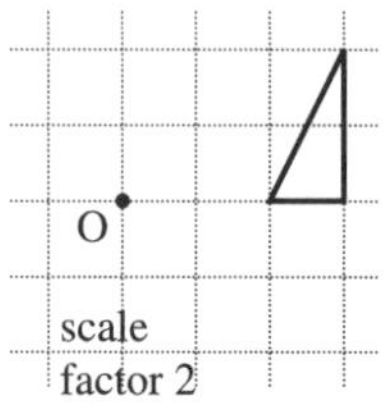

5.

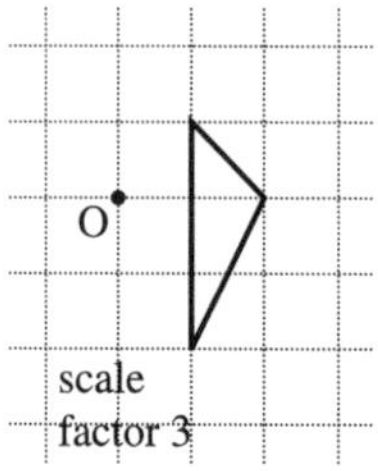

6.

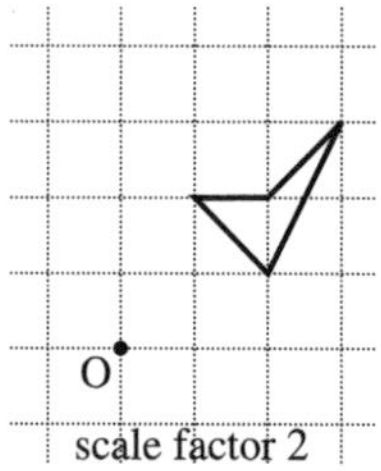

7. Copy the diagram
Draw an enlargement of the triangle with scale factor 2 and centre of enlargement (0, 0).

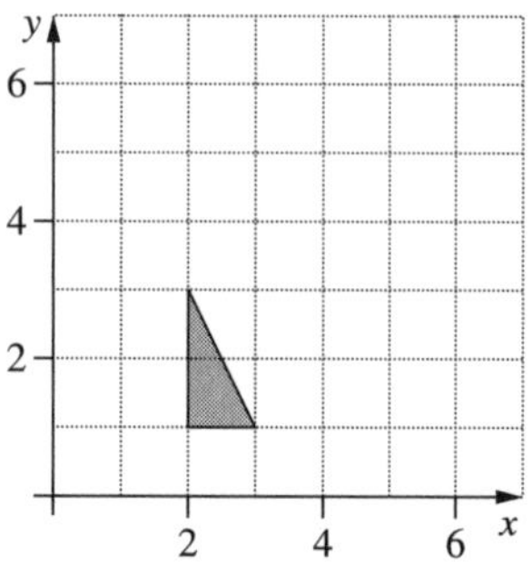

8. For (a), (b) and (c) draw a grid similar to the one in Question 7.
Draw an enlargement of each shape.

Shape	Centre of enlargement	Scale factor
(a) (1, 1) (2, 1) (2, 2) (1, 2)	(0, 0)	3
(b) (2, 1) (4, 2) (2, 2)	(0, 0)	2
(c) (4, 5) (6, 5) (6, 6) (4, 6)	(8, 8)	2

9. (a) Draw axes with values from 0 to 12 and draw △1 with vertices at (5, 4), (3, 4), (3, 6).
(b) Draw △2, the image of △1 under enlargement with scale factor 2, centre (5, 2).
(c) Draw △3, the image of △1 under enlargement with scale factor 3, centre (2, 3).
(d) Draw △4, the image of △3 (not △1!) under enlargement with scale factor $\frac{1}{2}$, centre (11, 0).
(e) Draw △5, the image of △3 under enlargement with scale factor $\frac{1}{6}$, centre (11, 12).
(f) Write down the coordinates of the right angled vertex in △2, △3, △4 and △5.

10. Copy the diagram. (You will need it because you have to draw several construction lines). Find the scale factor and centre for each of the following enlargements:
(a) △A → △F
(b) △B → △C
(c) △D → △C
(d) △B → △E
(e) △B → △D.

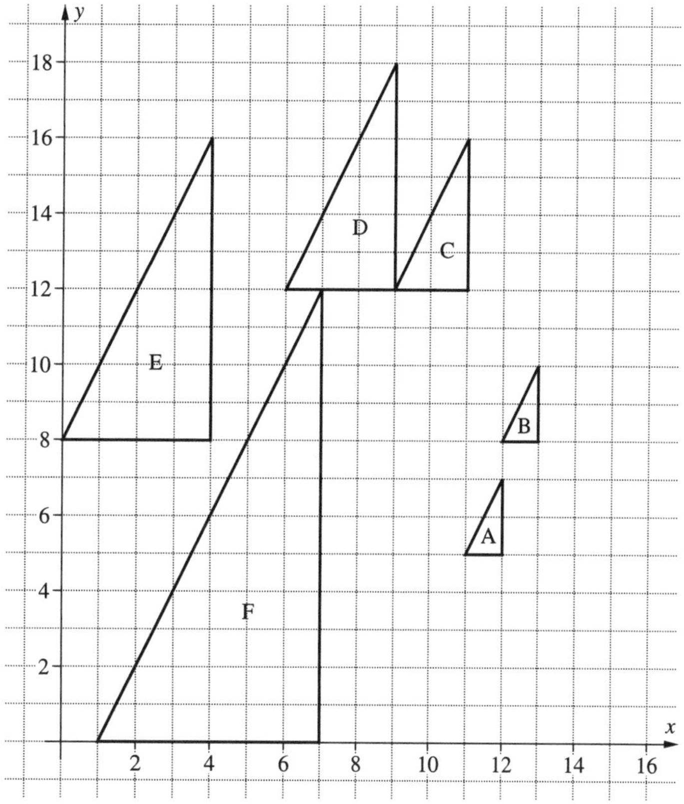

11. Draw axes with values from 0 to 14.
Draw quadrilateral ABCD at A(2, 12), B(4, 10), C(2, 8), D(3, 10).
(a) A′B′C′D′ is an enlargement of ABCD with A′ at (4, 14) and C′ at (4, 6). Complete the quadrilateral A′B′C′D′.
(b) A*B*C*D* is an enlargement of ABCD with A* at (8, 12) and B* at (14, 6). Complete the quadrilateral A*B*C*D*.
(c) Draw A°B°C°D°, which is an enlargement of A*B*C*D* with scale factor $\frac{1}{6}$ and centre of enlargement (2, 6).
(d) Write down the coordinates of A°.

12. Copy the diagram. Describe fully each of the following enlargements
(a) square 1 → square 3
(b) square 2 → square 5
(c) square 2 → square 7
(d) square 3 → square 5
(e) square 7 → square 5

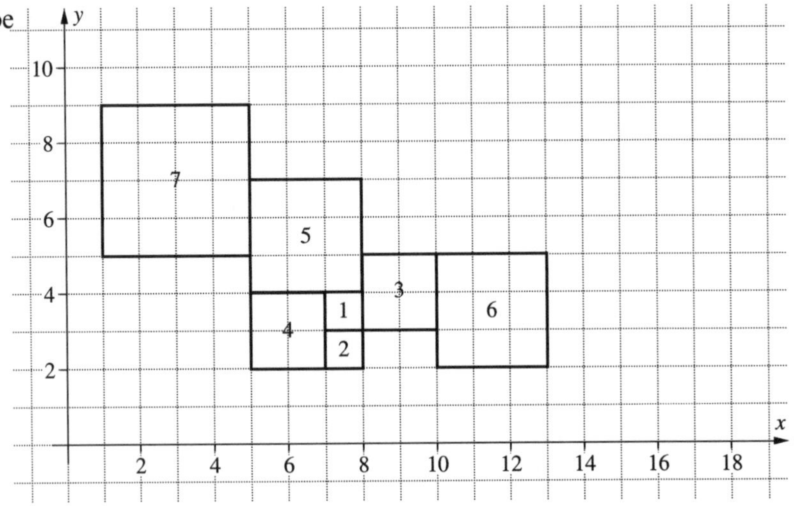

13. Copy shape A inside the rectangle shown. Shape A is enlarged so that it just fits inside the rectangle.
Draw the enlargement of shape A and mark the centre of enlargement.

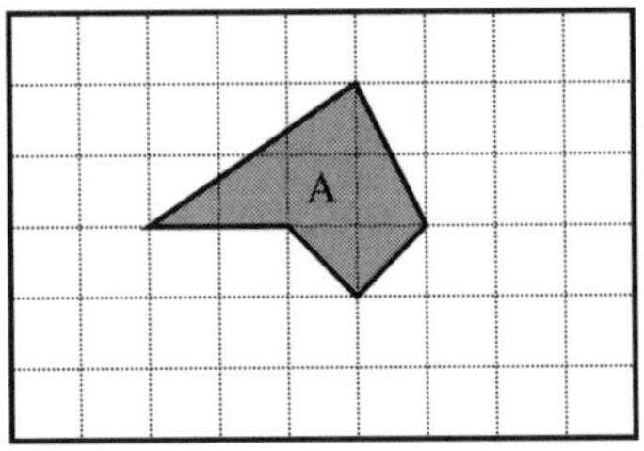

14. (a) Draw axes with values from 0 to 14.
(b) Draw the following shapes:
(i) Rectangle A at (9, 11), (11, 11), (11, 12), (9, 12)
(ii) Triangle B at (2, 10), (2, 12), (1, 12)
(iii) Square C at (3, 6), (4, 6), (4, 7), (3, 7)
(c) Enlarge A onto A′ with scale factor 2, centre (10, 14)
(d) Enlarge B onto B′ with scale factor 3, centre (0, 11)
(e) Enlarge C onto C′ with scale factor 4, centre (3, 8)
(f) Write down the areas of shapes A, A′, B, B′, C, C′.
(g) Work out the ratios: $\left(\frac{\text{area of A}'}{\text{area of A}}\right)$; $\left(\frac{\text{area of B}'}{\text{area of B}}\right)$; $\left(\frac{\text{area of C}'}{\text{area of C}}\right)$.
(h) Write down any connection you observe between the ratios above and the scale factor for each enlargement.

5.3 Sequences, the *n*th term

(a) For the sequence 4, 8, 12, 16, 20,... the rule is 'add 4'.

Here is the *mapping diagram* for the sequence.

Term number (n)		Term
1	$\longrightarrow$	4
2	$\longrightarrow$	8
3	$\longrightarrow$	12
4	$\longrightarrow$	16
⋮		⋮
10	$\longrightarrow$	40
⋮		⋮
n	$\longrightarrow$	$4n$

The terms are found by multiplying the term number by 4.
So the 10th number is 40, the 20th term is 80.

A *general* term in the sequence is the nth term, where n stands for any number.
The nth term of this sequence is $4n$.

(b) Here is a more difficult sequence: 4, 7, 10, 13,...

The rule is 'add 3' so, in the mapping diagram, we have written a column for 3 times the term number [i.e. $3n$].

Term number (n)		$3n$		Term
1	$\longrightarrow$	3	$\longrightarrow$	4
2	$\longrightarrow$	6	$\longrightarrow$	7
3	$\longrightarrow$	9	$\longrightarrow$	10
4	$\longrightarrow$	12	$\longrightarrow$	13

We see that each term is 1 more than $3n$.
So, the 10th term is $(3 \times 10) + 1 = 31$
the 15th term is $(3 \times 15) + 1 = 46$
the nth term is $(3 \times n) + 1 = 3n + 1$

(c) Look at these two mapping diagrams. Decide what the missing numbers would be.

Term number (n)		$2n$		Term
1	$\longrightarrow$	2		3
2	$\longrightarrow$	4		5
3	$\longrightarrow$	6		7
4	$\longrightarrow$	8		9
⋮		⋮		⋮
10	$\longrightarrow$	□	$\longrightarrow$	□
⋮				
n	$\longrightarrow$	$2n$	$\longrightarrow$	□

Term number (n)		$5n$		Term
1	$\longrightarrow$	5	$\longrightarrow$	7
2	$\longrightarrow$	10	$\longrightarrow$	12
3	$\longrightarrow$	15	$\longrightarrow$	17
4	$\longrightarrow$	20	$\longrightarrow$	22
⋮		⋮		⋮
20	$\longrightarrow$	□	$\longrightarrow$	□
⋮		⋮		⋮
n	$\longrightarrow$	□	$\longrightarrow$	□

Exercise 1

1. Copy and complete these mapping diagrams.

(a)

Term number (n)		Term
1	→	6
2	→	12
3	→	18
4	→	24
⋮		⋮
12	→	□
⋮		⋮
n	→	□

(b)

Term number (n)		Term
1	→	8
2	→	16
3	→	24
4	→	32
⋮		⋮
8	→	□
⋮		⋮
n	→	□

(c)

Term number (n)		Term
1	→	10
2	→	20
3	→	30
⋮		⋮
15	→	□
⋮		⋮
n	→	□

2. Copy and complete these mapping diagrams. Notice that an extra column has been written.

(a)

Term number (n)		$4n$		Term
1	→	4	→	5
2	→	8	→	9
3	→	12	→	13
4	→	16	→	17
⋮		⋮		⋮
20	→	□	→	□
⋮		⋮		⋮
n	→	□	→	□

(b)

Term number (n)		$5n$		Term
1	→	5	→	4
2	→	10	→	9
3	→	15	→	14
4	→	20	→	19
⋮		⋮		⋮
12	→	□	→	□
⋮		⋮		⋮
n	→	□	→	□

3. Write down each sequence and select the correct expression for the nth term from the list given.

(a) 3, 6, 9, 12, ...
(b) 5, 10, 15, 20, ...
(c) $1^2, 2^2, 3^2, 4^2, \ldots$
(d) 7, 14, 21, 28, ...
(e) 2, 3, 4, 5, 6, ...
(f) $1^3, 2^3, 3^3, 4^3, \ldots$
(g) 1, 3, 5, 7, 9, ...

n^3 | $3n$ | $n+1$ | $7n$ | $2n-1$ | n^2 | $5n$

4. Here you are given the nth term. Copy and complete the diagrams.

(a)

Term number (n)	$7n$	Term
1 →	7 →	8
2 →	☐ →	☐
3 →	☐ →	☐
4 →	☐ →	☐
⋮	⋮	⋮
n →	$7n$ →	$7n+1$

(b)

Term number (n)	$3n$	Term
1 →	3 →	1
2 →	☐ →	☐
3 →	☐ →	☐
4 →	☐ →	☐
⋮	⋮	⋮
n →	$3n$ →	$3n-2$

(c)

Term number (n)	$5n$	Term
1 →	5 →	☐
2 →	☐ →	☐
3 →	☐ →	☐
8 →	☐ →	☐
⋮		
n →	$5n$ →	$5n+1$

(d)

Term number (n)	$10n$	Term
1 →	☐ →	☐
2 →	☐ →	☐
5 →	☐ →	☐
10 →	☐ →	☐
⋮	⋮	⋮
n →	$10n$ →	$10n+1$

- It is convenient to use the notation: T(1) for the first term,
  T(2) for the second term,
  T(3) for the third term and so on.

  The nth term of a sequence is written as T(n).

- The nth term of a sequence is $3n+1$.
  So we have $T(n) = 3n + 1$.

The first term, $T(1) = 3 \times 1 + 1 = 4$
The second term, $T(2) = 3 \times 2 + 1 = 7$
The seventh term, $T(7) = 3 \times 7 + 1 = 22$

Remember:
For the first term, put $n = 1$
For the second term, put $n = 2$.

Exercise 2

1. For the sequence 3, 5, 7, 9, 11, 13, ... write down
   (a) T(1) (b) T(2) (c) T(5)

> Remember:
> T(1) means 'the first term'
> T(2) means 'the second term'
> ... and so on.

2. For the sequence 2, 4, 6, 8, 10, ... write down
   (a) T(1) (b) T(4) (c) T(6)

3. The nth term of a sequence is $T(n)$ and $T(n) = 2n + 1$.
   Copy and complete the following
   (a) $T(1) = 2 \times 1 + 1 = \square$
   (b) $T(2) = 2 \times \square + 1 = \square$
   (c) $T(3) = 2 \times \square + 1 = \square$
   (d) $T(10) = 2 \times \square + 1 = \square$

4. The nth term of a sequence in $T(n)$ and $T(n) = 4n$.
   Find (a) T(1) (b) T(2) (c) T(20)

5. For a sequence, $T(n) = 5n + 1$.
   Find (a) T(1) (b) T(3) (c) T(10)

6. For a sequence, $T(n) = 20 - n$.
   Find (a) T(2) (b) T(5) (c) T(11)

7. The nth term of a sequence is $3n - 1$.
   Find (a) T(1) (b) T(100)

8. Write the first five terms of the sequence whose nth term, $T(n) = 2n + 3$.

9. Write the first five terms of the sequence where $T(n)$ is:
   (a) $n + 2$ (b) $5n$ (c) $10n - 1$
   (d) $n - 2$ (e) $\frac{1}{n}$ (f) n^2

Finding the *n*th term

- In an *arithmetic* sequence the difference between successive terms is always the same number.
  Here are some arithmetic sequences:
  5, 7, 9, 11, 13,
  12, 32, 52, 72, 92,
  20, 17, 14, 11, 8,
- The expression for the nth term of an arithmetic sequence is always of the form $an + b$

  The *difference* between successive terms is equal to the number a.
  The number b can be found by looking at the terms.

Find the nth term of the sequence 5, 7, 9, 11, 13, ...

This is an arithmetic sequence, so the nth term is of the form $an + b$.
The difference between terms is 2, so $a = 2$.

Put the sequence in a table and write a column for $2n$.

n	$2n$	term
1	2	5
2	4	7
3	6	9
4	8	11

We can see that the term is always 3 more than $2n$, so $b = 3$.

The nth term is $2n + 3$.

Exercise 3

1. Look at the sequence 5, 9, 13, 17, ...

The difference between terms is 4.
Copy the table, which has a column for $4n$.
Copy and complete: 'The nth term of the sequence is $4n + \square$.'

n	$4n$	term
1	4	5
2	8	9
3	12	13
4	16	17

2. Look at the sequence and the table underneath. Find the nth term in each case.

(a) Sequence 7, 10, 13, 16, ...

n	$3n$	term
1	3	7
2	6	10
3	9	13
4	12	16

nth term = $\square$

(b) Sequence 4, 9, 14, 19, ...

n	$5n$	term
1	5	4
2	10	9
3	15	14
4	20	19

nth term = $\square$

3. In the sequence 6, 10, 14, 18, ... the difference between terms is 4. Copy and complete the table and write an expression for the nth term of the sequence.

n	$\square$	term
1	$\square$	6
2	$\square$	10
3	$\square$	14
4	$\square$	18

4. Look at the sequence 5, 8, 11, 14, ...
Write down the difference between terms.
Make a table like the one in Question **3** and use it to find an expression for the nth term.

5. Write down each sequence in a table and then find the nth term.
(a) 8, 10, 12, 14, 16, ...
(b) 3, 7, 11, 15, ...
(c) 8, 13, 18, 23, ...

6. Make a table for each sequence and write the nth term.
(a) 11, 19, 27, 35, ...
(b) $2\frac{1}{2}$, $4\frac{1}{2}$, $6\frac{1}{2}$, $8\frac{1}{2}$, ...
(c) -7, -4, -1, 2, 5, ...

7. Here is a sequence of shapes made from sticks

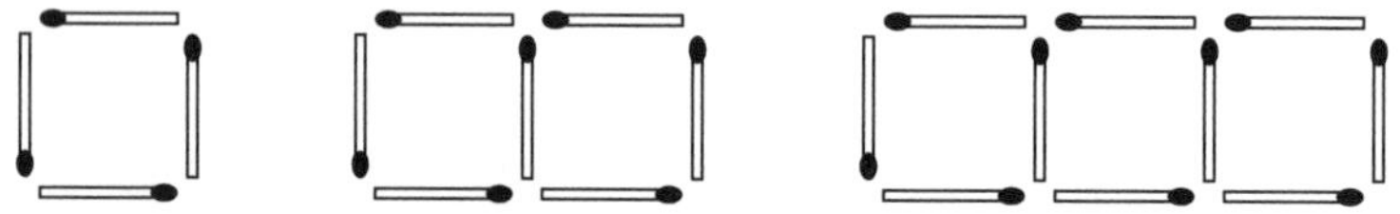

Shape number:	n = 1	n = 2	n = 3
Number of sticks:	4	7	10

The number of sticks makes the sequence 4, 7, 10, 13, ...
Make a table for the sequence and find the nth term.

In Questions **8** to **13** you are given a sequence of shapes made from sticks or dots. For each question make a table and find the nth term of the sequence.

8. Here is a sequence of triangles made from dots. Draw the next diagram in the sequence. How many dots are in nth term?

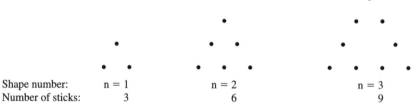

Shape number:	n = 1	n = 2	n = 3
Number of sticks:	3	6	9

9. Here is a sequence of 'steps' made from sticks.
Draw the next diagram in the sequence and make a table. How many dots are in the nth term?

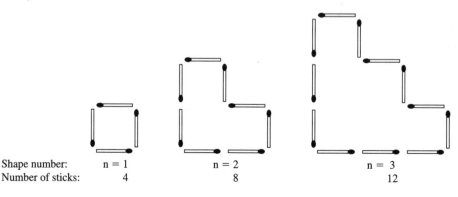

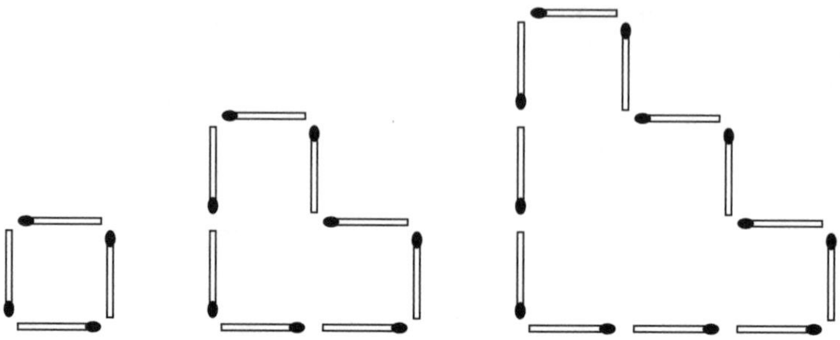

Shape number:	n = 1	n = 2	n = 3
Number of sticks:	4	8	12

10. Louise makes a pattern of triangles from sticks.

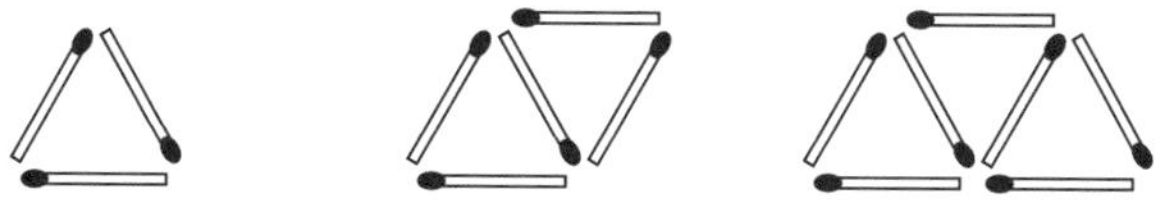

Shape number:	n = 1	n = 2	n = 3
Number of sticks:	3	5	7

(a) Draw shape number 4 and shape number 5 and make a table. How many sticks are in the *n*th term?

11. Here is a sequence of houses made from sticks

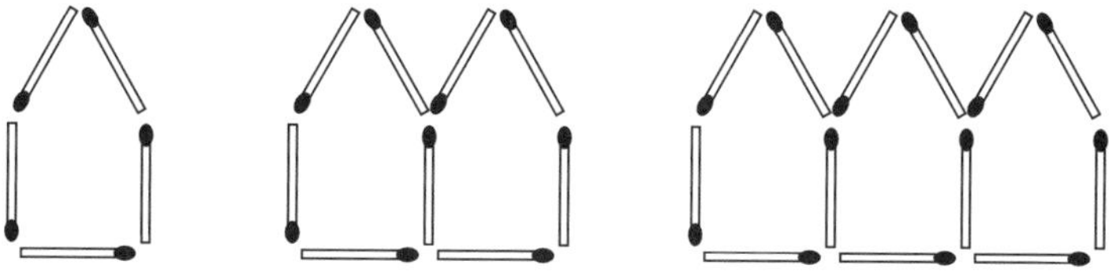

Shape number:	n = 1	n = 2	n = 3
Number of sticks:	5	9	13

Draw shape number 4 and make a table. How many sticks are in the *n*th term?

12. Paul makes a pattern of squares from dots.

Shape number:	n = 1	n = 2	n = 3
Number of sticks:	4	6	8

Draw shape number 4 and shape number 5 and make a table. How many dots are in the *n*th term?

13. Here is another sequence made from dots.

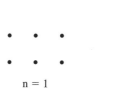

Shape number:	n = 1	n = 2	n = 3
Number of dots:	6	10	☐

Draw shape numbers 4 and 5 and make a table. How many dots are in the *n*th term?

In Questions **14** to **18** find the number of squares, dots or sticks in the *n*th term of the sequence.

14. In these diagrams black squares are surrounded on three sides by white squares.

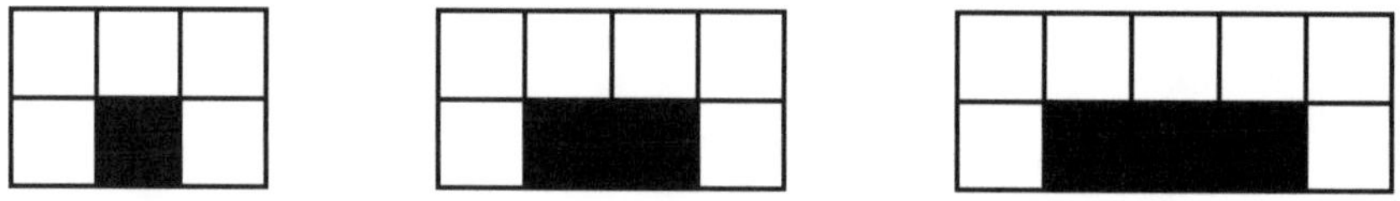

White squares: $w = 5$ $w = 6$ $w = 7$

15. In this sequence black squares are surrounded by white squares.

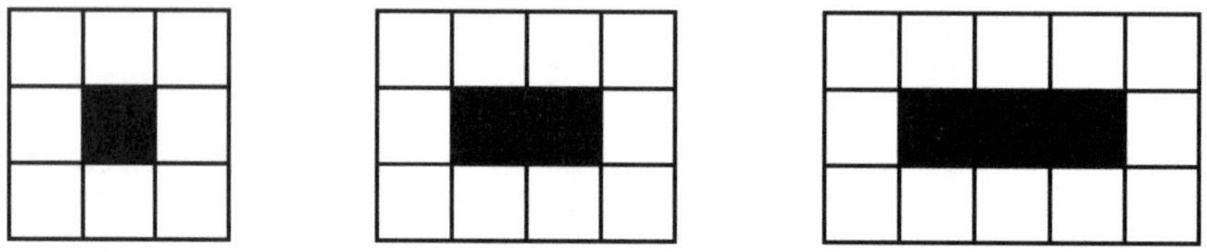

White squares: $w = 8$ $w = 10$ $w = 12$

16. In the diagrams below rectangles are joined together and dots are drawn around the outside with 2 dots on a long side and one dot on a short side.

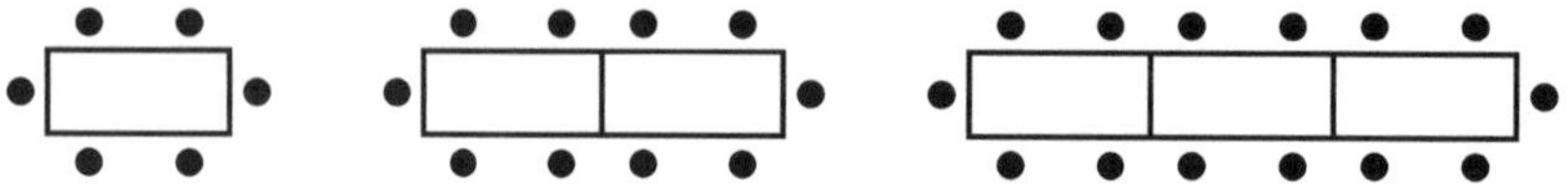

17. Now the rectangles are joined along their longer sides.

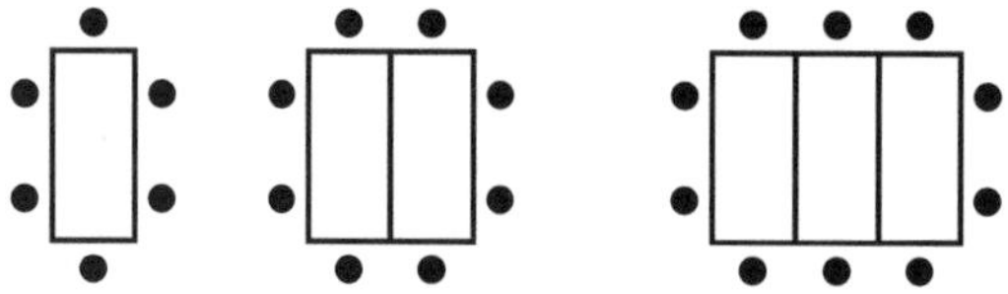

18.

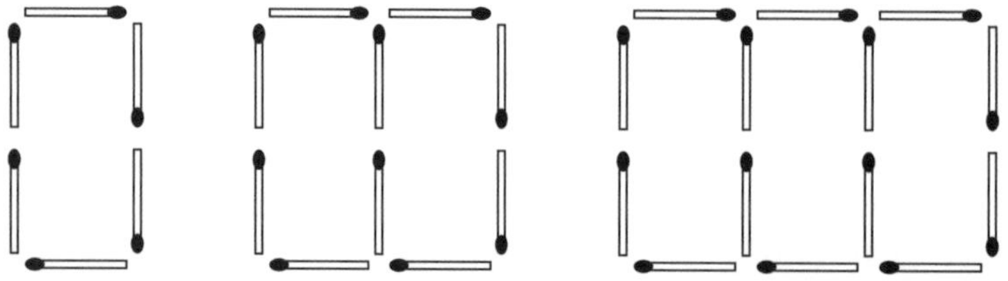

19. Design a sequence of shapes using sticks or squares. Find an expression for the *n*th term of the sequence.

5.4 Drawing graphs

- We have seen that when a calculation [like $5 + 7 \times 3$] is performed, the order of operations follows 'BIDMAS'.

  The same rules apply for the expressions involved in graphs.

  Brackets
  Indices
  Divide
  Multiply
  Add
  Subtract

- Consider the graph $y = 3x - 1$. Two operations are performed: 'multiply by 3', 'subtract 1'.
  Multiply is done before subtract and a *flow chart* can be drawn

  $x \rightarrow \boxed{\times 3} \rightarrow \boxed{-1} \rightarrow y$

  So when $x = 2$, $y = 2 \times 3 - 1 = 5$. On the graph plot (2, 5)
  when $x = 4$, $y = 4 \times 3 - 1 = 11$. On the graph plot (4, 11)
  when $x = 7$, $y = 7 \times 3 - 1 = 20$. On the graph plot (7, 20)

- Consider the graph $y = 2(x + 1)$. The operation in brackets is done first.
  The flow chart is:

  $x \rightarrow \boxed{+1} \rightarrow \boxed{\times 2} \rightarrow y$

  When $x = 2$, $y = (2 + 1) \times 2 = 6$. Plot (2, 6)
  $x = 3$, $y = (3 + 1) \times 2 = 8$. Plot (3, 8)
  $x = 5$, $y = (5 + 1) \times 2 = 12$. Plot (5, 12)

Using the flow diagram, complete the table below.
Hence draw the graph of $y = 2x + 4$ for x from 0 to 5

$x \rightarrow \boxed{\times 2} \rightarrow \boxed{+4} \rightarrow y$

x	0	1	2	3	4	5
y	4	6	8	10	12	14
coord-inates	(0, 4)	(1, 6)	(2, 8)	(3, 10)	(4, 12)	(5, 14)

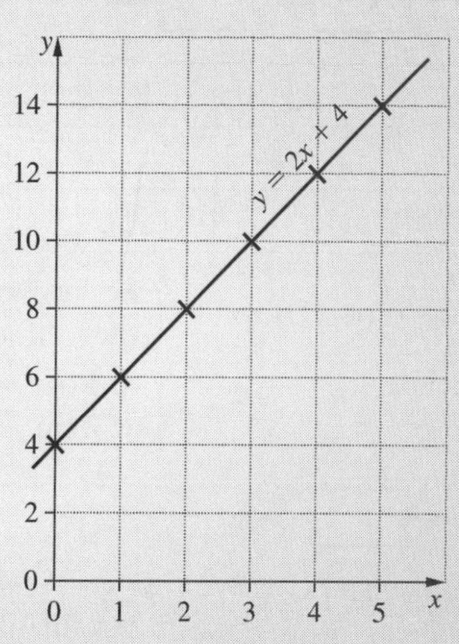

Exercise 1

For each question copy and complete the table using the flow diagram. Then draw the graph using the scales given.

1. $y = 2x + 1$ for x: 0 to 6 $\begin{pmatrix} x\text{: 1 cm} = \text{1 unit} \\ y\text{: 1 cm} = \text{1 unit} \end{pmatrix}$

$x \rightarrow \boxed{\times 2} \rightarrow \boxed{+1} \rightarrow y$

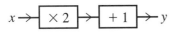

x	0	1	2	3	4	5	6
y					9		
coordinates					(4, 9)		

2. $y = x + 4$ for x: 0 to 7 $\begin{pmatrix} x\text{: 1 cm} = \text{1 unit} \\ y\text{: 1 cm} = \text{1 unit} \end{pmatrix}$

$x \rightarrow \boxed{+4} \rightarrow y$

x	0	1	2	3	4	5	6	7
y			6					
coordinates			(2, 6)					

3. $y = 3x - 2$ for x: 0 to 5 $\begin{pmatrix} x\text{: 1 cm} = \text{1 unit} \\ y\text{: 1 cm} = \text{2 units} \end{pmatrix}$

$x \rightarrow \boxed{\times 3} \rightarrow \boxed{-2} \rightarrow y$

x	0	1	2	3	4	5
y	−2	1				
coordinates		(1, 1)				

4. $y = \dfrac{x}{2}$ for x: 0 to 7 (Set up your own table) $\begin{pmatrix} x\text{: 1 cm} = \text{1 unit} \\ y\text{: 2 cm} = \text{1 unit} \end{pmatrix}$

$x \rightarrow \boxed{\div 2} \rightarrow y$

5. $y = 6 - x$ for x: 0 to 6 (Set up your own table) $\begin{pmatrix} x\text{: 1 cm} = \text{1 unit} \\ y\text{: 1 cm} = \text{1 unit} \end{pmatrix}$

$x \rightarrow \boxed{\text{subtract from 6}} \rightarrow y$

6. $y = 12 - 2x$ for x: 0 to 6 $\begin{pmatrix} x\text{: } 1\text{ cm} = 1\text{ unit} \\ y\text{: } 1\text{ cm} = 1\text{ unit} \end{pmatrix}$

$x \rightarrow$ [× 2] $\rightarrow$ [subtract from 12] $\rightarrow y$

7. $y = 3(x + 1)$ for x: 0 to 5 $\begin{pmatrix} x\text{: } 1\text{ cm} = 1\text{ unit} \\ y\text{: } 1\text{ cm} = 2\text{ units} \end{pmatrix}$

$x \rightarrow$ [+ 1] $\rightarrow$ [× 3] $\rightarrow y$

8. $y = 3(6 - x)$ for x: 0 to 6 $\begin{pmatrix} x\text{: } 1\text{ cm} = 1\text{ unit} \\ y\text{: } 1\text{ cm} = 2\text{ units} \end{pmatrix}$

$x \rightarrow$ [subtract from 6] $\rightarrow$ [× 3] $\rightarrow y$

9. $y = 2x + 4$ for x: 0 to 8 $\begin{pmatrix} x\text{: } 1\text{ cm} = 1\text{ unit} \\ y\text{: } 1\text{ cm} = 2\text{ units} \end{pmatrix}$

$x \rightarrow$ [× 2] $\rightarrow$ [+ 4] $\rightarrow y$

10. $y = \frac{1}{2}x + 3$ for x: 0 to 8 $\begin{pmatrix} x\text{: } 1\text{ cm} = 1\text{ unit} \\ y\text{: } 2\text{ cm} = 1\text{ unit} \end{pmatrix}$

$x \rightarrow$ [÷ 2] $\rightarrow$ [+ 3] $\rightarrow y$

In Questions **11** to **16** the values of x include negative values.

11. $y = 2x + 2$ for x: -2 to $+4$ $\begin{pmatrix} x\text{: } 1\text{ cm} = 1\text{ unit} \\ y\text{: } 1\text{ cm} = 2\text{ units} \end{pmatrix}$

$x \rightarrow$ [× 2] $\rightarrow$ [+ 2] $\rightarrow y$

12. $y = 3x - 2$ for x: -2 to $+3$ $\begin{pmatrix} x\text{: } 1\text{ cm} = 1\text{ unit} \\ y\text{: } 1\text{ cm} = 2\text{ units} \end{pmatrix}$

$x \rightarrow$ [× 3] $\rightarrow$ [− 2] $\rightarrow y$

13. $y = 4x - 1$ for x: -2 to $+3$ $\begin{pmatrix} x\text{: } 1\text{ cm} = 1\text{ unit} \\ y\text{: } 1\text{ cm} = 2\text{ units} \end{pmatrix}$

$x \rightarrow$ [× 4] $\rightarrow$ [− 1] $\rightarrow y$

14. $y = 2 - 2x$ for x: -2 to $+3$ $\left(\begin{array}{l} x\text{: 1 cm} = \text{1 unit} \\ y\text{: 1 cm} = \text{5 units} \end{array}\right)$

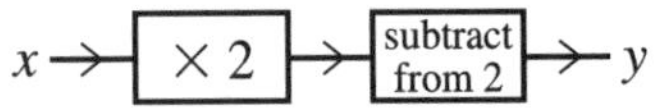

15. $y = 5 - 3x$ for x: -2 to $+3$ $\left(\begin{array}{l} x\text{: 1 cm} = \text{1 unit} \\ y\text{: 1 cm} = \text{5 units} \end{array}\right)$

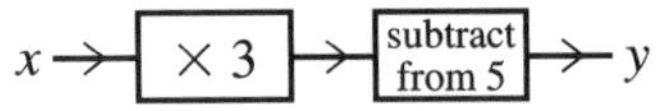

16. (a) Copy the graph of $y = 2x - 1$
(b) Using the same axes, draw the graph of $y = x + 2$. Take x from -2 to $+3$.
(c) Write down the coordinates of the point where the lines meet.

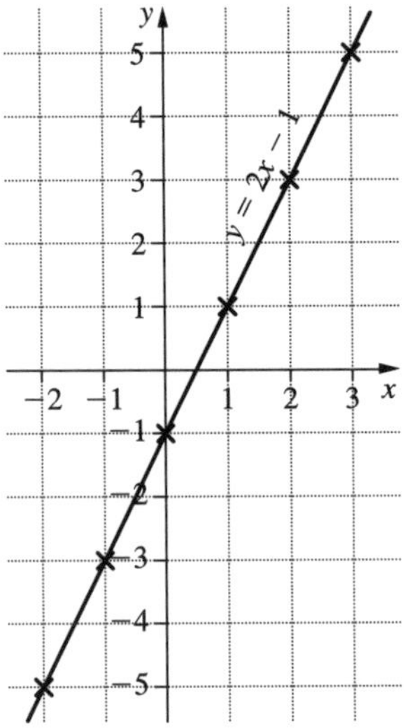

17. Draw $x + y = 5$; take x from 0 to 6.

18. Darw $2x + y = 10$; take x from 0 to 6.

19. Using the same axes, draw the graphs of $y = x + 1$ and $x + y = 7$. Take values of x from 0 to 6.
Write down the coordinates of the point where the lines meet.

20. On the same graph, draw the lines $y = 2x - 3$,
$y = \frac{1}{2}x$,
$x + y = 9$.

Take values of x from 0 to 8.
Write down the coordinates of the three vertices of the triangle formed.

21. On the same graph, draw the lines $x + y = 8$,
$y = 2x + 2$,
$y = 2$.

Take values of x from 0 to 8.
Find the area of the triangle formed.

Exercise 2

Use a graphical calculator or a graph plotter on a computer.

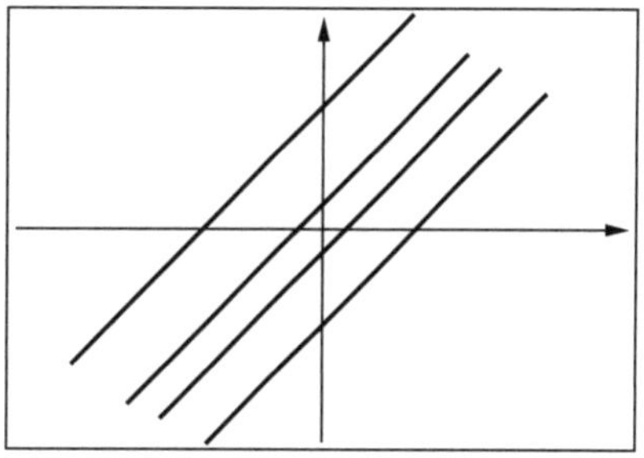

1. Draw the graphs of $y = x + 5$, $y = x + 3$, $y = x - 1$, $y = x - 4$

Write down what you notice. [Look at the point where the lines cut the y axis.]

2. Draw the graphs of $y = 2x + 1$, $y = 2x - 3$, $y = 2x + 5$. Write down what you notice.

3. Draw the graphs of $y = 3x$, $y = 3x - 5$, $y = 3x + 6$ What do you notice?

4. (a) Where do you expect $y = 4x + 7$ to cut the y axis?
(b) Where do you expect $y = 4x - 3$ to cut the y axis?

5. Write down the equations of any line parallel to $y = 6x + 3$.

6. Draw the graphs of $y = x^2$, $y = 12 \div x$, $y = x^2 - 5$

7. State which of the following represents straight line graphs

$y = 3x + 2$ $\qquad$ $y = 10 \div x$ $\qquad$ $y = 5x - 1$ $\qquad$ $y = x^3$

8. Experiment with different equations until you can obtain three lines which form a triangle like those shown.

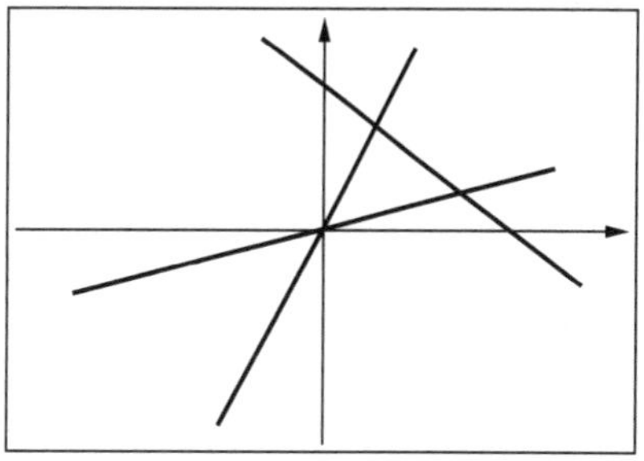

9.

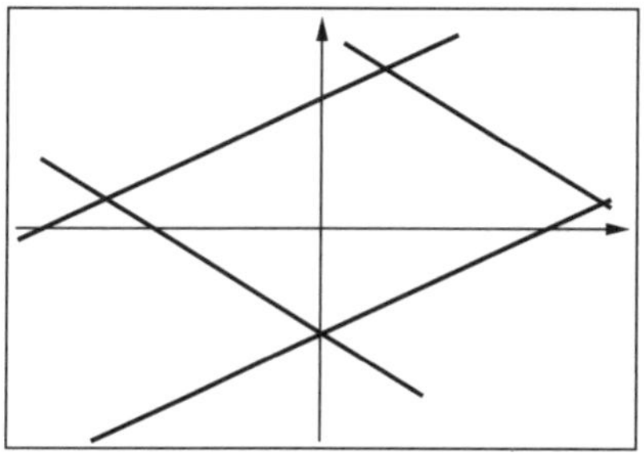

Experiment with different graphs until you obtain a parallelogram like the one shown here.

Curved graphs

Draw the graph of $y = x^2 - 3$ for values of x from -3 to $+3$.

$x = -3$, $y = (-3)^2 - 3 = 6$
$x = -2$, $y = (-2)^2 - 3 = 1$
$x = -1$, $y = (-1)^2 - 3 = -2$
$x = 0$, $y = 0^2 - 3 = -3$
$x = 1$, $y = 1^2 - 3 = -2$
$x = 2$, $y = 2^2 - 3 = 1$
$x = 3$, $y = 3^2 - 3 = 6$

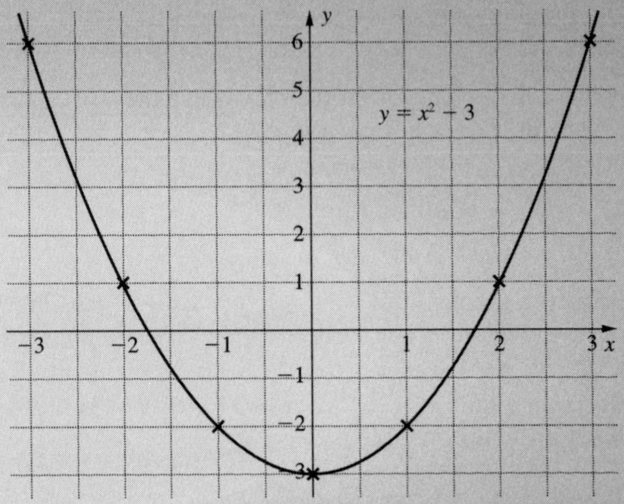

Draw a *smooth* curve through the points.
It helps to turn the page upside down so that your hand can be 'inside' the curve. Try not to look at the tip of your pencil. Instead look at next point through which you are drawing the curve.

Exercise 3

Draw the graph, using a scale of 2 cm to 1 unit on the x axis and 1 cm to 1 unit on the y axis (as in the above example).

1. $y = x^2$; take x from -3 to $+3$.
2. $y = x^2 + 2$; take x from -3 to $+3$.
3. $y = (x + 1)^2$; take x from -3 to $+3$.
4. $y = (x - 2)^2$; take x from -1 to $+5$.
5. $y = x^2 + x$; take x from -3 to $+3$.
6. $y = x^2 + x + 2$; take x from -3 to $+3$.
7. Draw the graph of $y = x^2 - 3x$ for values of x from -3 to $+3$.
   (a) What is the lowest value of y?
   (b) For what value of x does the lowest value occur?
8. Using the same axes, draw the graphs of $y = x^2 - 6x + 16$ and $y = 6x - x^2$ for values of x from 0 to 6.
   Write down the equation of the line which can be drawn through the two points of intersection.
9. Draw the graphs of $y = 2x^2 + x - 6$ and $y = 2x + 3$ for values of x from -3 to $+3$. Write down the x coordinates, correct to 1 d.p., of the two points where the line cuts the curve.

Using graphs

Exercise 4

1. A car hire firm charges an initial fee plus a charge depending on the number of miles driven, as shown.

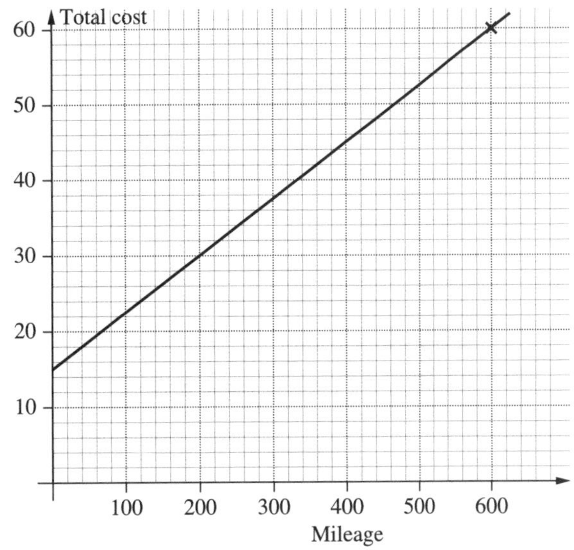

   (a) Find the total cost for driving 140 miles.
   (b) Find the total cost for driving 600 miles.
   (c) Find how many miles I can drive for a cost of £45.

2. A teacher has marked a test out of 80 and wishes to convert the marks into percentages. Draw axes as shown and draw a straight line through the points (0, 0) and (80, 100).

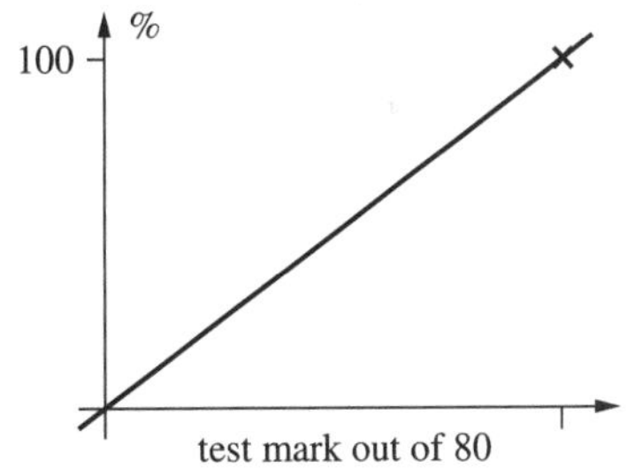

   (a) Use your graph to convert
      (i) 63 marks into a percentage
      (ii) 24 marks into a percentage
   (b) The pass mark was 60%. How many marks out of 80 were needed for a pass?

3. The graph converts pounds into French francs.

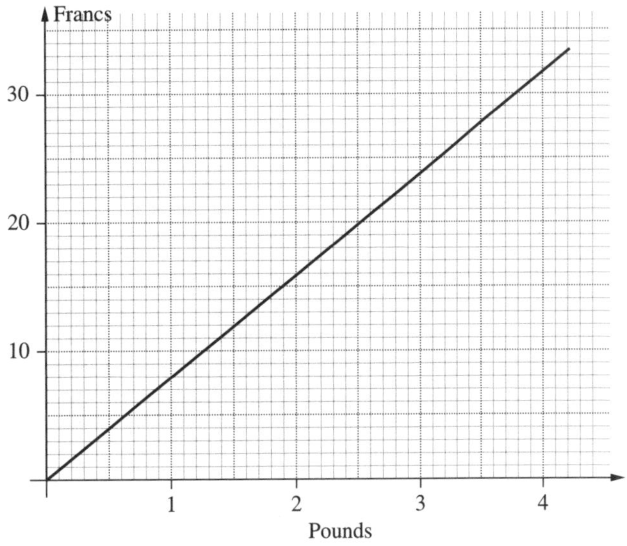

   (a) convert into francs
      (i) £2 (ii) £3·50
   (b) convert into pounds
      (i) 20F (ii) 12F.
   (c) A Mars bar costs 75p. Find the equivalent price in France.
   (d) A few years ago, the exchange rate was about 10 francs to the pound. Is it cheaper or more expensive nowadays as a British tourist in France?

4. (a) Draw axes, as shown, with a scale of 1 cm to 5°. Two equivalent temperatures are 32°F = 0°C and 86°F = 30°C.

(b) Draw a line through the points above and use your graph to convert:

(i) 20°C into °F

(ii) −10°C into °F

(iii) 50°F into °C

(c) The normal body temperature of a healthy person is 98°F. Susie's temperature is 39°C. Should she stay at home today, or go to school as usual?

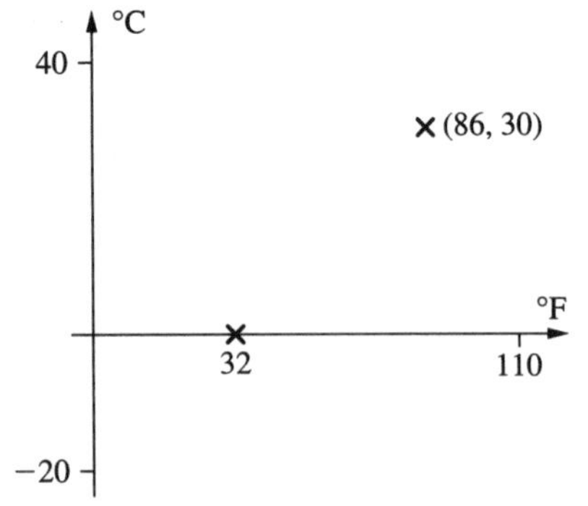

5. In the U.K., petrol consumption for cars is usually quoted in 'miles per gallon'. In other countries the metric equivalent is 'km per litre'.

(a) Convert 20 m.p.g. into km per litre.

(b) Convert 5 km per litre into m.p.g.

(c) A car travels 9 km on one litre of petrol. Convert this consumption into miles per gallon. Work out how many gallons of petrol the car will use, if it is driven a distance of 100 miles.

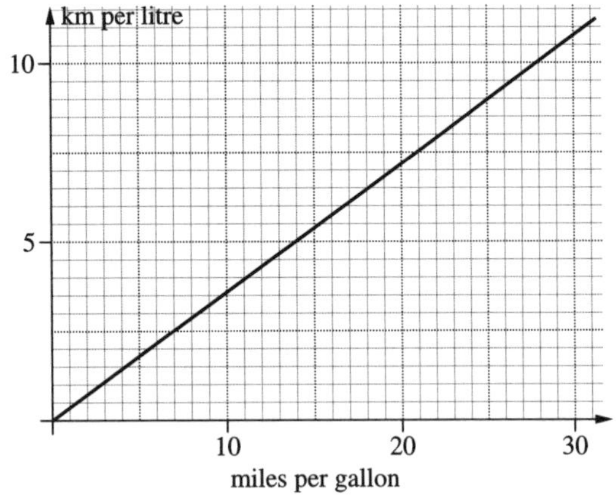

6. Selmin and Katie make different charges for people wanting pages typed professionally.

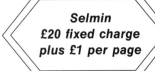

Selmin
£20 fixed charge
plus £1 per page

Katie
£1·50 per page

(a) How much would Selmin charge to type 30 pages?

(b) How much would Katie charge to type 10 pages?

(c) Draw axes for the number of pages typed and the total cost, using the scales given.

(d) On the same diagram, draw a graph for each typist to show their charges for up to 60 pages.

(e) Use your graphs to decide for what number of pages Selmin is the cheaper typist to choose.

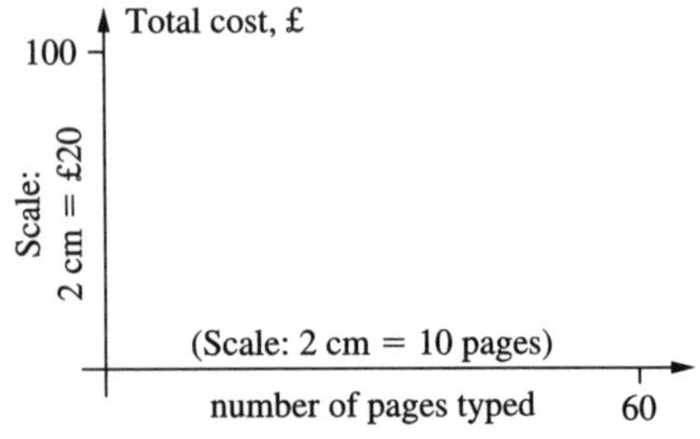

5.5 Congruent shapes, tessellation

Congruent shapes are exactly the same in shape and size. Shapes are congruent if one shape can be fitted exactly over the other.

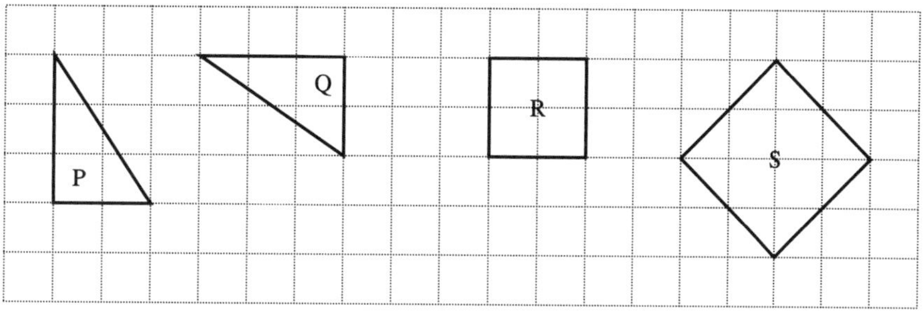

P and Q are congruent R and S are not congruent

Exercise 1

1. Decide which shapes are congruent pairs. [You can use tracing paper]

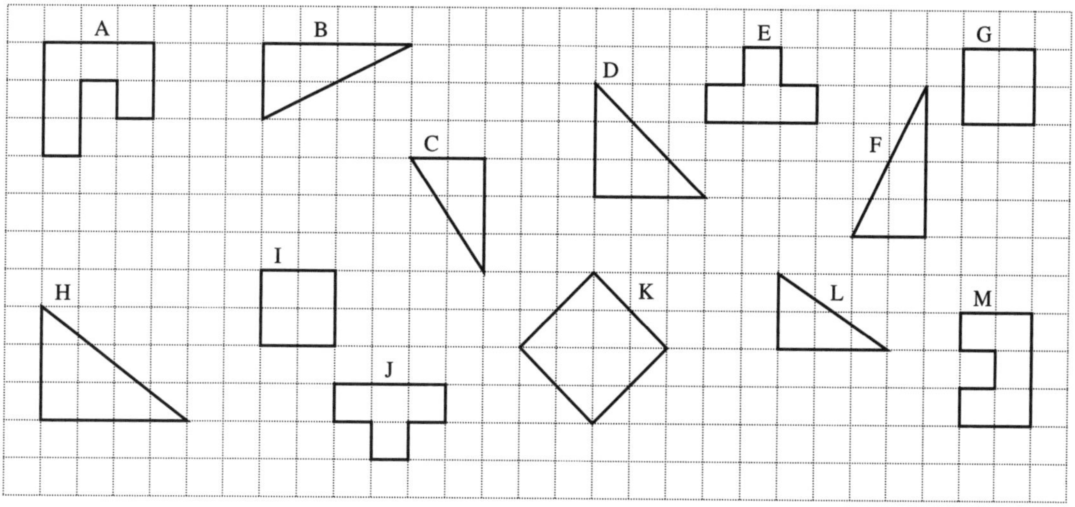

2. Copy the diagram and colour in congruent shapes with the same colour.

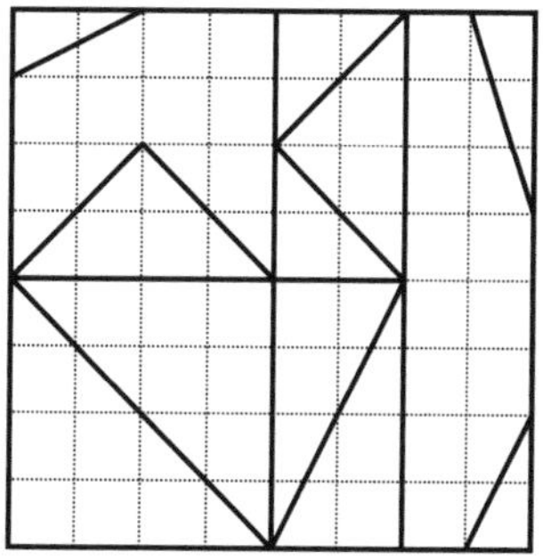

3.

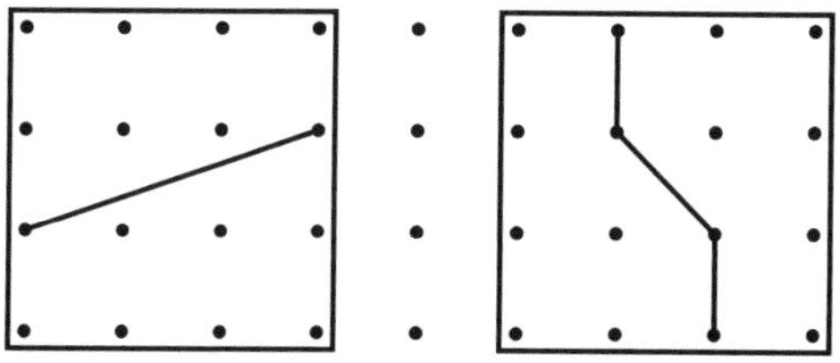

The 4 × 4 grids are divided into two congruent shapes.
Do this in as many different ways as possible.

4. Two congruent right angled triangles are joined together along equal sides
(a) How many shapes are possible?
(b) How many shapes are possible if the congruent triangles are scalene … or equilateral?

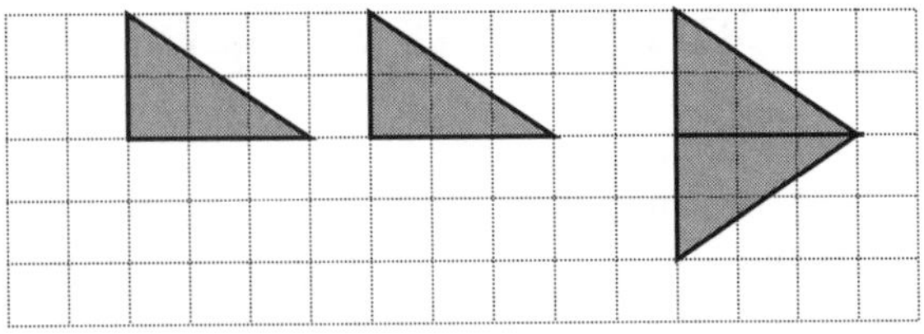

5. 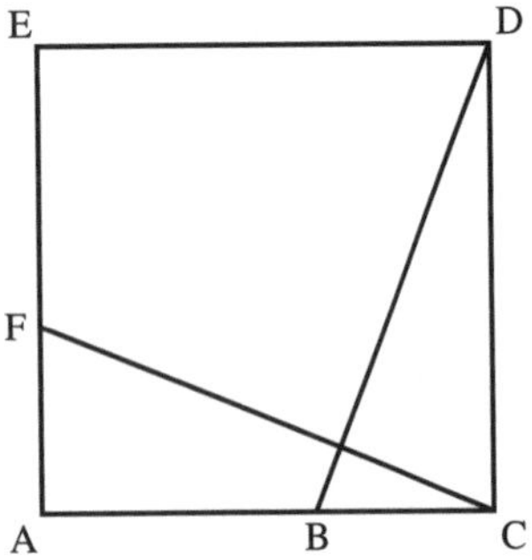

You are told that triangles DBC and CFA are congruent. Copy and complete:

(a) side AF = side ☐

(b) side CF = side ☐

(c) angle CFA = angle ☐

(d) angle ☐ = angle CDB.

Tessellation

- in tessellation we study the different ways we can regularly tile any flat surface, no matter how large. The examples below show tessellation using quadrilaterals:

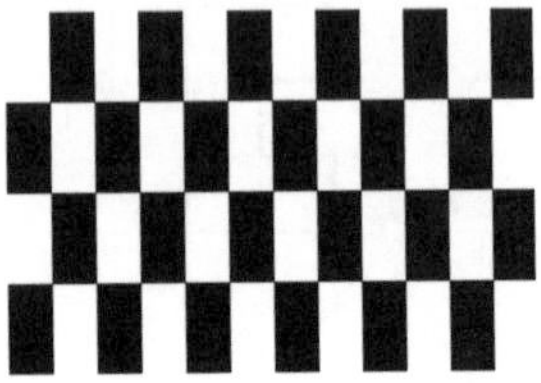

(Rectangles)

(Kites)

- Draw *any* quadrilateral on card and make a tessellation.

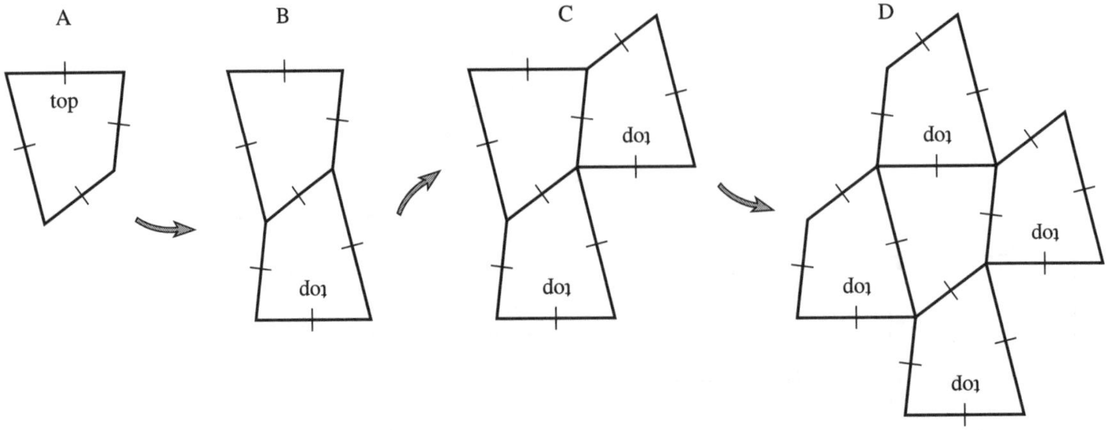

Interesting tessellations may be formed using sets of different shapes, provided the lengths of their sides are compatible

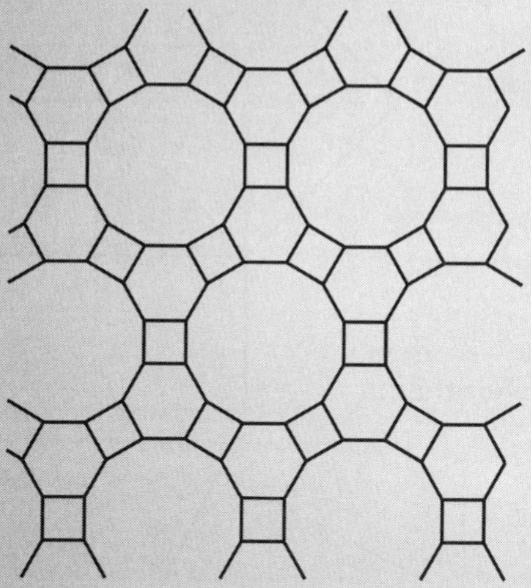

Exercise 2

1. Draw and cut out a template on card for each of the shapes below:
(You can trace the shapes below to save time. All their sides are compatible).

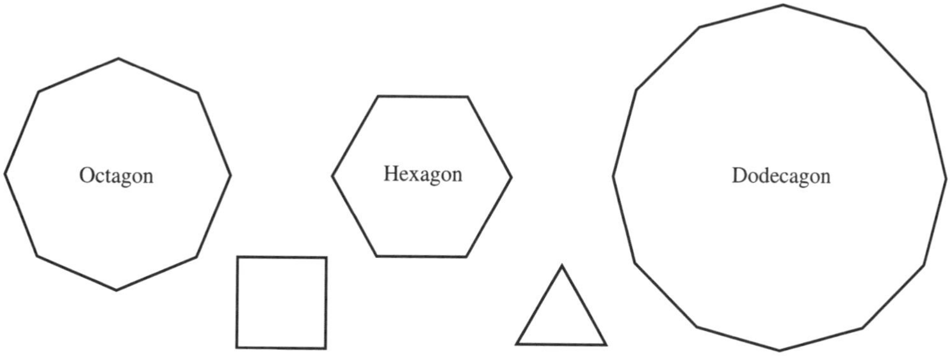

2. Either (i) draw a tessellation on plain paper or (ii) draw a tessellation directly onto tracing paper, using:
(a) only hexagons
(b) only octagons and squares
(c) only dodecagons and equilateral triangles.
(d) only hexagons, squares and equilateral triangles.
(e) only dodecagons, hexagons and squares.
(f) only squares and equilateral triangles.

3. For each tessellation in **2**, colour the pattern in an interesting way.

5.6 Pythagoras' theorem

Below are two dissections which demonstrate a result called Pythagoras' theorem. Pythagoras was a famous Greek mathematician who proved the result in about 550 B.C. The first dissection works only for isosceles right angled triangles.

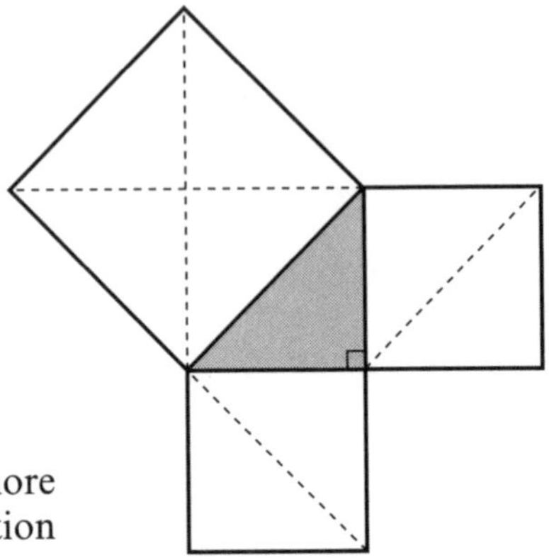

The second dissection, which is Perigal's dissection, is more impressive. It has been left for you to complete as a demonstration of Pythagoras' Theorem.

- Copy triangle ABC on dotted paper.
- Find the point X which is the centre of square ①
- Draw PQ parallel to AB and draw RS perpendicular to PQ.
- Cut out square ② and the four pieces of square ①.
- Rearrange these five pieces to fit exactly into square ③

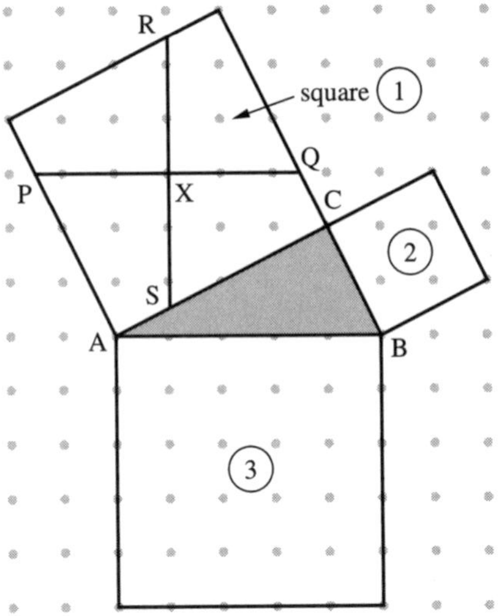

Both of these dissections demonstrate Pythagoras' theorem....

'In a right angled triangle, the square on the hypotenuse is equal to sum of the squares on the other two sides.'

The 'hypotenuse' is the longest side in a right angled triangle.

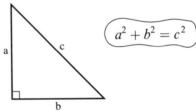

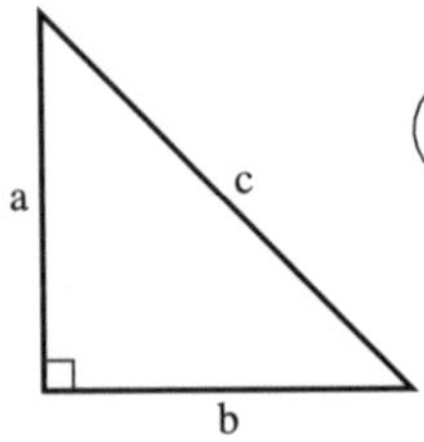

$$a^2 + b^2 = c^2$$

The theorem can be used to calculate the third side of a right angled triangle when two sides are known.

Find the length x

(a)

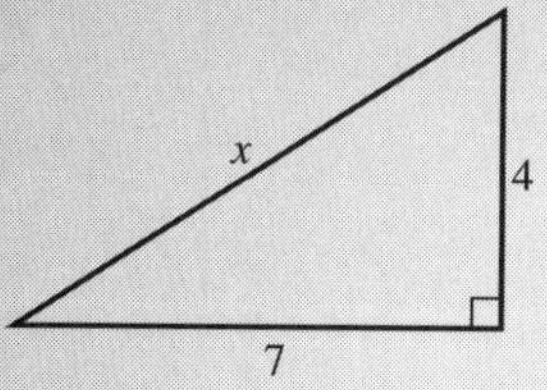

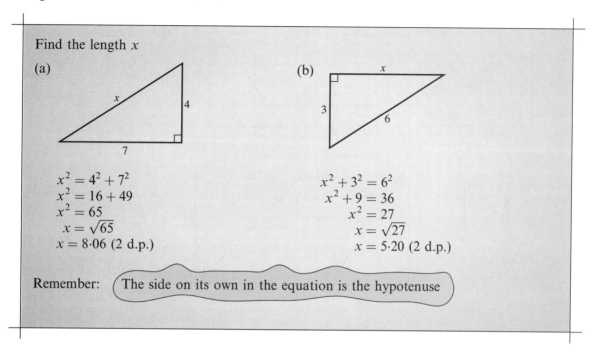

$x^2 = 4^2 + 7^2$
$x^2 = 16 + 49$
$x^2 = 65$
$x = \sqrt{65}$
$x = 8{\cdot}06$ (2 d.p.)

(b)

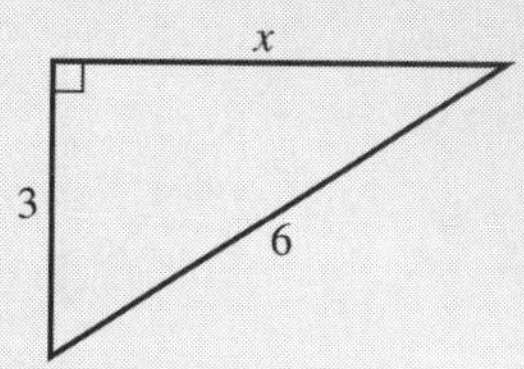

$x^2 + 3^2 = 6^2$
$x^2 + 9 = 36$
$x^2 = 27$
$x = \sqrt{27}$
$x = 5{\cdot}20$ (2 d.p.)

Remember: The side on its own in the equation is the hypotenuse

Exercise 1

Give your answers correct to 2 d.p. where necessary. The units are cm unless you are told otherwise.

1. Find x.

(a)

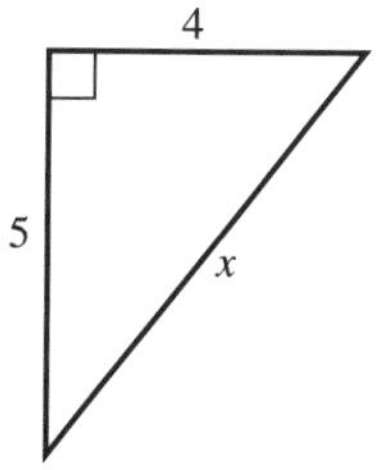

(b)

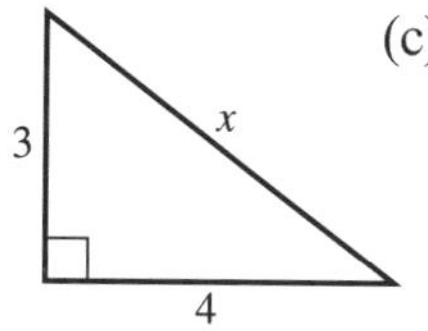

(c)

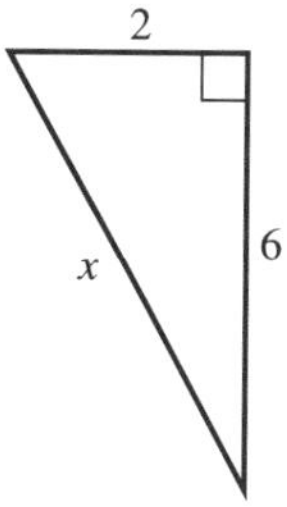

(d)

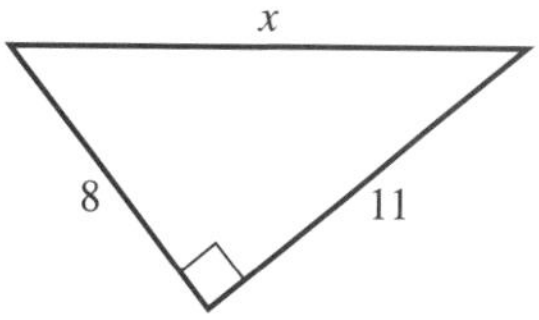

(e)

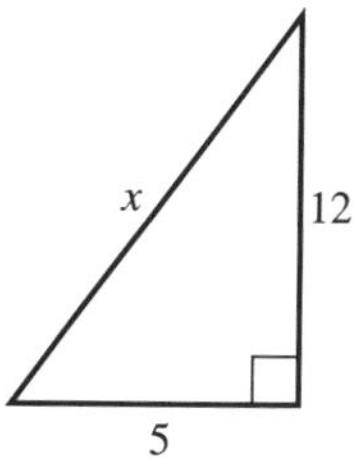

(f)

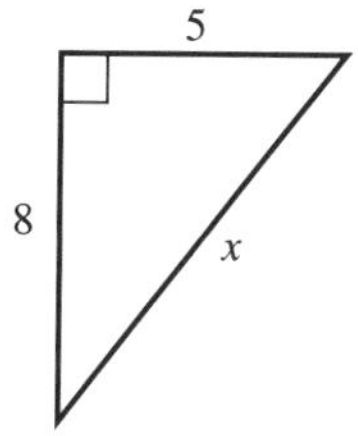

(g)

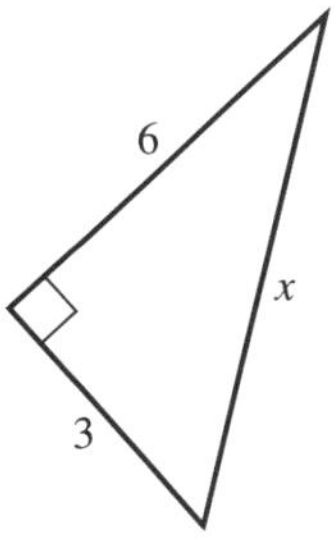

(h)

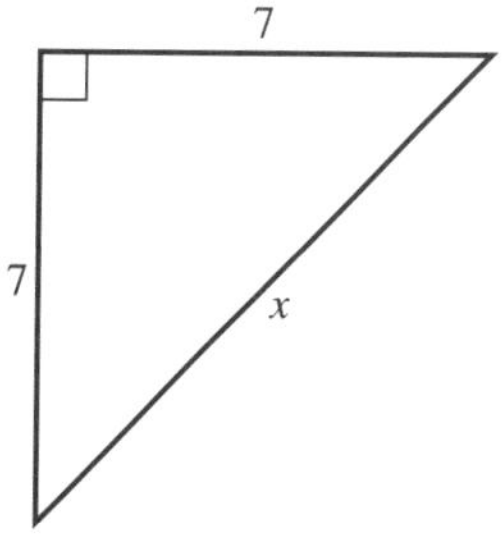

2. Find y.
Hint: In part (a) write $y^2 + 4^2 = 8^2$

(a)
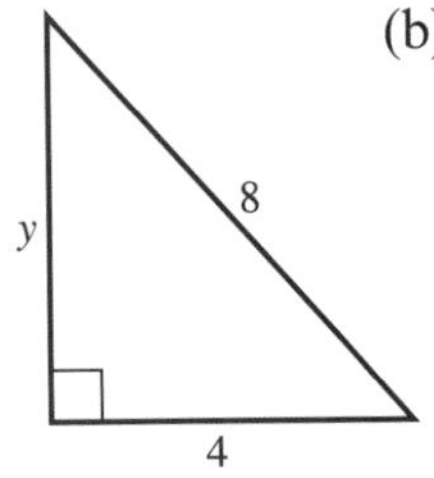

(b)
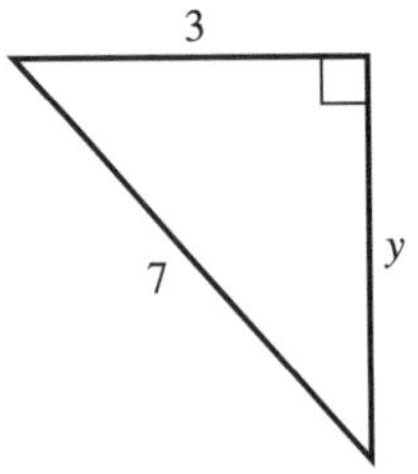

(c)
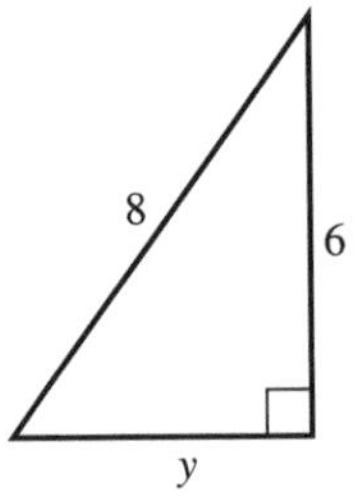

(d)
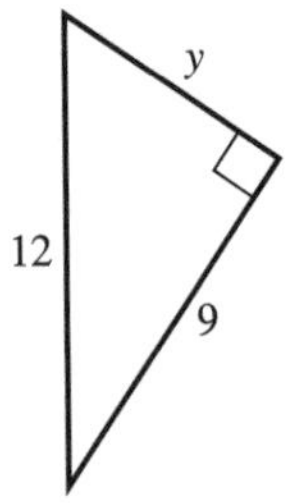

(e)
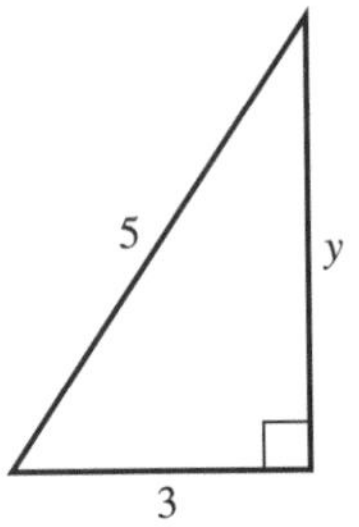

(f)
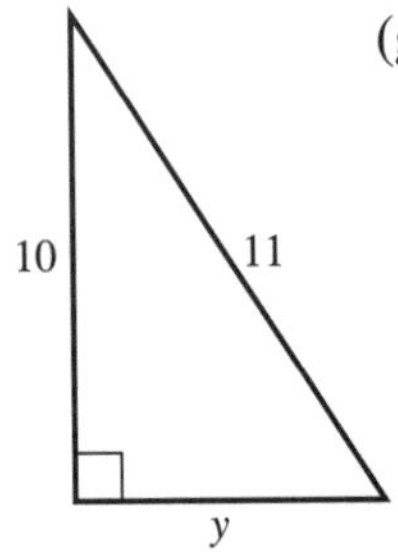

(g)
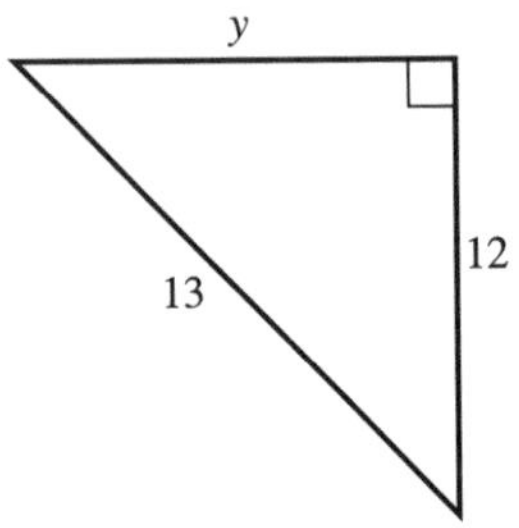

(h)
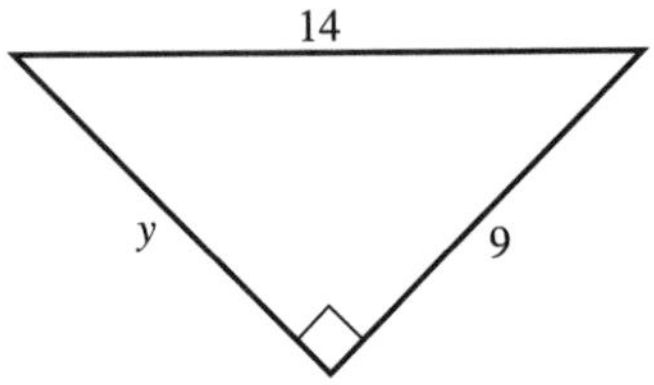

3. Find the side marked with a letter. It may be the hypotenuse or one of the other sides.

(a)
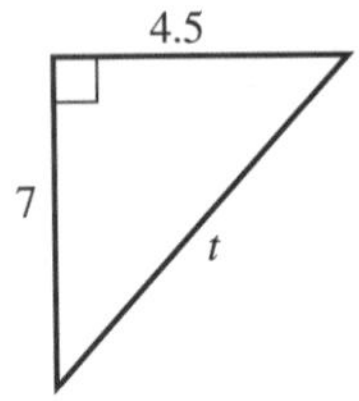

(b)
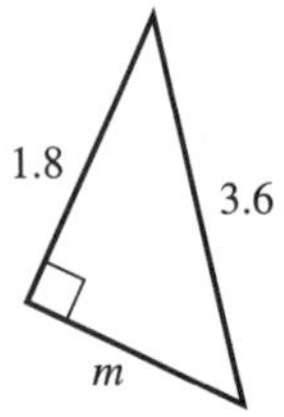

(c)
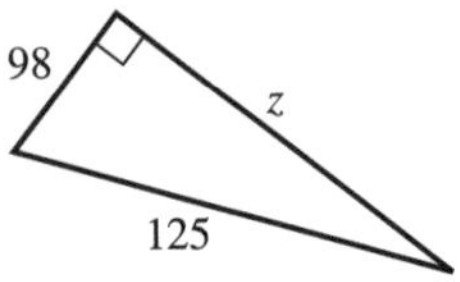

(d)
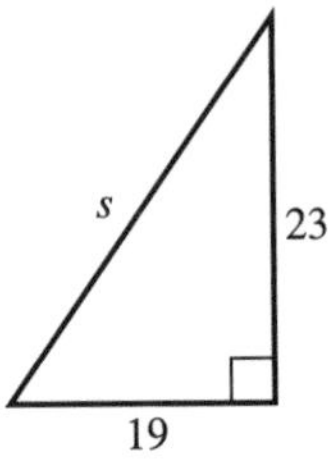

(e)
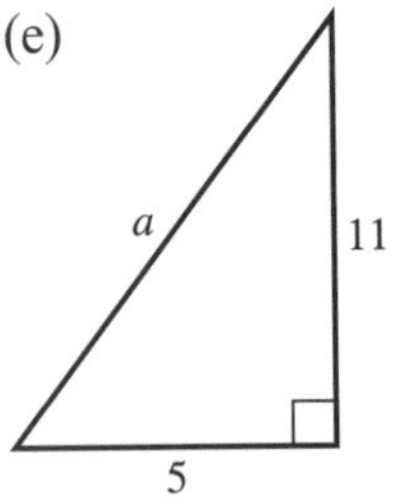

(f)
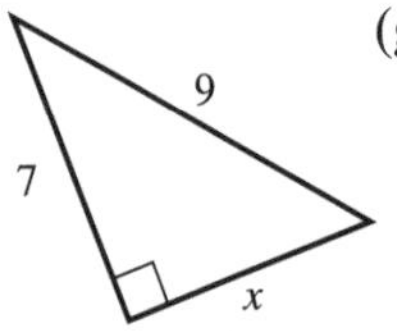

(g)
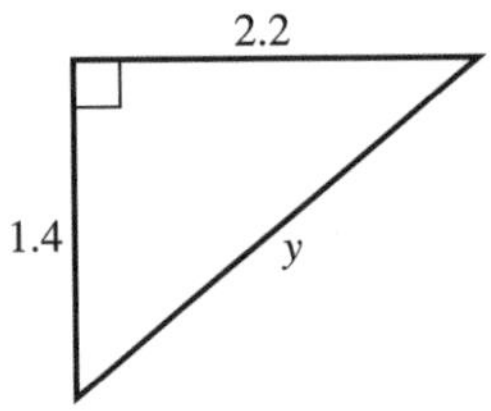

(h)
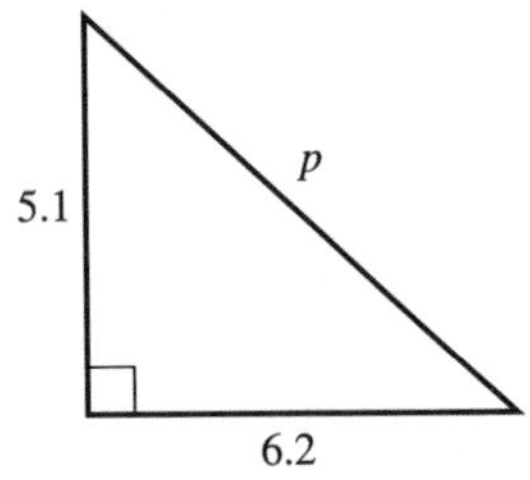

4. A ladder of length 5 m rests against a vertical wall, with its foot 2 m from the wall. How far up the wall does the ladder reach?

5. A ladder of length 4 m reaches 32 m up a vertical wall. How far is the foot of the ladder from the wall?

6. A boat sails from the harbour to the lighthouse. The lighthouse is 11 km to the south and 8 km to the east of the harbour.
Calculate the distance between the harbour and the lighthouse.

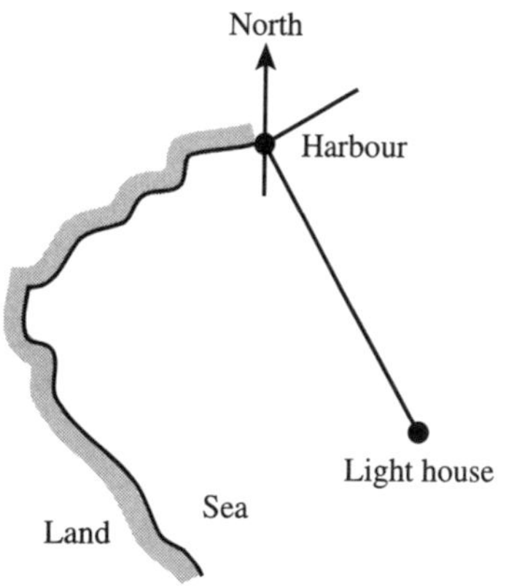

7. A farmer digs a drainage ditch across a rectangular field.
How long is the ditch, to the nearest metre?

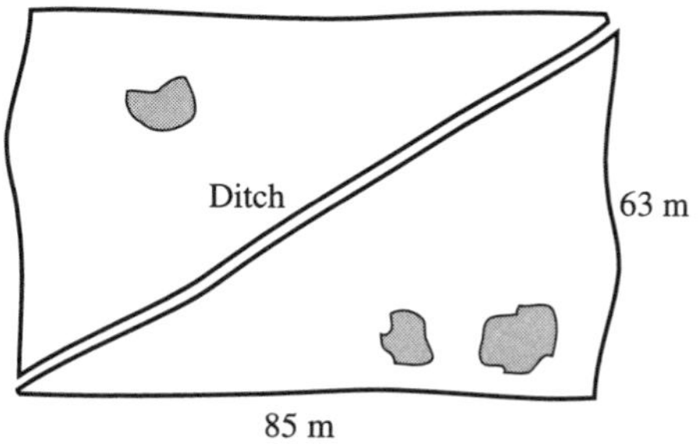

8. The square and the rectangle have the same perimeter. Which has the longer diagonal and by how much?

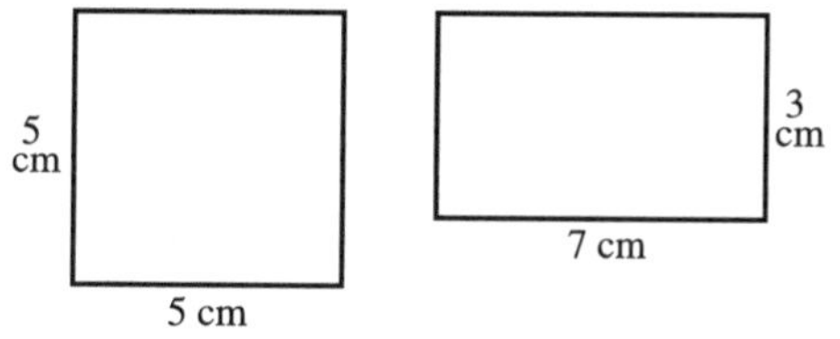

Exercise 2

Give answers correct to 2 d.p. where necessary. The units are cm unless you are told otherwise.

1. Find the side marked with a letter

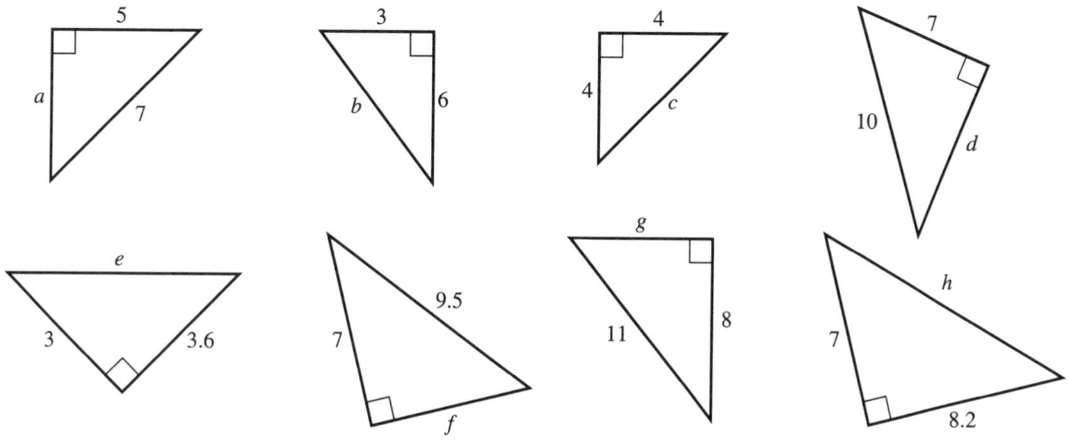

2. A ship sails 40 km due south and then a further 65 km due east. How far is the ship from its starting point?

3. A square has diagonals of length 24 cm. Find the length of a side of the square to the nearest cm.

4. What is the longest shot you could have to play on a snooker table measuring 12 feet by 6 feet?

5. Calculate the height of the isosceles triangle shown.

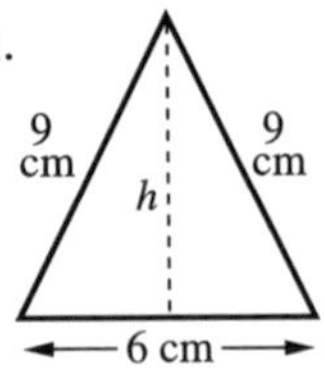

6. Calculate the vertical height and hence the area of an equilateral triangle of side 14 cm.

7. Calculate the length of a side of the largest square which can be drawn inside a circle of radius 10 cm.

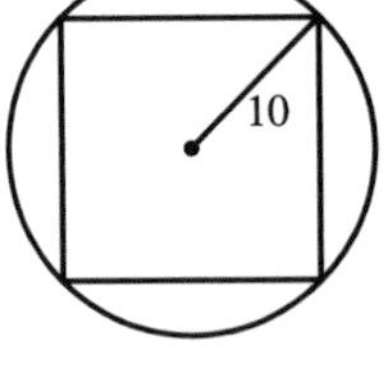

8. A car driver can take one of two routes from A to C:
Route 1. From A to B and then B to C. This route is along main roads and he travels at 50 mph. The angle between AB and BC is 90°.
Route 2. From A straight to C along a short cut. This is a minor road and he drives at only 30 mph.
(a) Which route takes the shorter length of time?
(b) By how much in hours is it shorter?

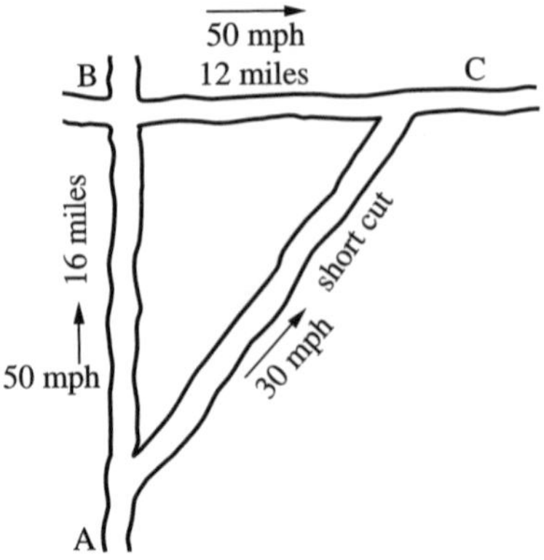

9. [More difficult] Find the length x

(a)

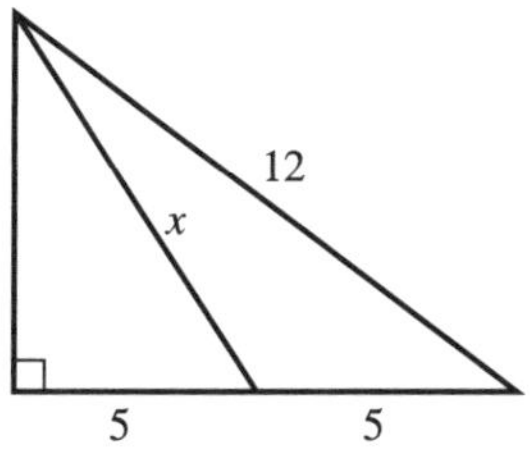

(b)

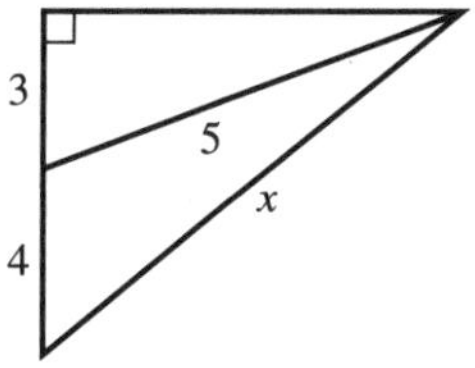

(c)

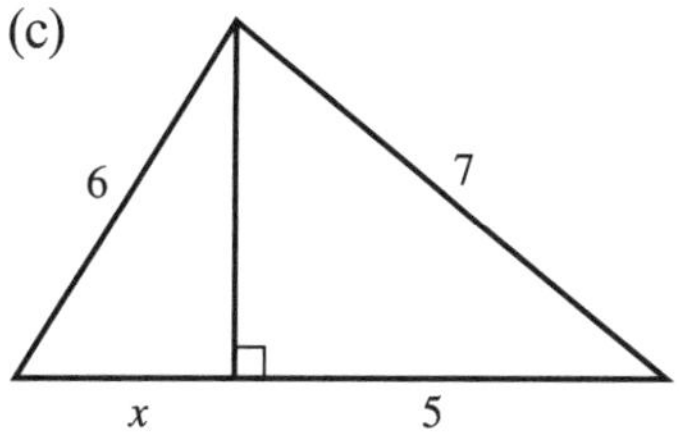

(d)

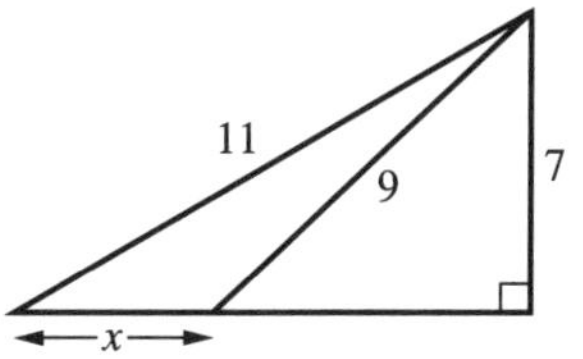

(e)

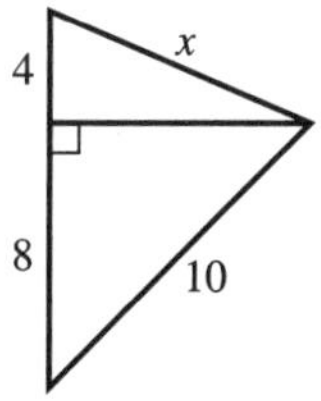

(f)

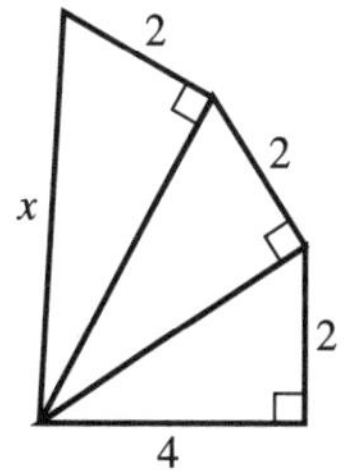

10. The diagonal of a square has length 5 cm. What is the area of the square (in cm^2)?

11. The diagram shows a rectangular box (a cuboid).
Calculate the length of
(a) AB
(b) AC
(c) AD. [Draw triangle ACD].

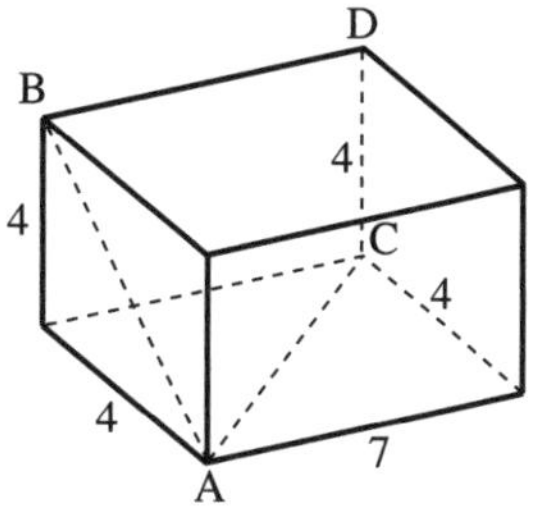

12. Calculate the length of the longest diagonal of a cube of side 10 cm.

13. The inside dimensions of a removal lorry are 2·5 m by 3 m by 4 m. A pole vaulter's pole is 5·7 m long. Will it fit inside the lorry?

14. The diagram shows water lying in a semi-circular channel. Calculate the maximum depth d of water in the channel.

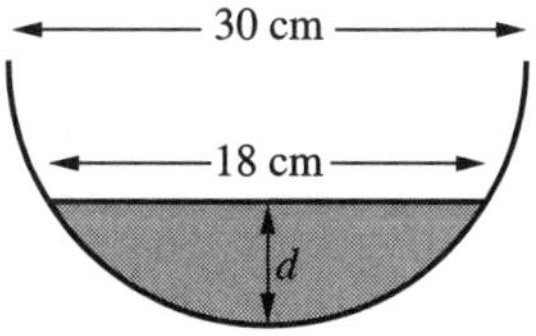

15. Calculate x and y.

(a)

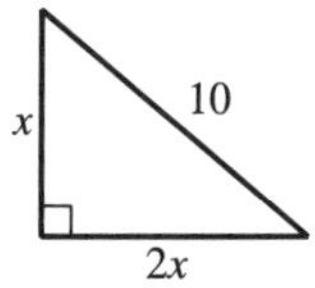

(b)

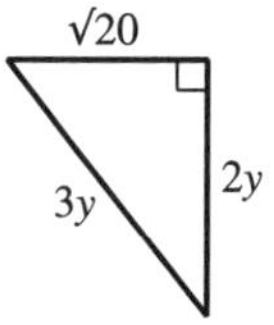

5.7 Mathematical reasoning

Break the codes

1. The ten symbols below each stand for one of the digits 0, 1, 2, 3, 4, 5, 6, 7, 8, 9 but not in that order.

   $\odot$ $\triangledown$ $\square$ $*$ $\uparrow$? $\ominus$ π $\mp$ I

   Use the clues below to work out what number each symbol stands for.

   (a) $* + * = ?$
   (b) $\triangledown \times \triangledown = \ominus$
   (c) $? + ? + ? = \odot$
   (d) $\square - * = \odot$
   (e) $\pi + \mathrm{I} = \ominus$
   (f) $\pi \times \uparrow = \uparrow$
   (g) $\mp - \mathrm{I} = \mathrm{I}$

2. The ten symbols used in part 1 are used again but with different values.
   The clues are more difficult to work out.

   (a) $\ominus + \mp = \mathrm{I}$
   (b) $\triangledown + \square = \mathrm{I}$
   (c) $\odot \times \square = \odot$
   (d) $\odot \times ? = ?$
   (e) $\pi \div \mp = \odot$
   (f) $\square + \square + \square + \square = \odot$
   (g) $\pi - \mp = \triangledown$
   (h) $* \times * = \uparrow$

3. Again the same ten symbols are used but with different values.

   (a) $\triangledown + \odot = \uparrow$
   (b) $\mp - \pi = *$
   (c) $\ominus \times \ominus \times \ominus = \square$
   (d) $* \times \uparrow = \uparrow$
   (e) $\square \div \triangledown = \ominus$
   (f) $\pi - \triangledown = *$
   (g) $? - \uparrow = \ominus$
   (h) $\odot \times \odot = ?$

Puzzles

1. The totals for the rows and columns are given. Find the values of the letters.

(a)

B	C	A	A	37
C	C	C	C	44
D	A	D	A	[redacted]
A	B	B	A	37
35	40	35	32	

(b)

T	S	T	R	T	27
P	Q	S	R	T	36
T	R	T	R	T	26
S	P	R	R	P	47
T	T	S	R	R	35
25	36	36	50	24	

2. Show how the cross can be cut along the broken lines and the pieces rearranged to make a square.

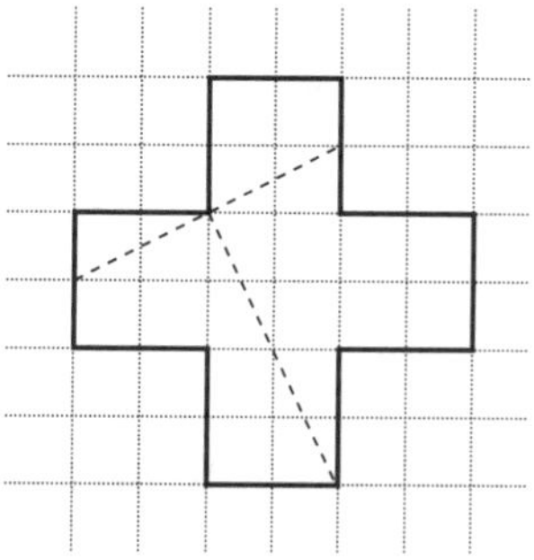

3 Fill in the space in words so that it is correct:
'*This sentence has ______ letters.*'

4. Replace the question marks with three mathematical symbols (+, −, ×, ÷) so that the calculation is correct.

(105 ? 7) ? 3 ? 7 = 38

5. For this multiplying box, there are five *outside* numbers [5, 7, 11, 2, 9] and
six *inside* numbers [10, 14, 22, 45, 63, 99].

	5	7	11
2	10	14	22
9	45	63	99

Draw a 4 × 3 box and position the seven outside numbers [26, 45, 11, 15, 9, 33, 22] and the twelve inside numbers [495, 99, 572, 135, 286, 990, 390, 495, 675, 363, 198, 726] so that the box works like the one above.

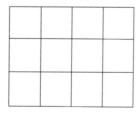

6. A lottery prize of £5555 was shared equally between a number of people so that each person received a whole number of pounds. There were between 20 and 100 people. How many people shared the prize and how much did each person receive?

7. A double-decker bus has just 10 seats. There are 5 seats in a line upstairs and 5 downstairs.

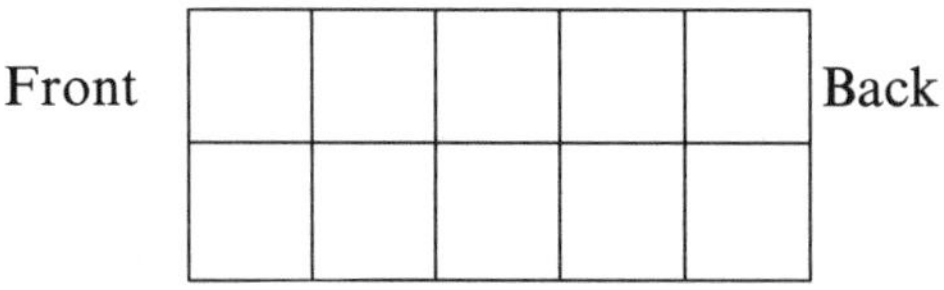

Dave is sitting directly below Karen and in front of eight people. Philip is sitting right at the back, directly above Neha. Lisa is directly in front of Greg and directly above Richard. Chris is just behind Jim and directly below Bob. Who is directly behind Karen?

8. The diagram on the right is the net of a cube made from cardboard.
Which of the six cubes below could not be made from this net?

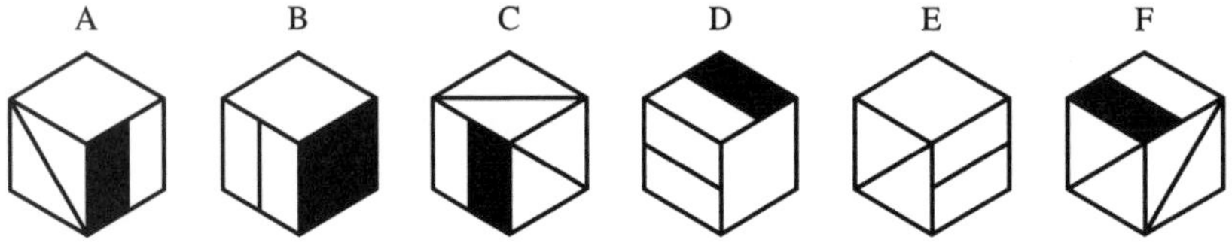

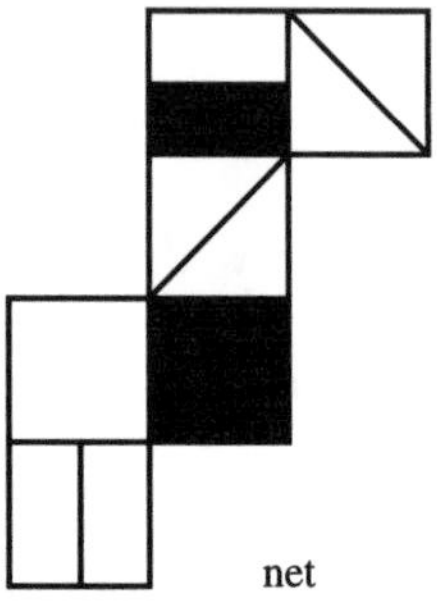

Perimeters and common edges: an investigation

In this work, one centimetre squares touch either along an edge or at a corner.

Shape A has 2 common edges, shown by the thick lines, and shape B has 3 common edges.

The perimeter of shape A is 12 cm and the perimeter of shape B is 10 cm.

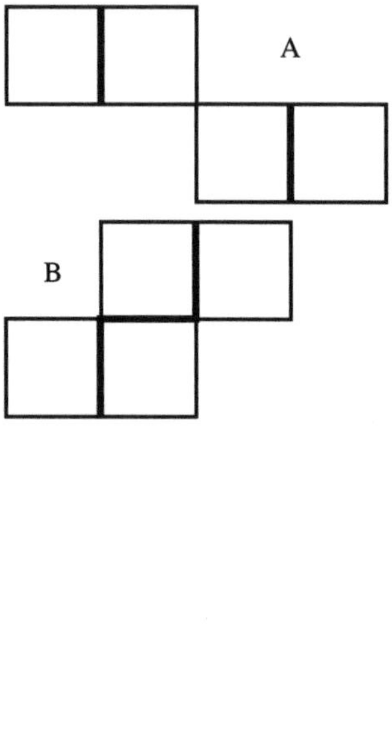

- Using four squares, draw a shape with 1 common edge ($c = 1$). Write down the perimeter, p cm.
  Is there more than one shape with one common edge? Do all shapes with one common edge have the same perimeter?
- Again using four squares, draw a shape with 4 common edges ($c = 4$). Write down the perimeter, p, of the shape.
- Draw shapes with $c = 2$, $c = 3$, $c = 0$ and each time write down the perimeter.
- Try to find a connection between c and p. Either write the connection in words or as a formula, '$p = \ldots$'.

Five squares or more

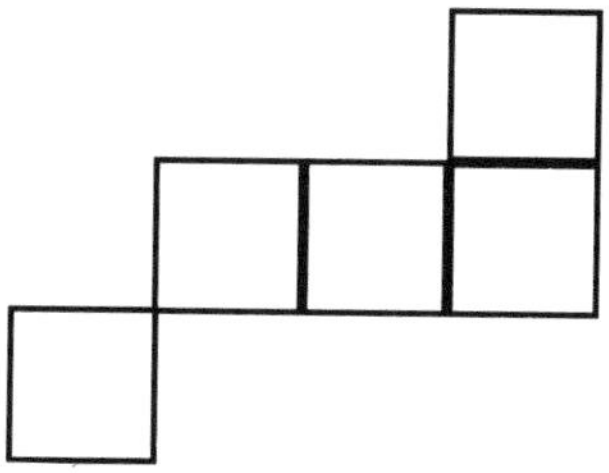

- Draw several shapes with 5 squares with $c = 0, 1, 2 \ldots.$
  Find a formula connecting c and p. [Write $p = \ldots$]
- Now draw diagrams with 6 squares and again find a formula connecting c and p.
- Look at your formulas for shapes with 4, 5 and 6 squares. *Predict*, without drawing any more shapes, what the formula might be for 7 squares.
- Now draw several shapes with 7 squares, count c and p for each one, and check if the formula you predicted *does* work.
- Now go further. Predict a formula for shapes with 10 squares or 100 squares.
  The most *general* case is the shape consisting of n squares, where n is any whole number (greater than 1).
  Try to write a formula connecting c, p and n.

Extension

- Equilateral triangles can be drawn on isometric paper.
  For shape X, $c = 2$ and $p = 8$.
  For shape Y, $c = 1$ and $p = 10$.
- Find a formula connecting p and c for shapes with 4 triangles.

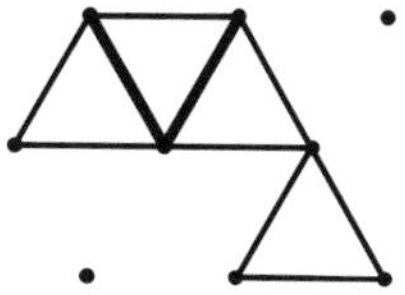

X

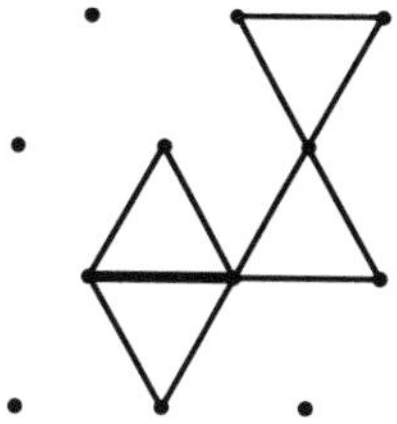

Y

- Work methodically and try to find a formula for shapes with *any* number of triangles.

Further extension

- *Without* drawing any shapes, try to predict a formula, connecting p and c, for 3 hexagons.
- Draw shapes with 3 hexagons and check if your formula works.

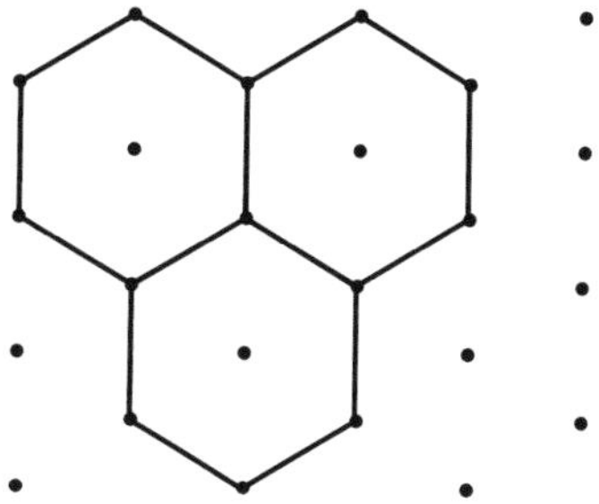

Logic problems

- In logic problems we often have to look at what has changed, and what has stayed the same, in order to help us solve them. There is no, straight forward method which works for each one. Sometimes trial and error is a useful starting point.

(a)

(b)

(c)

○ = How many △'s?

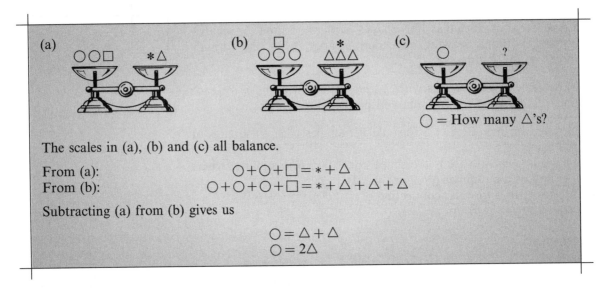

The scales in (a), (b) and (c) all balance.

From (a): ○+○+□ = * + △

From (b): ○+○+○+□ = * + △ + △ + △

Subtracting (a) from (b) gives us

○ = △ + △

○ = 2△

Solve these loigic problems.

1. (a)

(b)

(c)

* * * = How many □'s?

2. (a)

(b)

(c)

* = How many □'s?

3. (a) △□ = * * *
(b) □ = *
(c) △△ = How many *'s?

4. (a) △△○ = □*
(b) ○△△△ = □* **
(c) △ = How many *'s?

5. (a) □ = △△
(b) ∗ = □○
(c) ○ = □△△
(d) ∗ = How many △'s?

6. (a) ∗ = △○○
(b) □ = ○○○
(c) ∗○ = □△△
(d) ○○ = How many △'s?

7. (a) ∗□ = △○
(b) □□ = △
(c) □ = ○○
(d) ∗ = How many ○'s?

8. (a) △△ = □○
(b) □△ = ∗
(c) △○ = ∗□
(d) △△△△ = How many □'s?

Questions **9** to **12** are difficult.

9. (a) ∗□ = ○○
(b) □△ = ○
(c) ∗○ = □□□□
(d) □□ = How many △'s?

10. (a) ∗ = △○
(b) △ = ○□□
(c) ∗○ = △△□
(d) ○ = How many □'s?

11. (a) ○○□ = ∗○
(b) ∗∗ = ○○○
(c) □∗ = ○○
(d) ∗ = How many □'s?

12. (a) ∗△ = □
(b) ∗ = △○
(c) ∗∗△ = □○○
(d) △ = How many ○'s?

Diagonals

Look at the squares below.

4×4

1			8
	2	7	
	6	3	
5			4

8 squares along the diagonals

5×5

1				9
	2		8	
		3		
	7		4	
6				5

9 squares along the diagonals

6×6

1					12
	2			11	
		3	10		
		9	4		
	8			5	
7					6

12 squares along the diagonals

(a) Draw a similar diagram for a 7×7 square and count the squares along the two diagonals.
(b) How many squares are there along the diagonals of
(i) a 10×10 square? (ii) a 15×15 square?
(c) A square wall is covered with square tiles. There are 33 tiles altogether long the two diagonals. How many tiles are there on the whole wall?
(d) Another square wall has 40 tile altogether along the two diagonals. How many tiles are there on the whole wall?
(e) A square wall is covered by 900 square tiles. How many tiles are there along the two diagonals?

How many dots?: an investigation

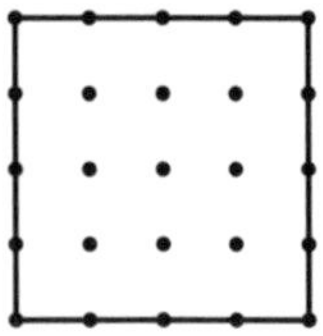

1. The diagram shows a 5 × 5 square of dots.
   There are 16 dots on the perimeter
   and 9 dots inside the square.
   (a) Draw a 3 × 3, a 4 × 4 and a 6 × 6 square of dots. For each diagram, count the number of dots on the perimeter and the number of dots inside the square.
   (b) For a 100 × 100 square of dots, how many dots are on the perimeter?
   (c) For a 57 × 57 square of dots, how many dots are inside the square?

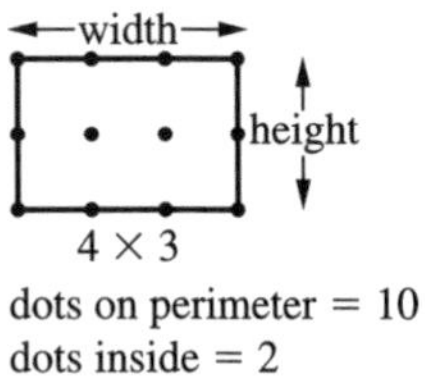

2. Rectangles are drawn so that the width is always 1 unit more than the height. The number of dots on the perimeter and the number of dots inside the rectangle are counted.
   (a) How many dots are on the perimeter of a 101 × 100 rectangle?
   (b) How many dots are inside a 9 × 8 rectangle?
   (c) (Much harder) How many dots are inside a 52 × 51 rectangle?

Around and around: an investigation

- Using a calculator, go around the flow diagram several times.
  What do you notice about the numbers you write down?
  Does it change if you start with a different number?

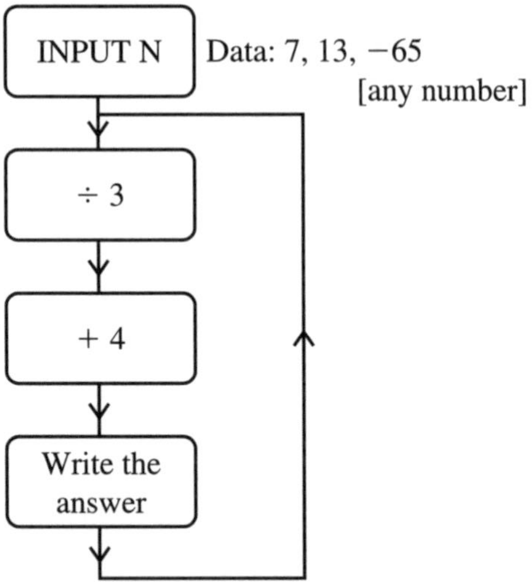

- Using a calculator, go around the diagram several times (say 20 or 30 times).
  Write down what you notice.
  Is there a connection between the input number N and the numbers you write down?
  [The data can be any positive number.]

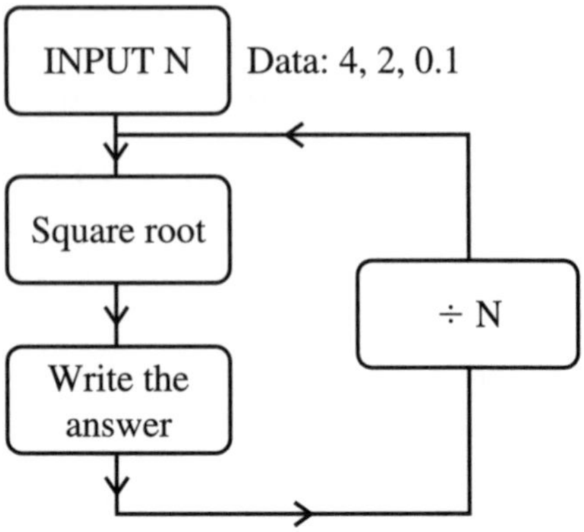

Finding areas by counting dots

- Shapes can be drawn on dotty paper, with vertices on dots.

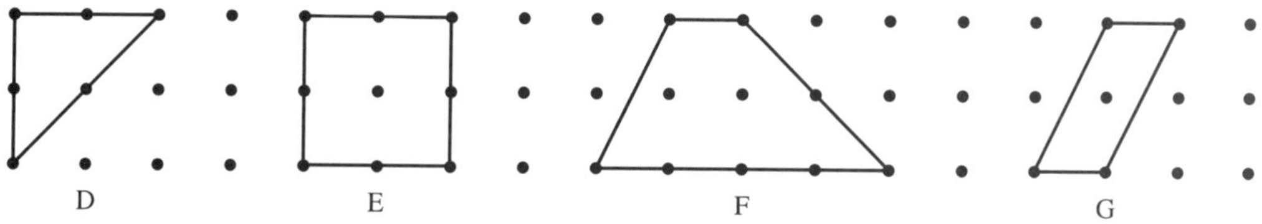

Triangle D has 6 dots on its perimeter. For short, we will write $p = 6$.
Square E has 8 dots on its perimeter and 1 dot inside. We will write $p = 8$, $i = 1$.
Write down the values of p and i for shapes F and G.

- Is there a connection between the values for p, i and the *area* A for each shape?
Here are some of the areas:
For shape D: $p = 6$, $i = 0$, $A = 2$. (area is in square units)
For shape E: $p = 8$, $i = 1$, $A = 4$.
For shape F: $p = 8$, $i = 2$, $A = 5$.
For shape G: $p = 4$, $i = 1$, $A = 2$.
It is certainly not easy to see a connection or a formula that works for all the shapes.

- Make the problem simpler.
When you have a complicated problem it is often helpful to make it simpler.
We will start by drawing shapes with no dots inside [$i = 0$].

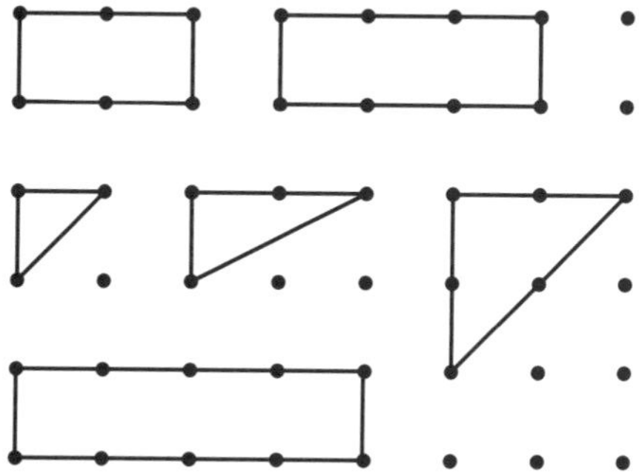

Record the values for p and A in a table:

p	A
6	2
8	3
10	
3	
5	

Try to find a connection between p and A.
Write it in the form 'A = ...'.

- Now draw shapes with one or more dots inside. Record the values for p, i and A in a new table. Try to find a connection between p, i and A.
  Write it in the form 'A = …'.

p	i	A
8	1	4
10	2	6
4	1	
5	3	

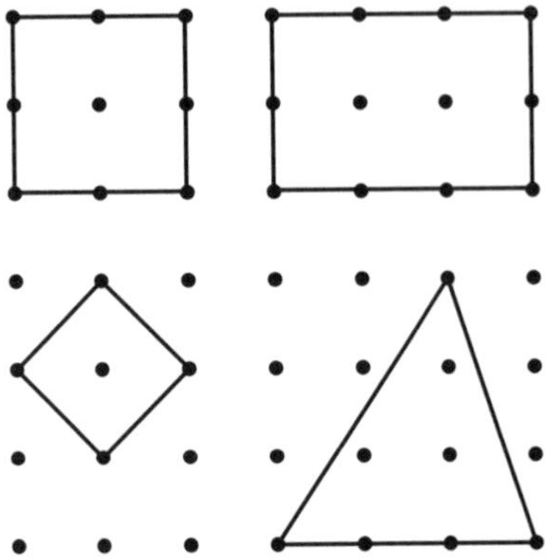

- Predictions
  If you think you have a formula for A, in terms of p and i, use it to predict the area of each of the shapes below.

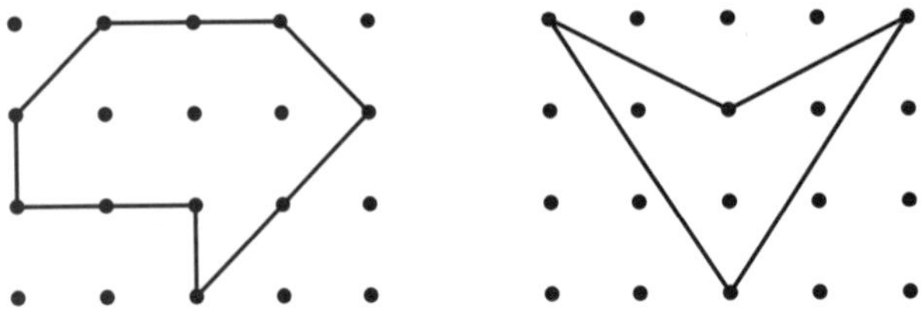

Check by calculating the areas by 'traditional' methods.

Part 6

6.1 Probability

Events occurring or not occurring

- If the probability of an event occurring is p, then the probability of it not occurring is $1 - p$.
- Ten identical discs numbered 1, 2, 3, 4, 5, 6, 7, 8, 9, 10 are put into a bag. One disc is selected at random.

  In this example there are 10 possible equally likely outcomes of a trial.

  (a) The probability of selecting a '2' $= \frac{1}{10}$

  This may be written p(selecting a '2') $= \frac{1}{10}$

  (b) p (not selecting a 2) $= 1 - \frac{1}{10}$

  $= \frac{9}{10}$

  (c) p (selecting a number greater than 7) $= \frac{3}{10}$

  (d) p (not selecting a number greater than 7) $= 1 - \frac{3}{10} = \frac{7}{10}$

Exercise 1

1. One card is picked at random from a pack of 52.
Find the probability that it is
(a) a diamond (b) not a diamond
(c) the King of hearts (d) not the King of hearts

2. A South Seas diver collected 965 oysters.
Just one of the oysters contained a pearl.
One oyster is chosen at random. Find the probability that
(a) it contains a pearl
(b) it does not contain a pearl.

3. Mo puts these numbered balls in a bag.
   (a) He shakes the bag and takes one ball without looking. What is the probability of getting a '2'?
   (b) Mo wants to put more balls in the bag so that the chance of getting a '4' is *twice* the chance of getting a '3'. What balls could he put in the bag?

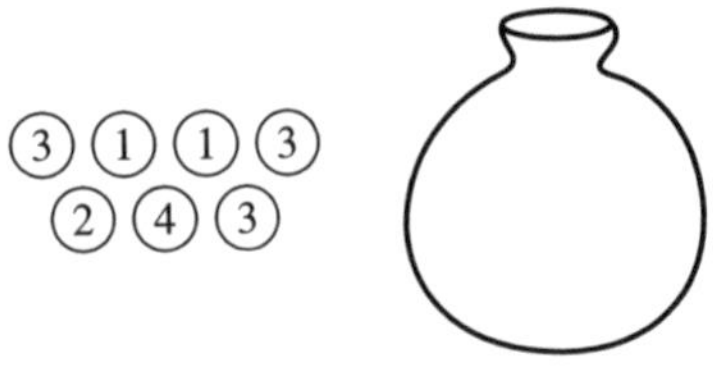

4. A dice has its faces numbered 2, 3, 3, 3, 4, 7.
   Find the probability of rolling
   (a) a '7'
   (b) an even number.

5. One card is selected at random from the nine cards shown.

   Find the probability of selecting
   (a) the ace of diamonds (b) a king
   (c) an ace (d) a red card

6. If Mala throws a 3 or a 5 on her next throw when playing 'Snakes and Ladders' she will slide down a snake on the board. What is the probability that she will avoid a snake on her next throw?

7. The 26 letters of the alphabet are written on discs. The five discs with vowels are put in bag A and the other discs are put in bag B. Find the probability of selecting
   (a) an 'o' from bag A
   (b) a 'z' from bag B
   (c) a 'w' from bag A

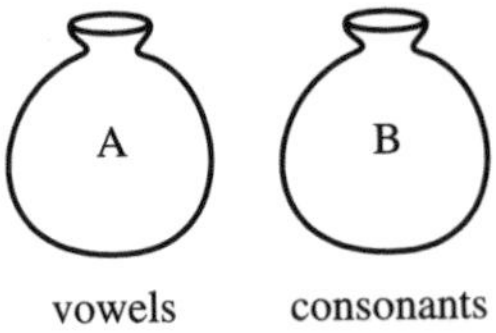

8. A shopkeeper is keen to sell his stock of left-handed scissors. He has read that 9% of the population is left-handed. What is the probability that the next person to enter his shop is right-handed?

9. A field contains 10 cows, 5 horses and 1 lion. The lion is thought to be tame and half of the cows are mad. One animal is chosen at random. Find the probability that the animal:
   (a) is mad
   (b) enjoys eating grass
   (c) might eat you.

10. Nicole has 3 kings and 1 ace. She shuffles the cards and takes one without looking.

Nicole asks two of her friends about the probability of getting an ace

Angie says:
'It is $\frac{1}{3}$ because there are 3 kings and 1 ace.'

Syline says
'It is $\frac{1}{4}$ because there are 4 cards and only 1 ace.'

Which of her friends is right?

11. A bag contains the balls shown. One ball is taken out at random. Find the probability that it is
(a) red (b) not red (c) blue
One more red ball and one more blue ball are added to the bag.
(d) Find the new probability of selecting a red ball from the bag.

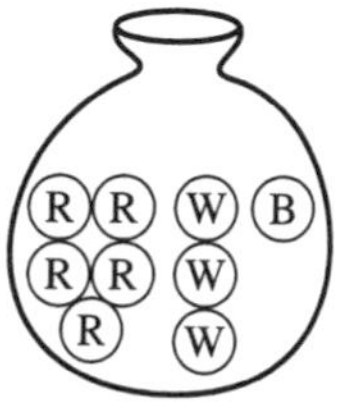

R = red
W = white
B = blue

12. A fair dice is rolled 480 times. How many times would you expect to roll:
(a) a 'two'
(b) an odd number?

13. A spinner, with 12 equal sectors, is spun 600 times. How often would you expect to spin:
(a) a shaded sector
(b) an even number
(c) a vowel
(d) a prime number?
[a prime number is divisible only by itself and by one]

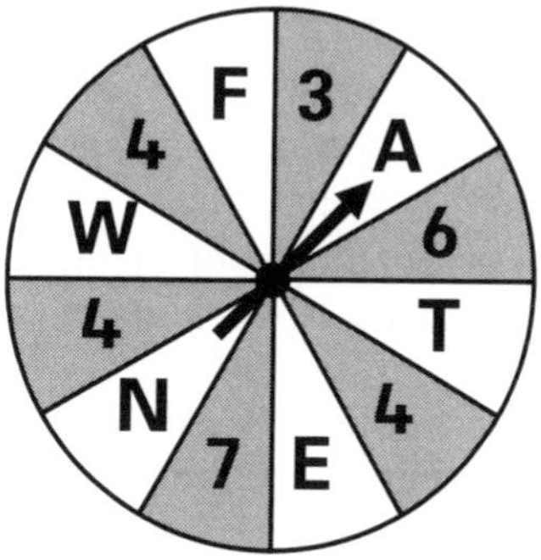

14. A coin is biased so that the probability of tossing a 'head' is 0·58.
(a) How many 'heads' would you expect when the coin is tossed 200 times?
(b) How many 'tails' would you expect when the coin is tossed 1000 times?

Exercise 2 (More difficult)

1. Each of the 11 letters of the word 'CALCULATION' was written on a small card. One card was selected at random. Find the probability that the letter drawn was
(a) a 'T'
(b) an 'A'

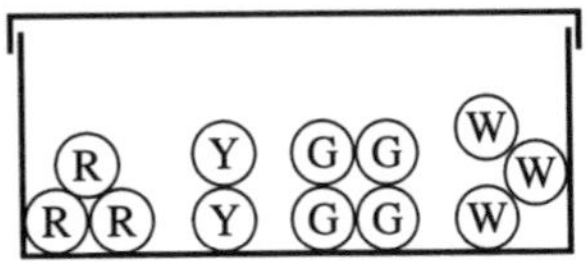

2. A box contains 12 balls: 3 red, 2 yellow, 4 green and 3 white.
(a) Find the probability of selecting
(i) a red ball
(ii) a yellow ball
(b) The 3 white balls are replaced by 3 yellow balls. Find the probability of selecting
(i) a red ball
(ii) a yellow ball.

3. A pack of cards is split into two piles. Pile P contains all the picture cards and aces and pile O contains all the other cards.

(a) Find the probability of selecting
(i) the Jack of hearts from pile P
(ii) a seven from pile O
(b) All the diamonds are now removed from both piles. Find the probability of selecting
(i) the King of clubs from pile P
(ii) a red card from pile O.

4. (a) Steve has taken a number of cards at random from a pack. The probability of picking a red card from Steve's cards is $\frac{3}{5}$. What is the probability of picking a black card?
(b) How many cards of each colour *could* there be in Steve's cards?
(c) Write down another possibility for the number of cards of each colour that are in Steve's cards.

5. One person is selected at random from the crowd of 14 750 watching a tennis match at Wimbledon. What is the probability that the person chosen will have his or her birthday that year on a Sunday?

6. One ball is selected at random from a bag containing x red balls and y white balls. What is the probability of selecting a red ball?

7. Helen played a game of cards with Michelle. The cards were dealt so that both players received two cards. Helen's cards were a seven and a four. Michelle's first card was a 10.

Find the probability that Michelle's second card was
(a) a picture card [a King, Queen or Jack]
(b) a seven.

8. A dice has its six faces marked
0p, 0p, 0p, 0p, 5p, 20p.
In a game at a school fair players pay 5p to roll the dice and they win the amount shown on the dice.

During the afternoon the game is played 540 times.
(a) How much money would be paid by the people playing the game?
(b) How many times would you expect the dice to show '20p'?
(c) How many times would you expect the dice to show '5p'?
(d) How much profit or loss would you expect the stall to make?

9. At another stall at the fair players pay 20p to spin the pointer on the board shown. Players win the amount shown by the pointer.

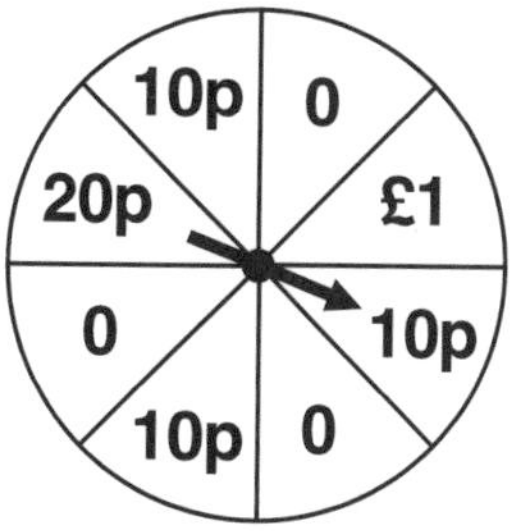

The game is played 800 times.

Work out the expected profit or loss on this game.

Listing possible outcomes: two events

- When a 10p coin and a 20p coin are tossed together there are four possible outcomes. So, for example, the probability of tossing two tails $= \frac{1}{4}$.

10p	20p
head	head
head	tail
tail	head
tail	tail

- Suppose a red dice and a blue dice are rolled together. This time there are *many* possible outcomes. With the red dice first the outcomes can be listed systematically:

(1, 1) (1, 2) (1, 3) (1, 4) (1, 5) (1, 6)
(2, 1) (2, 2) (2, 3) (2, 4) (2, 5) (2, 6)
(3, 1) (3, 2) , , , ,
, , , , , ,
, , , , , ,
, , , , (6, 5) (6, 6)

There are 36 equally likely outcomes

- A neat way of listing the outcomes is on a grid.

This is called a sample space

The point marked • shows a four on the red dice and a five on the blue dice.

The probability of rolling a four on the red dice and a five on the blue dice is $\frac{1}{36}$.

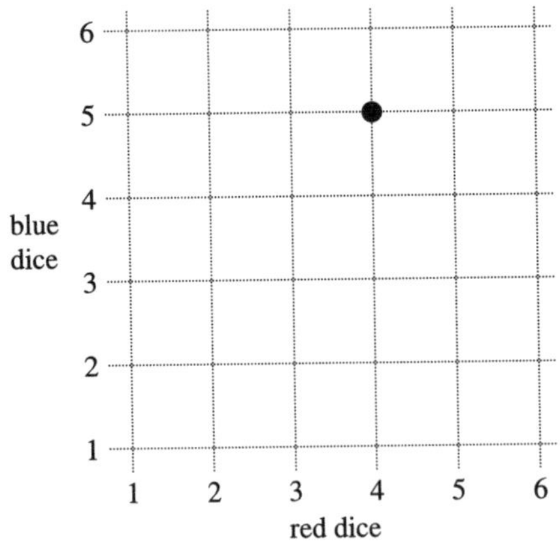

Exercise 3

1. Roll a pair of dice many times and in a tally chart record the frequency of obtaining the totals from 2 to 12.

Total	Frequency
2	
3	
⋮	
12	

2. (a) Work out the expected probability of getting a total of 5 when two dice are rolled together.
Compare your answer with the experimental probability of getting a total of 5 obtained in the experiment in Question **1**.
(b) Work out the expected probability of other totals and compare them with the experimental results.

3. A red dice is thrown first and then a blue dice is thrown.
(a) Find the probability that the score on the blue dice is the same as the score on the red dice.
(b) Find the probability that the score on the blue dice is one more than the score on the red dice.

4. Two dice are rolled together and the *difference* is found.
In the grid the point X has a difference of 3 obtained by rolling a 2 and a 5.

Find the expected probability of obtaining a difference of (a) 3
(b) 0

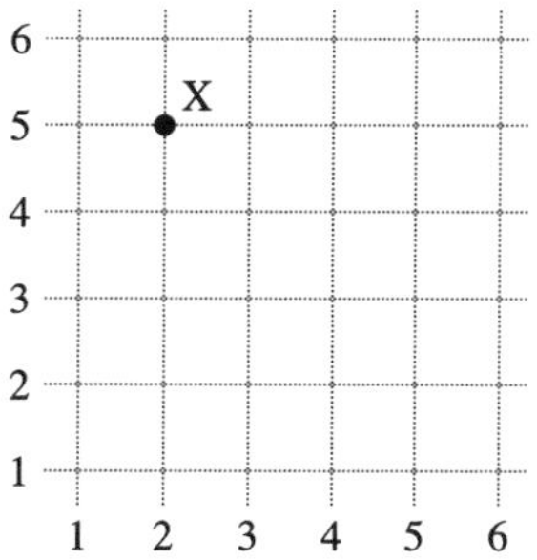

5. The spinner shown has six equal sections on the outside and three equal sections in the middle. The spinner shows a '5' and an 'A'.

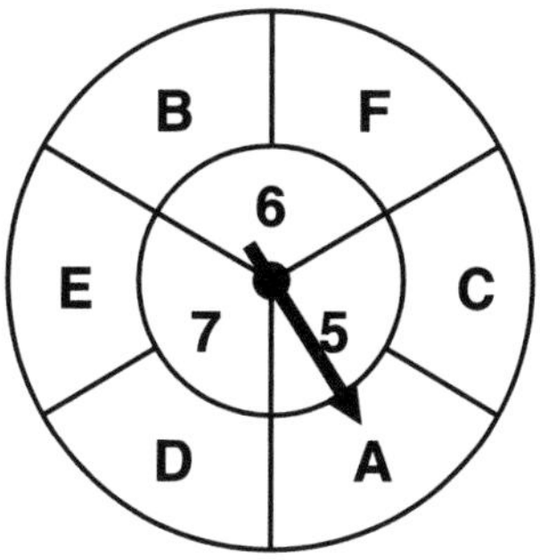

Find the probability of spinning
(a) a 'C'
(b) a '7'
(c) a '6' and an 'F' at the same time

6. A bag contains a 1p coin, a 10p coin and a 20p coin. Two coins are selected at random.
(a) List all the possible combinations of two coins which can be selected from the bag.
(b) Find the probability that the total value of the two coins selected is
(i) 11p
(ii) 30p

7. The four cards shown are shuffled and placed face down on a table.

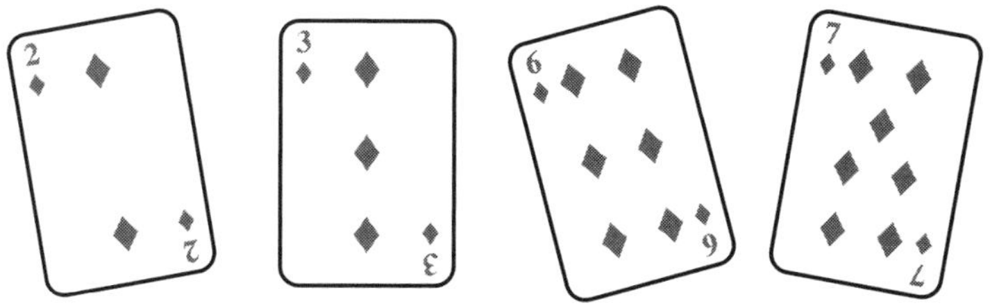

Two cards are selected at random.
(a) List all the possible pairs of cards which could be selected.
(b) Find the probability that the total of the two cards is
(i) 5
(ii) 9

8. Two spinners, with equal sectors, are numbered 0, 1, 2, ... 9. The two spinners are spun together and the difference between the scores is recorded. So a '5' and a '9' gives a difference of 4.

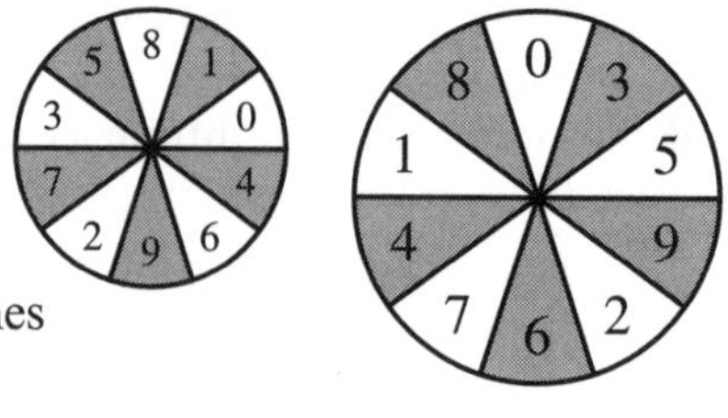

(a) Draw a grid to show all the possible outcomes and write the difference for each outcome.
(b) Find the probability of obtaining
(i) a difference of 4 (ii) a difference of 9
(c) What is the most likely number for the difference?

Experiment: Calculator simulation of two spinners

We can simulate two 10-sided spinners by using the RAN# button on a calculator.

When the RAN# button is pressed (possibly after 'SHIFT') the display shows a *random* 3 digit decimal number between 0·000 and 0·999.

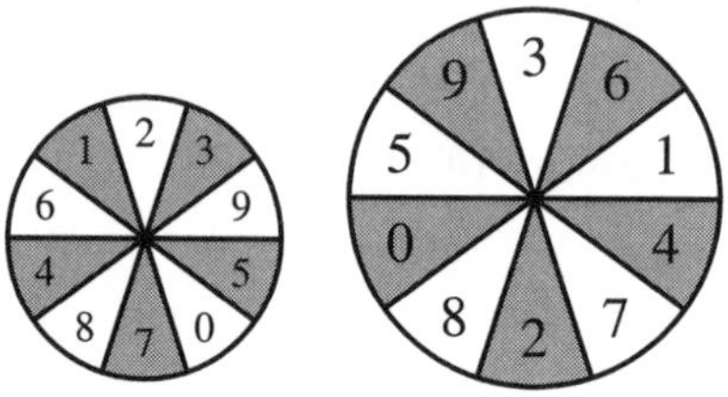

We can ignore the first digit after the point and use the last 2 digits to represent imaginary random scores on two spinners.

E.g. 0·~~0~~27 shows a '2' and a '7'
↑
ignore

0·~~8~~13 shows a '1' and a '3'

In question **8** of the last exercise you calculated the theoretical probability of getting a difference of 4 and a difference of 9, using two 10-sided spinners.

You can now use a calculator to see how closely the experimental results agree with the predicted results.

(a) Make a tally chart, recording the difference in the last two digits for every number you get using the RAN# button. Perform about 100 or 200 trials.

Difference	Tally
0	
1	
2	
⋮	
9	

(b) Collect together the results for the whole class. [Pass a sheet around the class].
(c) Work out the totals for each difference and also the total number of trials.
(d) Find the experimental probability of getting a difference of 4.
Find the experimental probability of getting a difference of 9.
(e) Compare your experimental results with the results you predicted in question **8** of the last exercise.

Experimental probability

Exercise 4

1. A bag contained coloured balls. Rajiv randomly selects a ball from the bag and then replaces it. Here are the results.

Colour	White	Green	Blue
Frequency	10	31	19

Estimate the probability that on his next draw he will select
(a) a white ball (b) a green ball.

2. Dimpna and Jenny both did the 'dropping a drawing pin' experiment. Here are their results.

Dimpna

Trials	20
'Point up'	10

Jenny

Trials	150
'Point up'	61

Another drawing pin is dropped.
(a) For Dimpna, what is the probability of getting 'point up'?
(b) For Jenny, what is the probability of getting 'point up'?
(c) Whose result is likely to be more reliable? Why?

3. Sean collected the results of 40 Liverpool home games. Estimate the probability that in their next home game:
(a) they will win
(b) they will lose.

Won	18
Lost	10
Drawn	12

For Liverpool's next 40 games, the results were:

Won	23
Lost	11
Drawn	6

Using all 80 results, estimate the probability of
(c) winning their next game.
(d) drawing their next game.

Would you expect these probabilities to be more accurate than those based on the first 40 matches? Why?

4. Roll a fair dice 60 times. How many 'ones' would you expect to roll?
Compare your experimental result with the theoretical one.

Suppose you do the experiment again (i.e. roll the dice another 60 times.)
Would you expect to get the same result?

6.2 Percentages

(a) Work out 16% of £15.

16% of £15

$= \frac{16}{100} \times \frac{15}{1}$

= £2·40

(b) Work out 14% of £260.
(Quick way)
14% = 0·14 as a decimal

So 14% of £260 = 0·14 × 260

= £36·40

(c) Work out, to the nearest penny:
8% of £11·99

$= \frac{8}{100} \times \frac{11.99}{1}$

= 0·9592

= £0·96, to the nearest penny

(d) Work out, to the nearest penny:
(Quick way)
21% of £6·92

= 0·21 × 6·92

= 1·4532

= £1·45, to the nearest penny

Exercise 1

Work out.

1. 12% of £600 **2.** 6% of £250 **3.** 81% of £9

4. 8% of £450 **5.** 7% of £440 **6.** 43% of £185

7. 5% of £22 **8.** 4% of £660 **9.** 8% of £2555

10. 85% of £400 **11.** 6·5% of £200 **12.** 7% of £6

13. 29% of £2000 **14.** 4·5% of £400 **15.** 17% of £175

16. The number of children having school dinners is 640. When chips are not on the menu the number goes down by 5%. How many fewer children have school dinners?

17. In a restaurant a service charge of 10% is added to the price of a meal. What is the service charge on a meal costing £28·50?

In Questions **18** to **32** give the answer correct to the nearest penny.

18. 13% of £2·13 **19.** 27% of £5·85 **20.** 15·1% of £7·87

21. 11% of £6·27 **22.** 13% of £6·17 **23.** 16% of £0·87

24. 37% of £5·20 **25.** 15% of £11·23 **26.** 4% of £0·65

27. 6·2% of £8·55 **28.** 31% of £35·04 **29.** 78% of £3·17

30. 8·9% of £17·10 **31.** 6·8% of £16·10 **32.** 23% of £18·05

33. At a garage 140 cars were given a safety test and 65% of the cars passed the test.
    (a) How many passed the test?
    (b) How many failed the test?

34. Of the 980 children at a school 45% cycle to school, 15% go by bus and the rest walk.
    (a) How many cycle to school?
    (b) How many walk to school?

35. A lottery prize of £65 000 is divided between Steve, Pete and Phil so that Steve receives 22%, Pete receives 32% and Phil the rest. How much money does Phil receive?

Percentage increase or decrease

At the end of the year the price of a car is increased from £9640 by 4%. What is the new price?

4% of £9640

$= \frac{4}{100} \times \frac{9640}{1}$

$= £385{\cdot}60$

; New price of car $= £9640 + £385{\cdot}60$
$= £10025{\cdot}60$

Exercise 2

1. The price of a painting was £6400 but it is increased by 6%. What is the new price?

2. In a closing-down sale, a shop reduces all its prices by 20%. Find the sale price of a jacket which previously cost £60.

3. The petrol consumption of a car is 35 miles per gallon. After a service the car does 6% more miles per gallon. What is the new consumption?

4. A dog normally weighs 28 kg. After being put on a diet for three months its weight is reduced by 35%. How much does it weigh now?

5. The length of a new washing line is 21 m. After being used it stretches by 3%. Find the new length.

6. A shop increases all its prices by 4%. What are the new prices of the items below?

£15

£49·50

7. A marathon runner weighs 55 kg at the start of a race. During the race his weight is reduced by 4%. How much does he weigh at the end of the race?

8. A hen weighs 2·7 kg. After laying an egg her weight is reduced by 1%. How much does she weigh now?

9. A mouse weighs 630 g. While escaping from a cat it loses its tail and its weight is reduced by 4%. How much does it weigh now?

10. A holiday costs £620. After a 12% increase the new price is 112% of £620. The 'quick' way to work this out is as follows:

$$\begin{aligned}\text{New price} &= 112\% \text{ of } £620\\ &= 1{\cdot}12 \times 620\\ &= £694{\cdot}40\end{aligned}$$

Use this quick method to find the new price of a boat costing £560, when the price is increased by 8%.

11. Copy and complete:
(a) To increase £400 by 6%, work out $1{\cdot}\square\square \times 400$.
(b) To reduce £720 by 15%, work out $0{\cdot}85 \times \square$.

12. Increase a price of £80 by 4%

13. Increase a price of £250 by 4%

14. Increase a price of £400 by 8%

15. Increase a price of £16 by 1%

16. Reduce a price of £3000 by 7%

17. Increase a price of £90 by 23%

18. Increase a price of £85 by 20%

19. Reduce a price of £8000 by 2·5%

20. Increase a price of £6500 by 2%

21. Reduce a price of £23 by 5·7%

22. A price of £650 is increased by 11% and then, a week later, it is increased by a further 8%. Find the final price.

6.3 Statistical problems

In general problems that can be answered by statistical methods are complicated! At the start you need to think carefully about questions which may be related.
It is helpful to go through the following procedure.

A Discuss the problem. Identify related questions

B Decide which data to collect

C Decide how to collect the data

D Present the data.

A Discuss the problem. Here is an example.

'Do parents watch more TV than their children?'

What counts as 'active TV watching'?
Does it count if you are just in the room?
If you conduct a survey, how can you make sure the data is accurate?
Can people remember accurately what they watched 24 hours ago?
Are people going to answer honestly?
Suppose one or both parents arrive home late every day. How would this affect the survey?
What about watching videos?

B Which data to collect.

For different problems you might obtain data from:
- a questionnaire or survey of a sample of people.
- secondary sources like newspapers, reference books, websites or historical records.

You should realise that data which you collect might be time consuming. On the other hand, you can decide exactly what questions to ask and to whom you ask them.

Realise also that a small sample may not accurately represent a large group.

Is a sample of 10 enough to represent a year group of 180?
Perhaps you should join with others to make a group effort.

C How to collect the data.

- You need to design a data collection sheet or questionnaire like those below.

data collection sheet

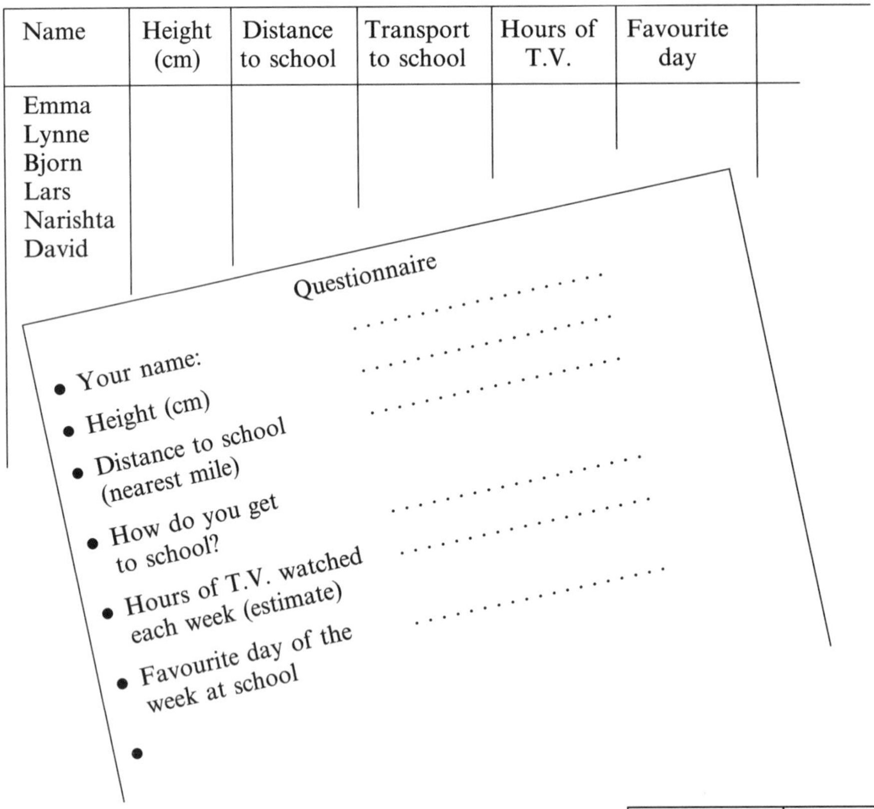
Name
Height (cm)
Distance to school
Transport to school
Hours of T.V.
Favourite day
Emma
Lynne
Bjorn
Lars
Narishta
David
Questionnaire
• Your name:
• Height (cm)
• Distance to school (nearest mile)
• How do you get to school?
• Hours of T.V. watched each week (estimate)
• Favourite day of the week at school
•

- For continuous data (like heights) you could use a frequency table. You might also use a two-way table.

height	frequency
151–160	11
161–170	8
171–180	5

D Present the data.

- Remember 'A picture paints a thousand words.' Use bar charts, pie charts, scatter graphs ......

Suppose you get 20 different answers to the question: 'What is your favourite T.V. program?'
A bar chart with a bar for each program will look very dull! You could try putting the programs into groups like 'comedy', 'soaps', 'sports', 'drama' etc. The choice is yours.

- Write a short report, interpreting results and write a clear *conclusion* to say what you found.

Collecting your own data

- For many people the most interesting data is the data *they* decide to find because it is what interests *them*. Below are some suggestions for the sort of problem you could attempt.

1. Are you more accurate at throwing with your writing hand than with your other hand?

Class activity: Each person throws a screwed-up ball of paper into a rubbish bin from a fixed distance. Throw five with each hand and collect results for the whole class.

On target	Writing hand	Other hand
0		
1		
2		
3		
4		
5		

2. Are absences from school equally likely on any day of the week?
Are Mondays and Fridays more frequent than other days for absences?
Are days when PE is taught more often chosen?
Do year 11 pupils take more days off school than year 7 pupils?

Where could information be obtained to answer these questions?

3. 'More babies are born in the spring than at any other time of year.'
What exactly do we mean by 'the spring'?

Investigate your year group to see if this is a true statement for your generation.

4.

Test the following theory:
'To find a child's potential height take the mean height of the parents, then add 8 cm for a boy and subtract 8 cm for a girl.'
What would be a suitable age group on which to test this theory? Collect data and draw two separate scatter graphs. Plot the mean height of parents on the horizontal axis and height of son or daughter on the vertical axis.

6.4 3-D Objects

A drawing of a solid is a 2-D representation of a 3-D object. Below are two pictures of the same object.
(a) On squared paper. (b) On isometric dot paper.

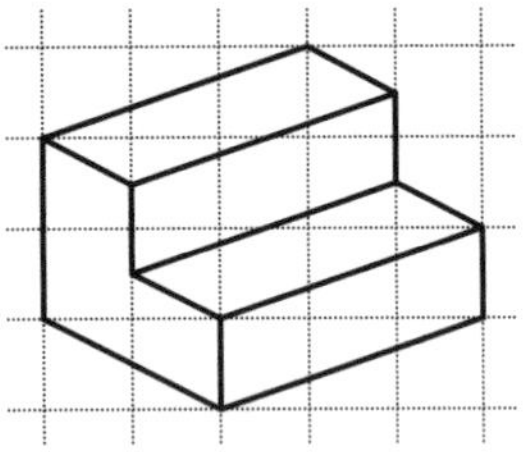

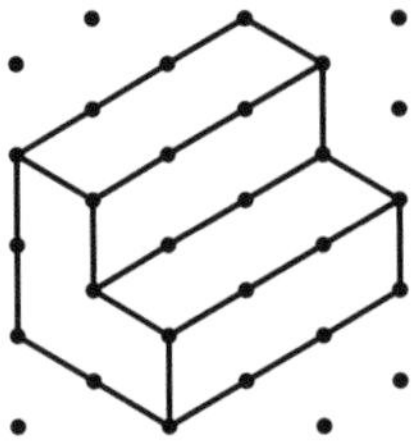

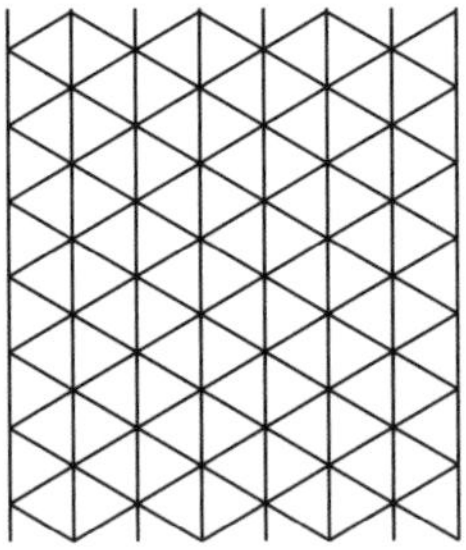

The dimensions of the object cannot be taken from the first picture but they can be taken from the second. Isometric paper can be used either as dots (as above) or as a grid of equilateral triangles. Either way, the paper must be the right way round (as shown here).

N.B. Most of the questions in this section are easier, and more fun to do, when you have an ample supply of 'unifix' or 'multilink' cubes.

Exercise 1

1. On isometric paper make a copy of each object below. Underneath each drawing state the number of 'multilink' cubes needed to make the object. (Make sure you have the isometric paper the right way round!)

(a)

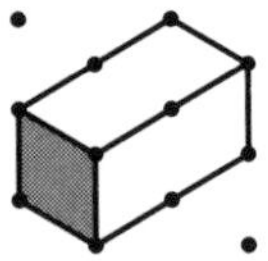

(b)

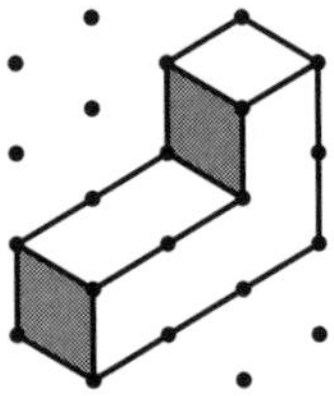

(c)

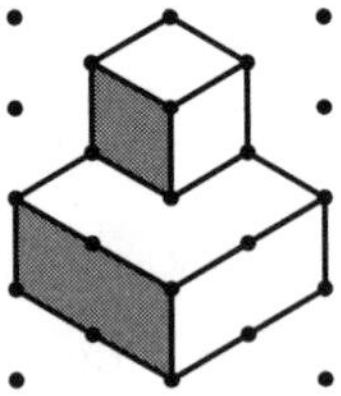

2. Using four cubes, you can make several different shapes. A and B are different shapes but C is the same as A.

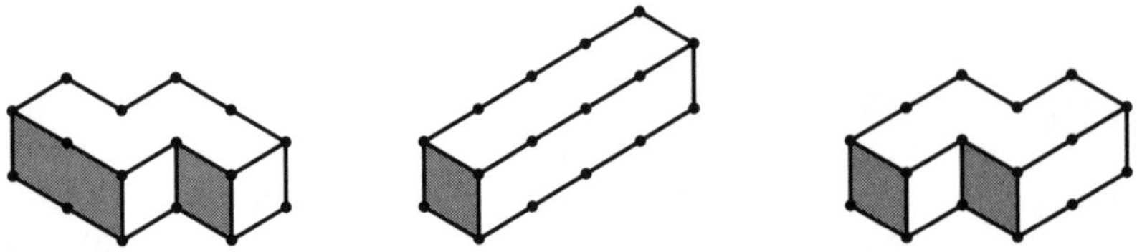

A✓ B✓ C✗

Make as many different shapes as possible, using four cubes, and draw them all (including shapes A and B above) on isometric paper.

3. Make the object shown using cubes.
Now draw the object *from a different view*.

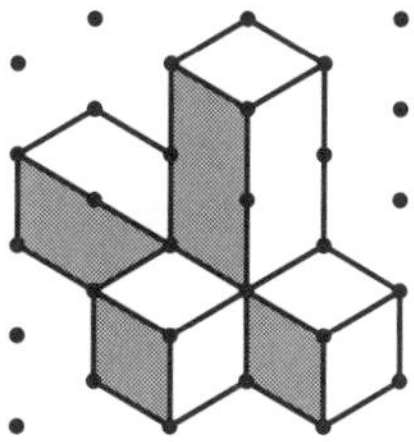

4.

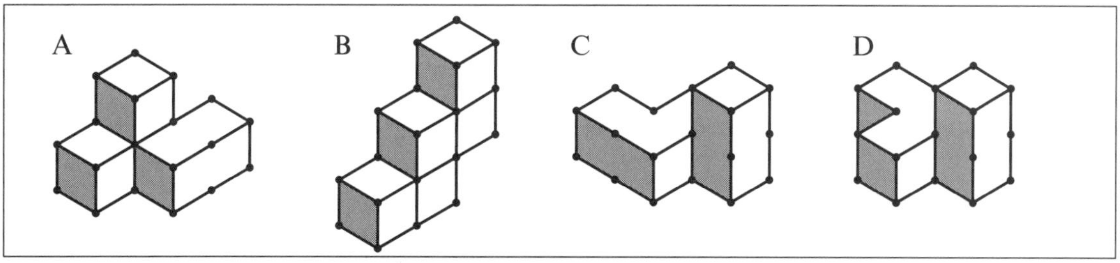

Build your own 3-D models of shapes A, B, C and D above. If possible use a different colour for each one.

Decide which of the shapes below are the same as shape A.
Repeat for shapes B, C and D.
Which shape is neither A, B, C nor D?

1.

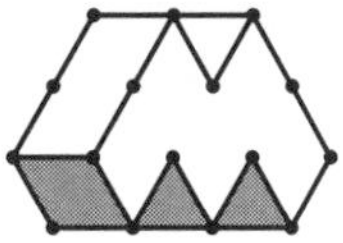

2.

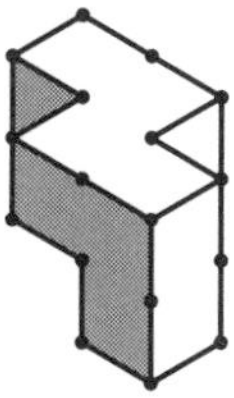

3.

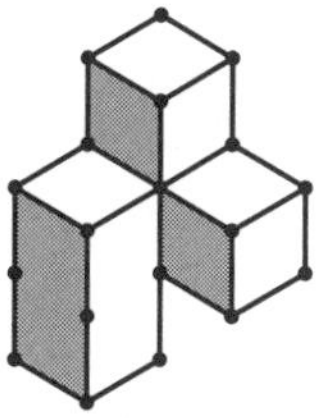

4.

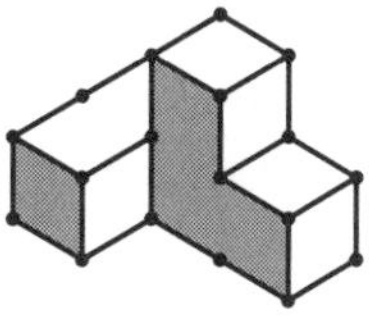

5.

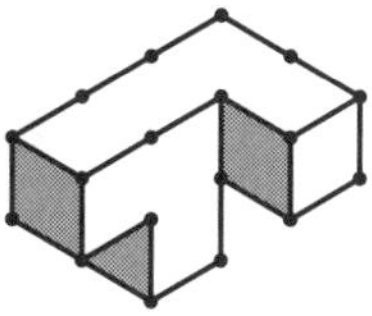

6.

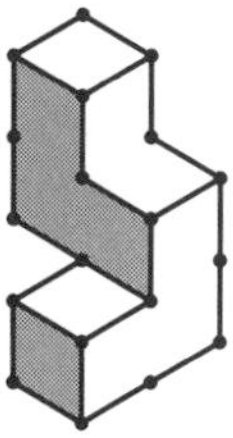

7.

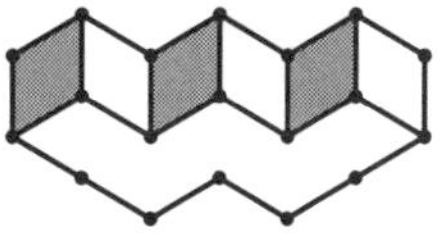

8.

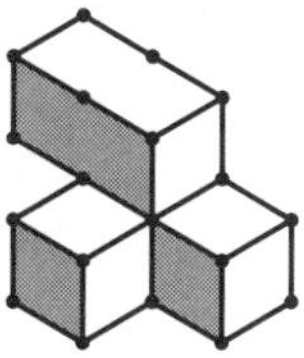

9.

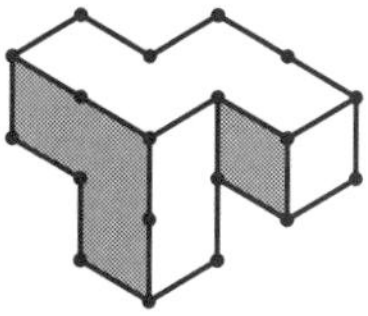

10.

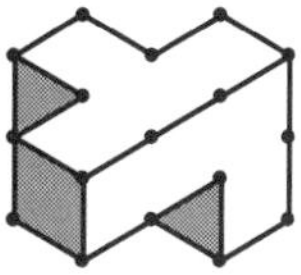

11.

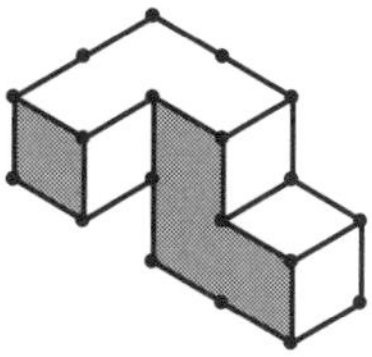

12.

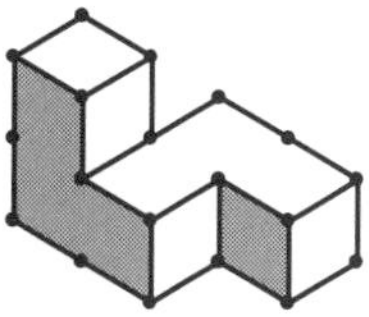

5. You need 18 cubes.
Make the two shapes below. Arrange them to make a $3 \times 3 \times 2$ cuboid by adding a third shape, which you have to find.
Draw the third shape on isometric paper.

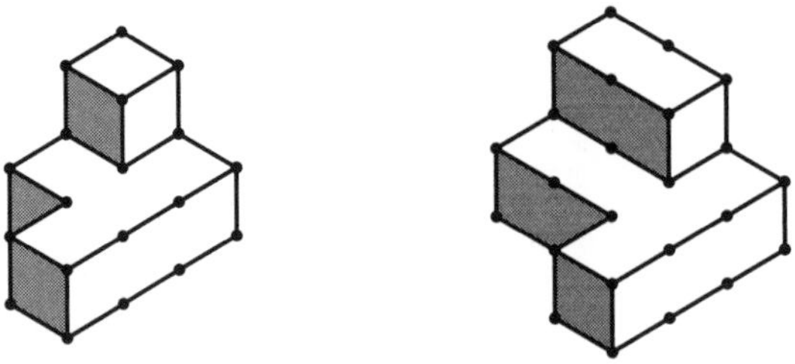

6. You need 27 small cubes for this question.
Make the four shapes below and arrange them into a $3 \times 3 \times 3$ cube by adding a fifth shape, which you have to find. Draw the fifth shape on isometric paper. (The number next to each shape indicates the number of small cubes in that shape).

(a)

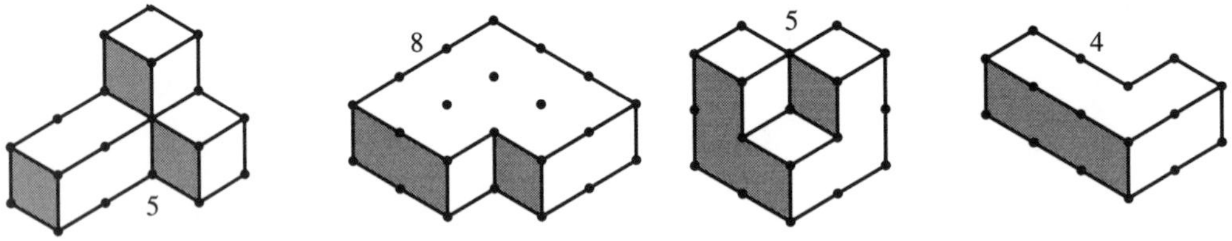

(b)

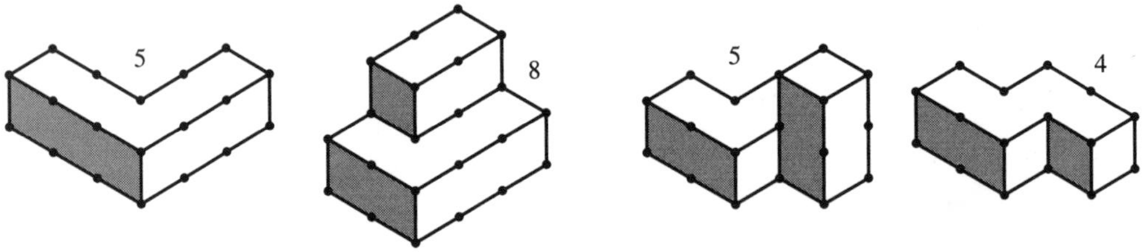

(c)

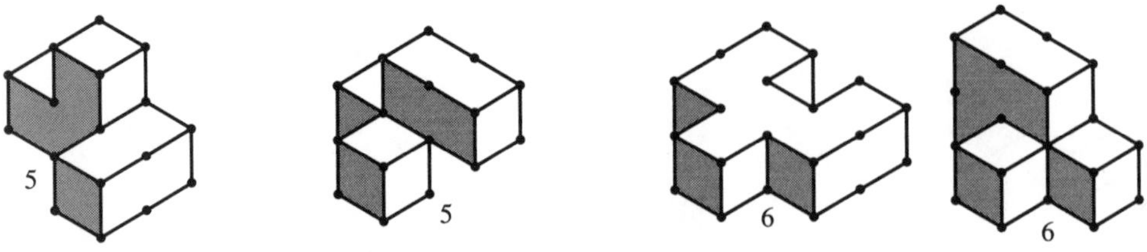

Three views of a shape

Here is a 3-D object made from centimetre cubes. We can draw 3 views of the object on squared paper.

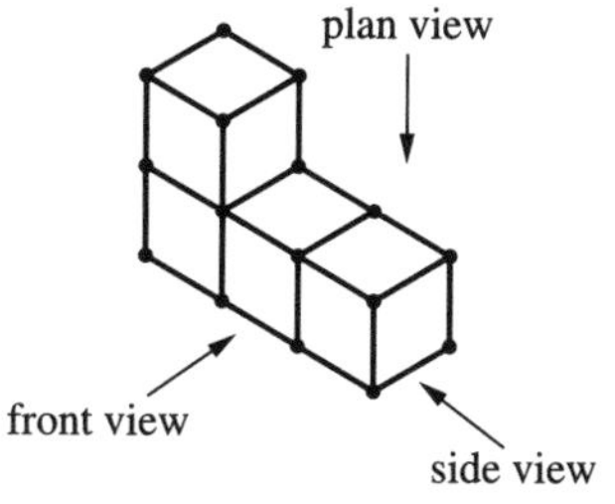

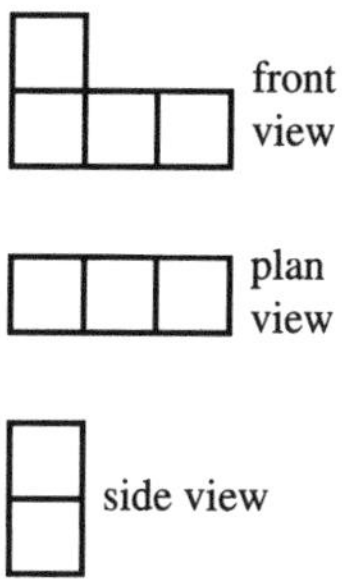

Exercise 2

In Questions **1** to **6** draw the plan view, the front view and the side view of the object

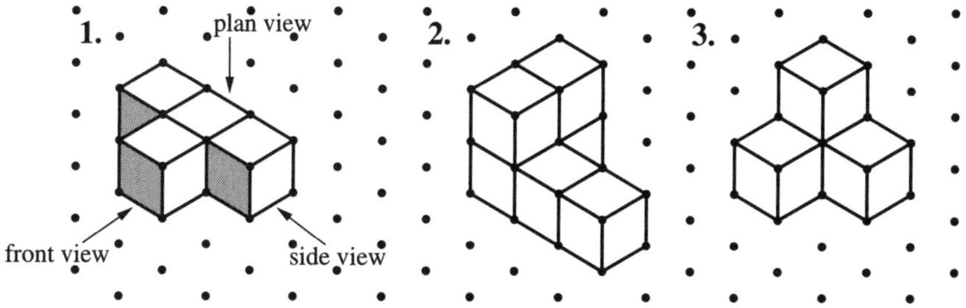

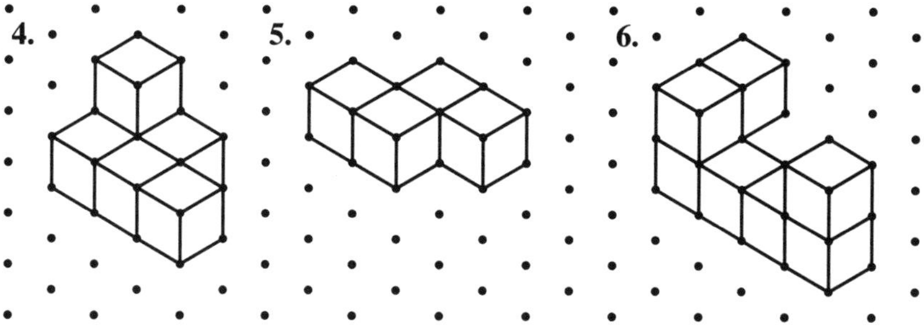

In Questions **7** to **10** you are given three views of a shape. Use the information to make the shape using centimetre cubes.

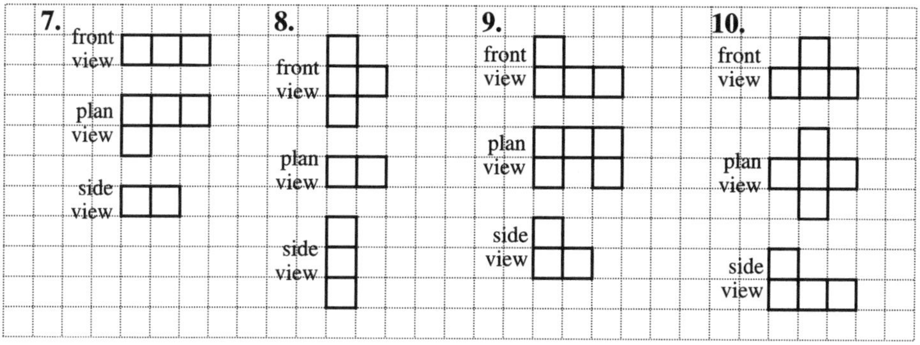

6.5 Bearings and scale drawing

Bearings are used by navigators on ships and aircraft and by people travelling in open country.
Bearings are measured from north in a *clockwise* direction. A bearing is always given as a three-figure number.

A bearing of 090° is due east. If you are going south-west, you are on a bearing 225°.

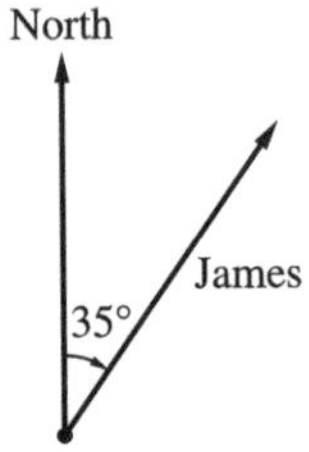

James is walking on a bearing of 035°.

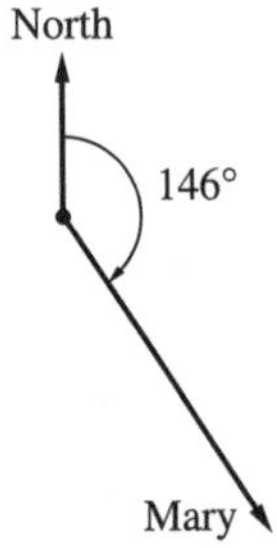

Mary is walking on a bearing of 146°

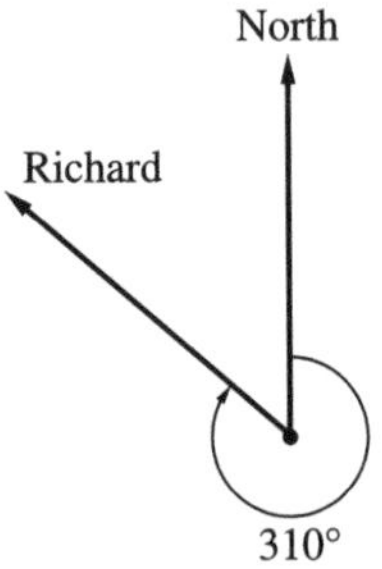

Richard is walking on a bearing of 310°

Exercise 1

1. Ten children on a treasure hunt start in the middle of a field and begin walking in the directions shown on the right. On what bearing is each child walking?

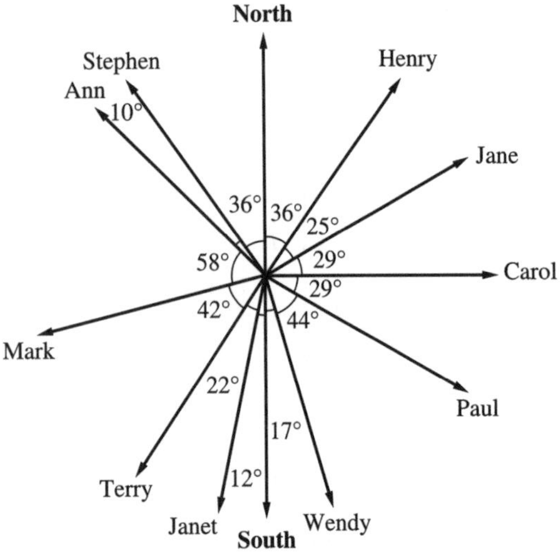

2. Ten pigeons are released and they fly in the directions shown below. On what bearing is each pigeon flying?

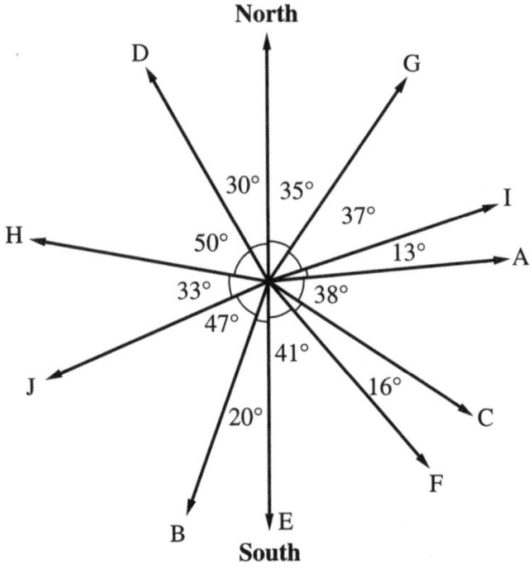

3. Measure the bearing on which each person is moving.

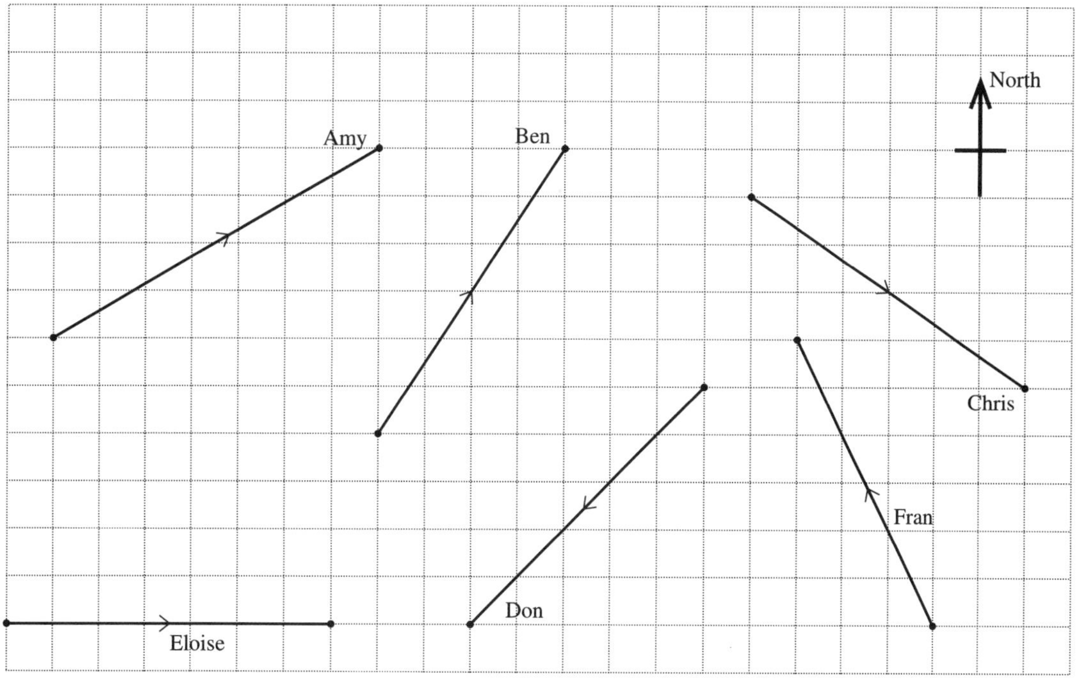

4. Measure the bearing of these journeys.

(a) A to B (b) B to C (c) A to C (d) A to D (e) C to D

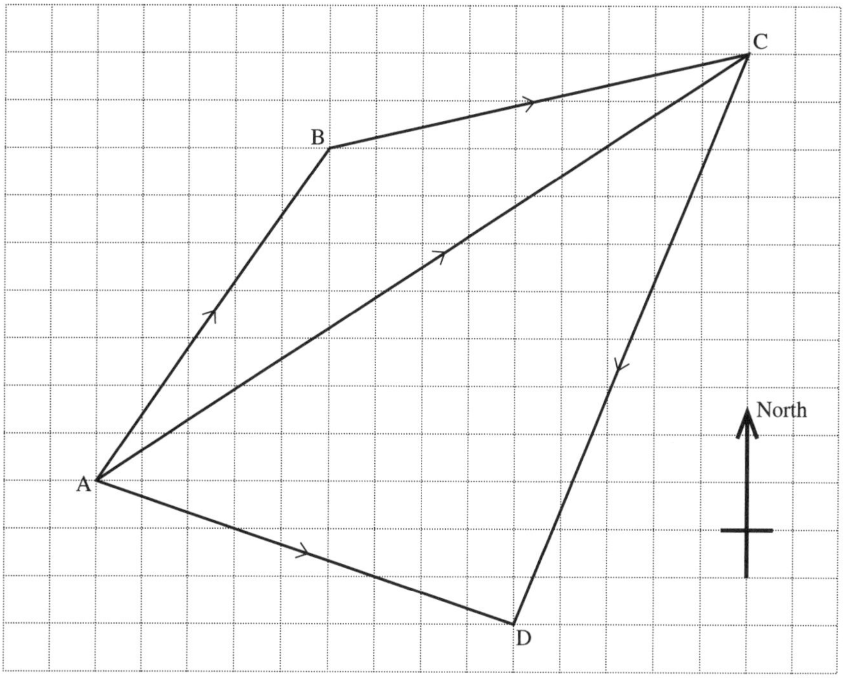

5. Draw lines on the following bearings.

(a) 040° (b) 075° (c) 120° (d) 200° (e) 300°

6. The map shows several features on and around an island. Axes are drawn to identify positions. [eg The coordinates of the cave are (9, 3).]

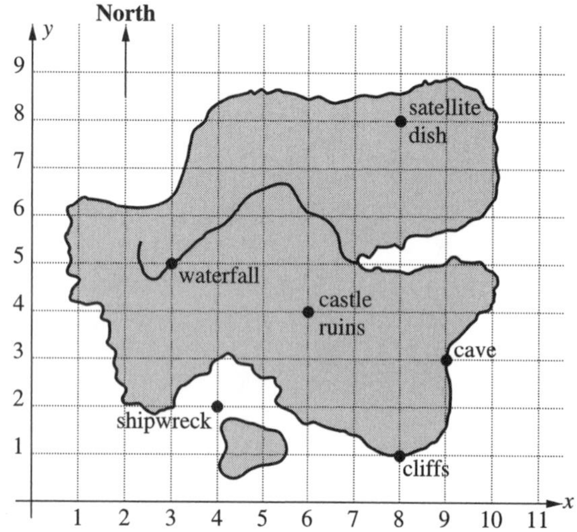

Four commandos, Piers, Quintin, Razak and Smudger, are in hiding on the island. Find the coordinates of the commandos, using the following information.

(a) The castle ruins are due south of Piers and the waterfall is due west of him.

(b) From Quintin, the bearing of the satellite dish is 045° and the shipwreck is due south of him.

(c) From Razak, the bearing of the waterfall is 315° and the bearing of the castle ruins is 045°.

(d) From Smudger, the bearing of the cave is 135° and the bearing of the waterfall is 225°.

(e) The leader of the commandos is hiding somewhere due north of the shipwreck in a hollow tree. From this tree, the castle ruins and the cliffs are both on the same bearing. Find the coordinates of this hollow tree.

7. For each diagram, write down the bearing of C from D.

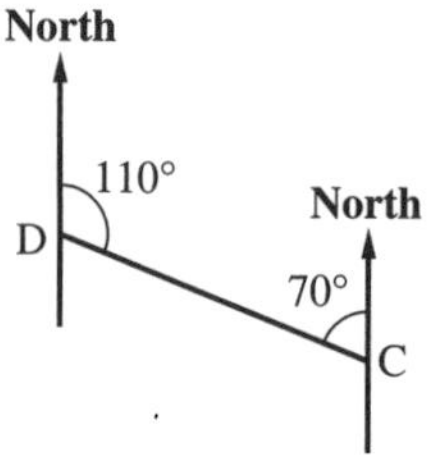

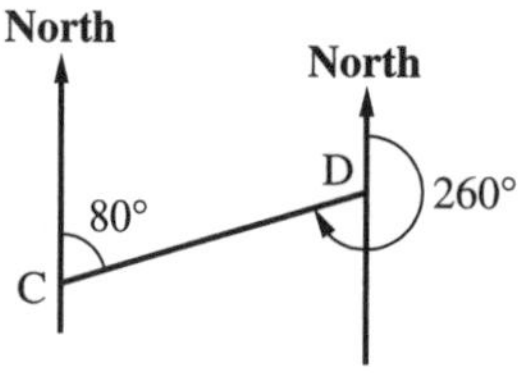

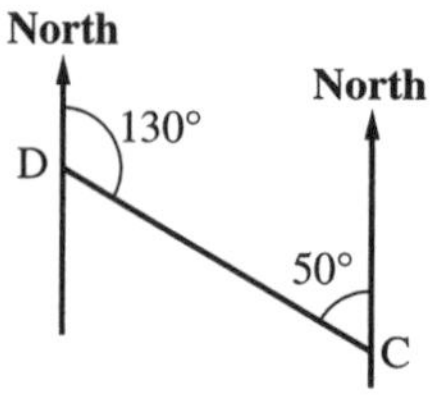

Scale drawing

Many problems involving lengths can be solved using a scale drawing. With questions about compass directions it is helpful to begin by drawing a small sketch to get an idea of where the lines will go. Choose as large a scale as possible for greater accuracy.

A ship sails 7 km north-east and then a further 10 km due south. How far is the ship from its starting point?

We will use a scale of 1 cm to 1 km.

(a) Mark a starting point S and draw a line at 45° to the lines on the page.
(b) Mark a point A, 7 cm from S.
(c) Draw a line vertically through A and mark a point F, 10 cm from A
(d) Measure the distance SF.
Answer: The ship is 7·1 km from its starting point.
(An answer between 7·0 km and 7·2 km would be acceptable.)

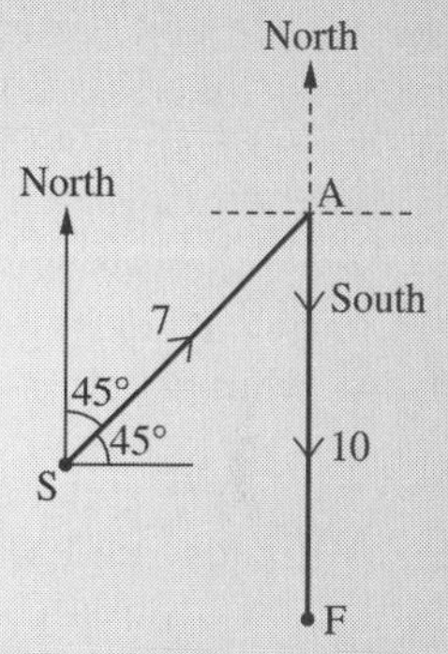

Exercise 2

In Questions **1** to **7** use a scale of 1 cm to represent 1 km.

1. A ship sails 7 km due east and then a further 5 km due south. Find the distance of the ship from its starting point.

2. A ship sails 10 km due west and then a further 4 km south-east. Find the distance of the ship from its starting point.

3. A ship sails 8 km due north and then a further 7 km on a bearing 080°.
How far is the ship now from its starting point?

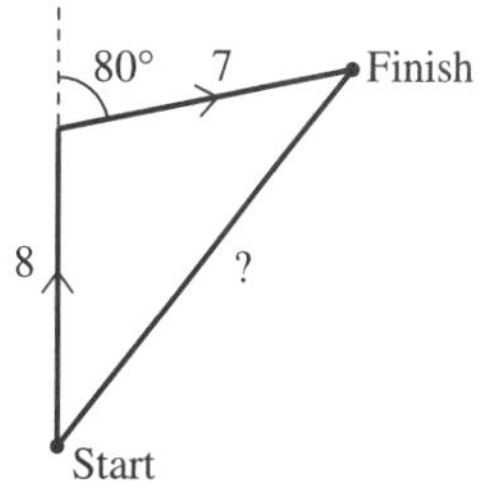

4. A ship sails 6 km on a bearing of 120° and then a further 4 km due south. How far is the ship from its starting point?

5. A ship sails 7 km on a bearing of 075° and then a further 5 km on a bearing of 130°. How far is the ship from its starting point?

6. Point G is 9 km from F on a bearing of 130° from F.
Point H is 10 km from F on a bearing of 212° from F.
What is the bearing of G from H?

7. Point X is 7·2 km from Y on a bearing 215° from Y.
Point X is also 8·5 km from Z on a bearing 290° *from* Z.
How far is Y from Z?

8. Use a scale of 1 cm to represent 10 km. Mark the fixed points P and Q so that P is 70 km due north of Q.
(a) At noon ship A is on a bearing 230° from P and 300° from Q.
At 1500 ship A is on a bearing 162° from P and 096° from Q.
(b) Mark the position of ship A at noon and at 1500.
(c) On what bearing is ship A sailing?
(d) At what speed is ship A sailing?

9. Two explorers, Tina and Karen, have a tent at camp A. Tina leaves the tent and walks on a bearing 064° for 12 km to reach point B. A little later Karen leaves camp A and walks on a bearing 111° for 8 km, to arrive at point C. Karen hears strange noises and decides that she would be better off with Tina, who has a big gun.
Draw a scale diagram to show Tina's route to point B and Karen's route to point C.
How far, and on what bearing, must Karen walk to arrive at point B?

10. A boat left Dornoch to sail to the oil rig O. After two hours it was at a point A, on a bearing of 252° from O and 329° from Banff.

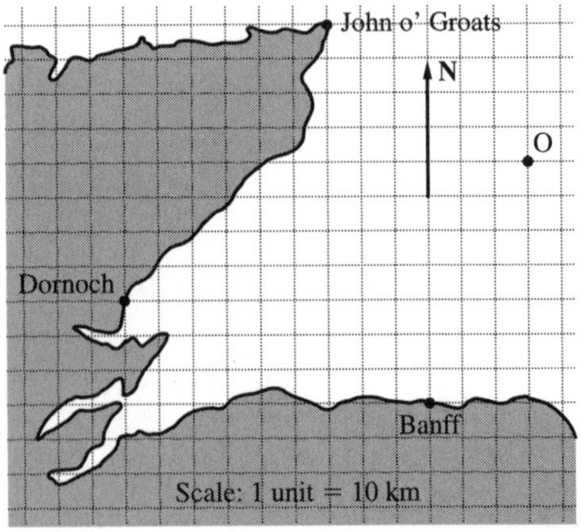

(a) Make a copy of the map on squared paper and find point A.
[Use the squared background to locate Dornoch, Banff, John o'Groats and point O.]
From A, the boat went on a bearing of 090° for 60 km to a new position B.
(b) Draw this part of the voyage on your map and mark position B.
The boat then began to sink and a rescue boat sailed, at a speed of 50 km/h, to point B from Banff.
(c) Measure the bearing to Banff from B.

11. One day at noon, on the radar screen of the Golden Hinde, Sir Francis Drake sees two ships. One is a defenceless Spanish galleon, laden with treasure, and the other is a French pirate ship.

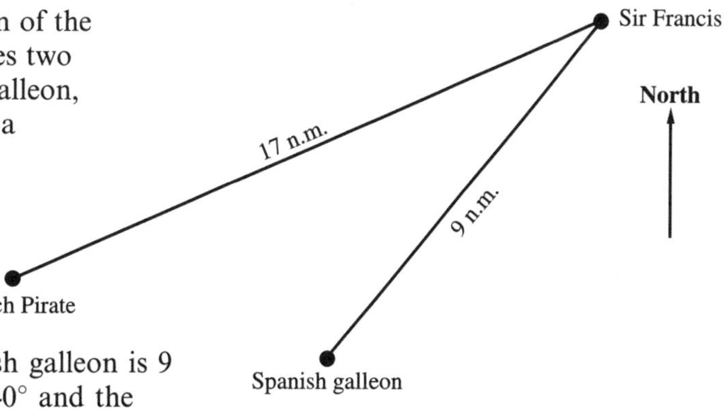

From the Golden Hinde, the Spanish galleon is 9 nautical miles away on a bearing 240° and the French pirate is 17 nautical miles away on a bearing 260°.
The Spanish galleon sails due south at 8 knots. The French pirate sails south-east at 11 knots and Sir Francis sails at 14 knots on a bearing 211°.
At 1300 the captain of the Spanish galleon surrenders to the nearest ship. Who gets the treasure?
[One knot is a speed of one nautical mile per hour].

12. At 0400 a customs patrol boat is 20 km due south of a suspect cargo ship. The cargo ship is sailing at a steady speed on a fixed bearing of 070°. The patrol boat sails on a fixed course at a speed of 26 km/h and intercepts the cargo ship at 0530.
(a) On what bearing did the patrol boat sail?
(b) At what speed was the cargo ship sailing?
[Use a scale of 1 cm to represent 2 km]

13.

Here is a totally accurate transcript of an actual radio conversation between a US naval vessel and the Canadian authorities off the coast of Newfoundland in October 1995. It was recently released by the chief of Naval Operations:
Americans: Please divert your course 15 degrees to the North to avoid a collision.
Canadians: recommend you divert YOUR course 15 degrees to the South to avoid a collision.
Americans: This is the Captain of a US Navy ship. I say again divert YOUR course.
Canadians: No. I say again, you divert YOUR course.
Americans: THIS IS THE AIRCRAFT CARRIER USS LINCOLN, THE SECOND LARGEST SHIP IN THE UNITED STATES ATLANTIC FLEET. WE ARE ACCOMPANIED BY THREE DESTROYERS, THREE CRUISERS AND NUMEROUS SUPPORT VESSELS. I DEMAND THAT YOU CHANGE YOUR COURSE 15 DEGREES NORTH, THAT'S ONE FIVE DEGREES NORTH, OR COUNTERMEASURES WILL BE UNDERTAKEN TO ENSURE THE SAFETY OF THIS SHIP.
Canadians: This a lighthouse. Its your call. . .

Read the clip from a newspaper. Write a question about bearings using this incident or one of your own invention

6.6 Volume

- Volume is a measure of how much physical space an object takes up.

Blocks A and B are each made from eight cubes, measuring 1cm × 1 cm × 1 cm. They each have a volume of 8 cubic cm, which is written 8 cm^3.

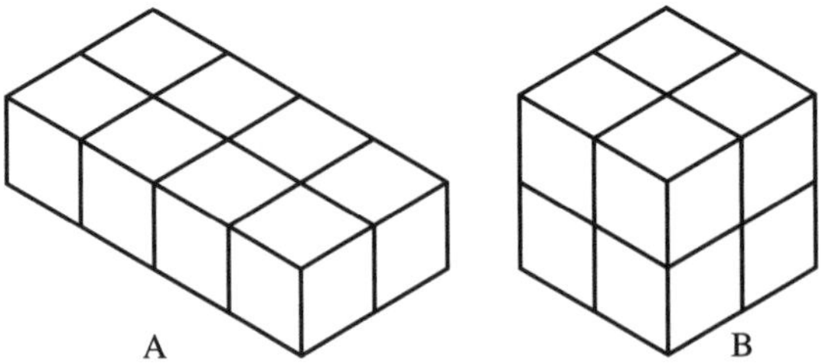

Rectangular blocks like these are called *cuboids*. A cube, like block B, is a special kind of cuboid.

- The volume of a cuboid is given by the formula,

Volume = (length) × (width) × (height)

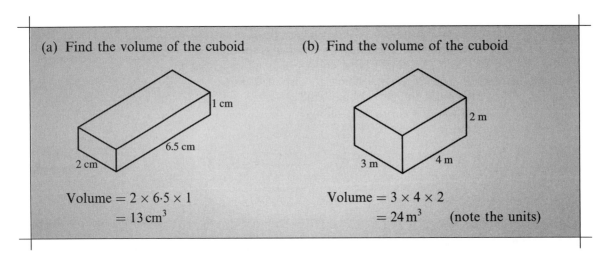

(a) Find the volume of the cuboid

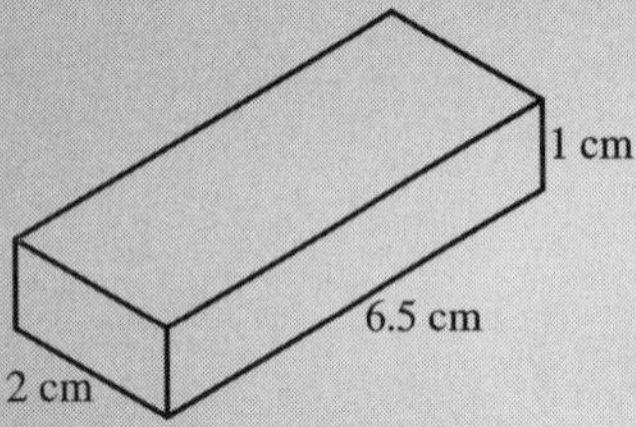

Volume = 2 × 6·5 × 1
= 13 cm^3

(b) Find the volume of the cuboid

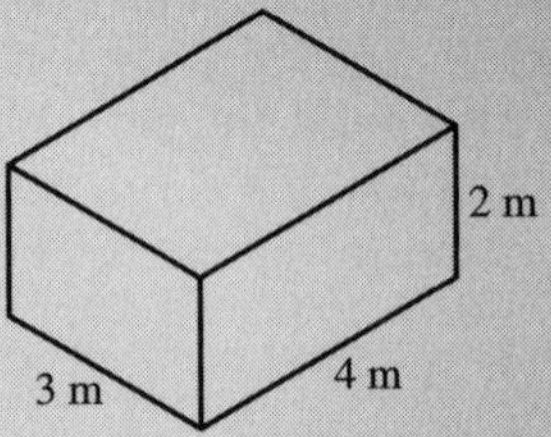

Volume = 3 × 4 × 2
= 24 m^3 (note the units)

Exercise 1

In Questions **1** to **9** work out the volume of each cuboid. Give your answer in the correct units

1.

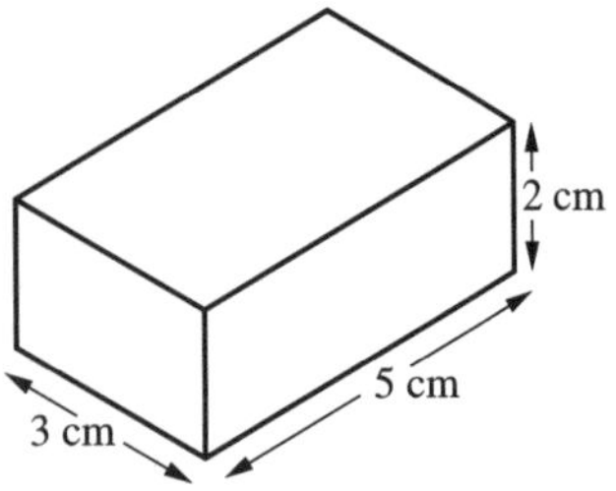

2.

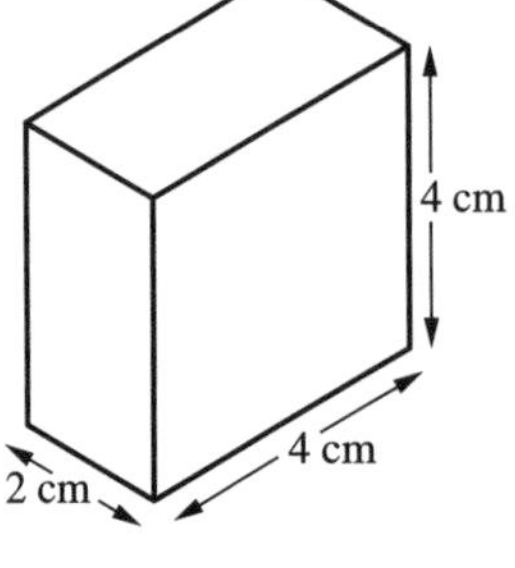

3.

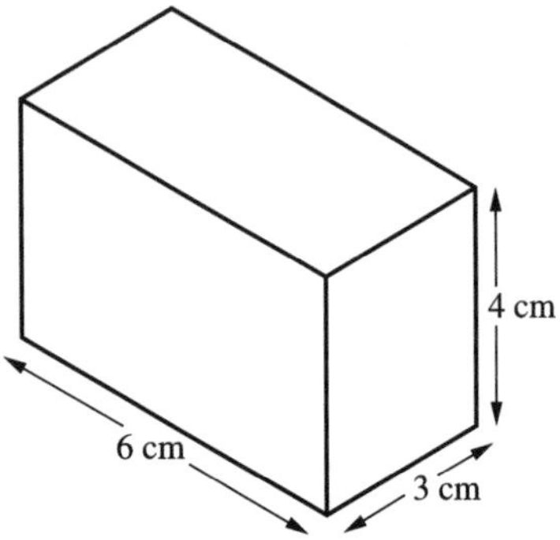

4.

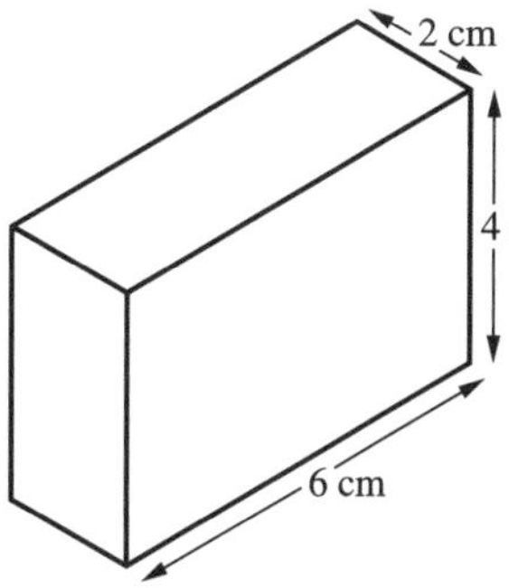

5.

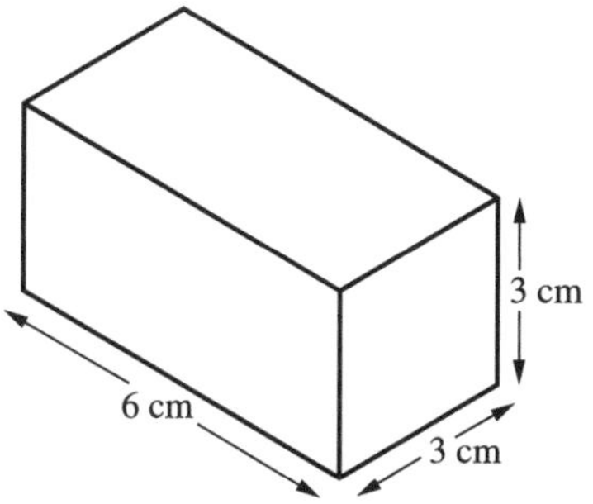

6.

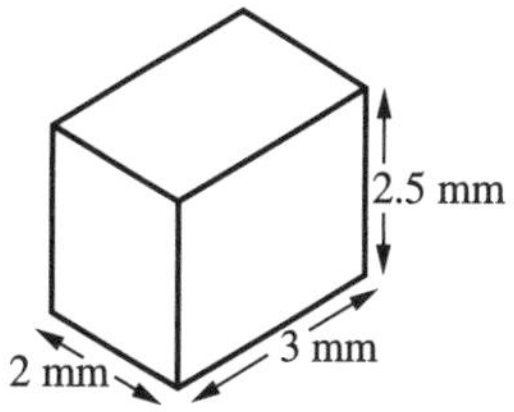

In Questions **7** to **12** write down the volume of the object. All the objects are made from centimetre cubes.

7.

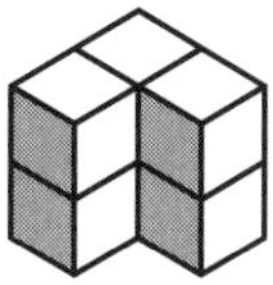

8.

9.

10.

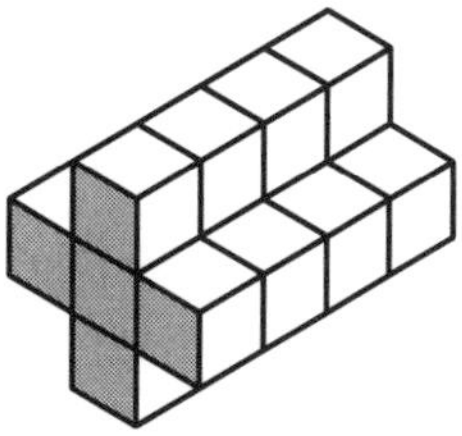

11.

12.

13. (a) Draw a sketch of 4 m by 4 m by 2 m cuboid.
(b) Calculate the volume of the cuboid.
(c) Calculate the total surface area of the cuboid.

14. Calculate the volume of each girder by splitting them into cuboids. All lengths are in cm.

(a)

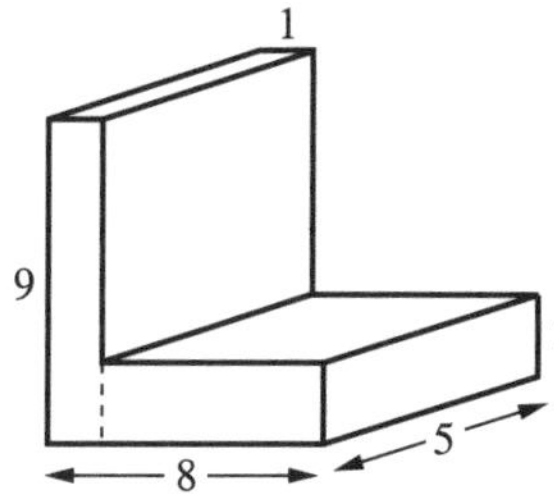

(b)

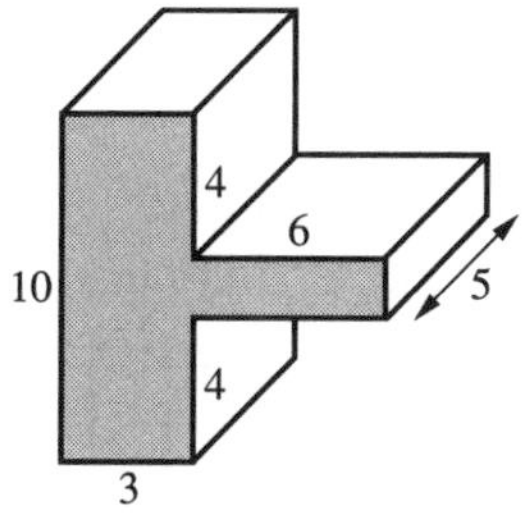

Exercise 2

1. How many times can the small box be filled from the large container which is full of grass seed?

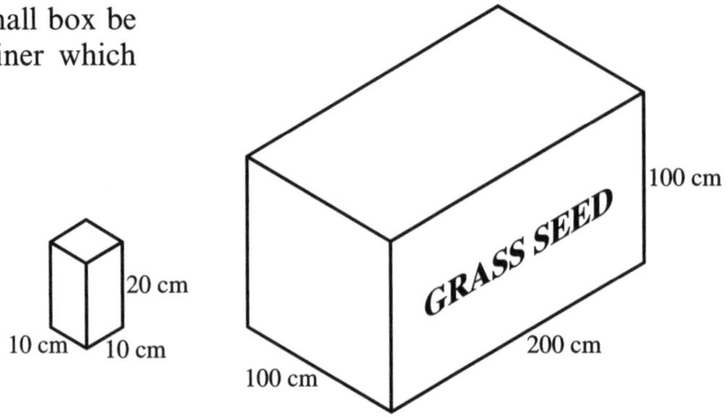

2. A mine shaft 400 m long is dug with the cross-section shown. Calculate the volume of earth which must be removed to make way for the shaft.

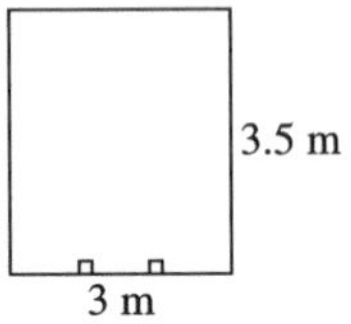

3. The diagram shows an empty swimming pool. Water is pumped into the pool at a rate of $2\,m^3$ per minute. How long will it take to fill the pool?

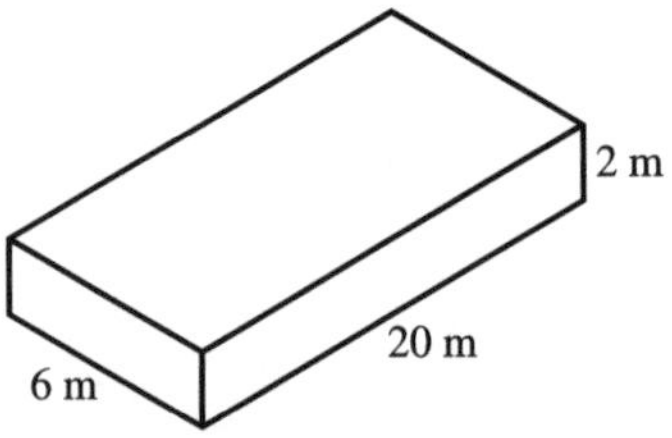

4. The large cube is cut into lots of identical small cubes as shown. Calculate the volume of each small cube.

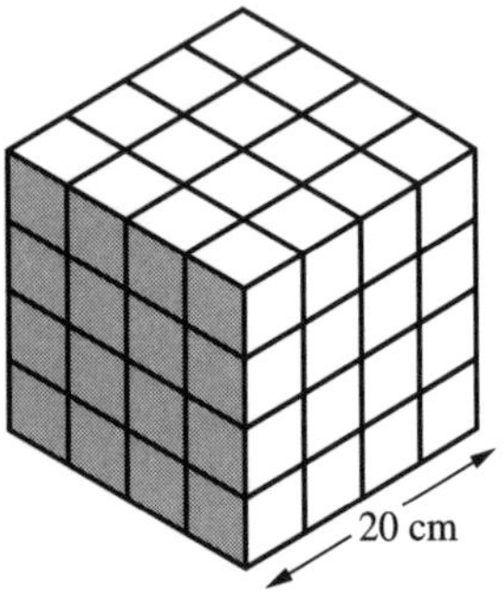

5. The shapes below are nets for closed boxes. Work out the volume of the box in each case, giving your answer in cubic cm.

(a)

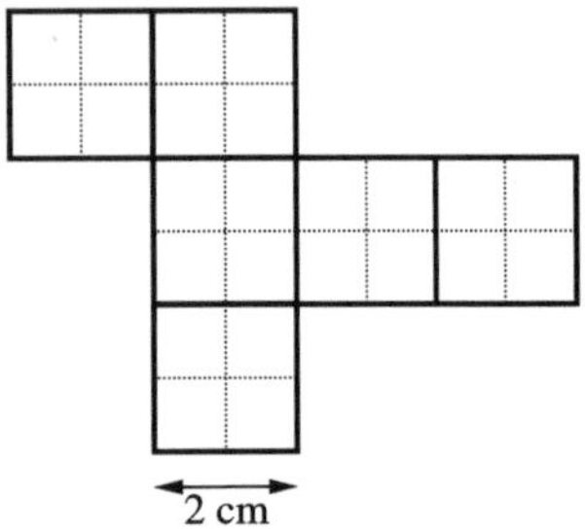

(b)

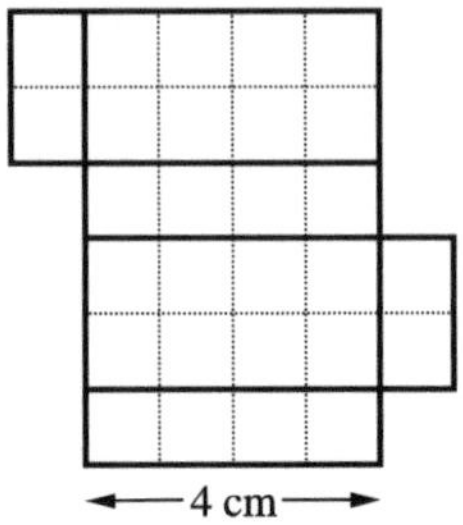

(c)

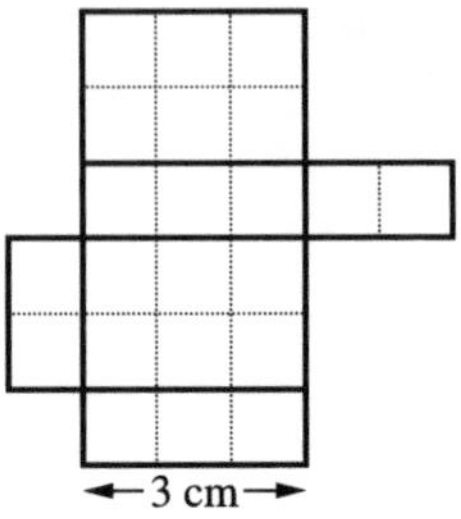

6. In a storm 2 cm of rain fell in 1 hour. Calculate the volume of water, in cm^3, which fell on the roof of the garage shown.

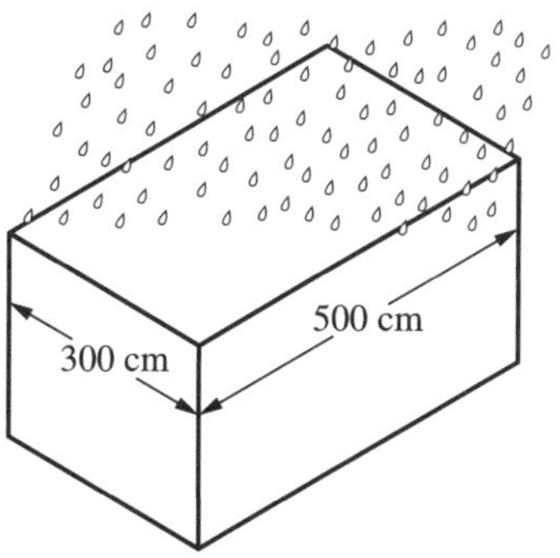

7. The inside of a spaceship orbiting the earth is a cuboid measuring 200 cm by 300 cm by 200 cm. Unfortunately air is leaking from the spaceship at a rate of $1000\ cm^3/sec$.
How long will it take for all the air to leak out?

8. Find the length x.

(a)

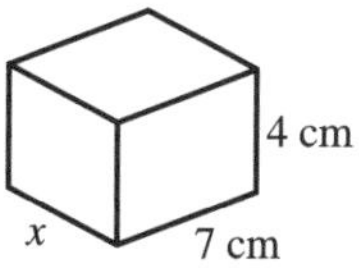

volume = $70\ cm^3$

(b)

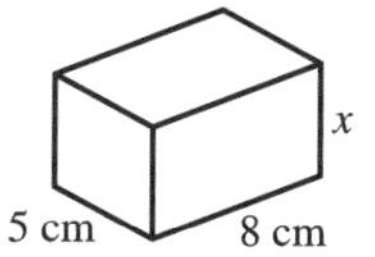

volume = $120\ cm^3$

(c)

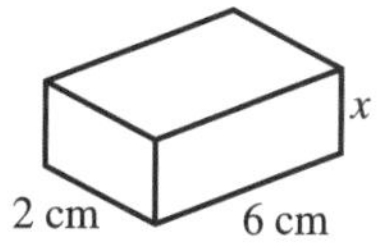

volume = $18\ cm^3$

(d)

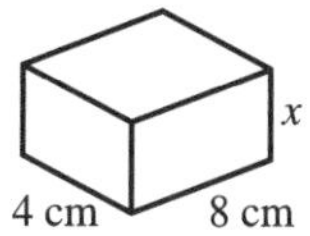

volume = $32\ cm^3$

(e)

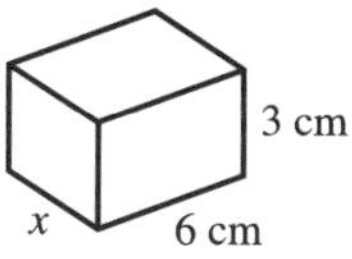

volume = $27\ cm^3$

(f)

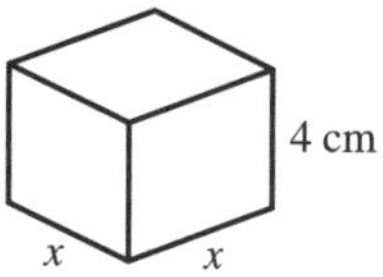

volume = $100\ cm^3$

9. The diagram shows an object of volume $7\ cm^3$.
Use isometric paper to draw the following objects:
(a) a cuboid with volume $45\ cm^3$
(b) a T-shaped object with volume $15\ cm^3$
(c) an L-shaped object with volume $20\ cm^3$
(d) any object with a volume of $23\ cm^3$.

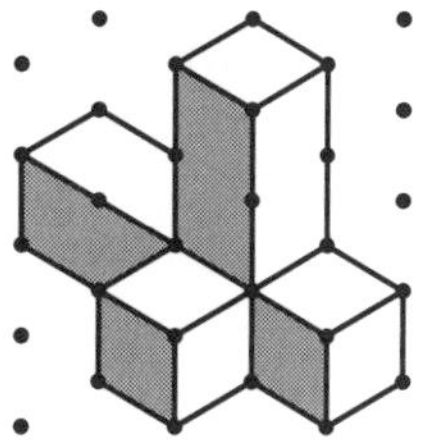

10. Sketch a cuboid a cm by b cm by c cm.
(a) Write an expression for the volume of the cuboid.
(b) Write an expression for the total surface area of the cuboid.

11. 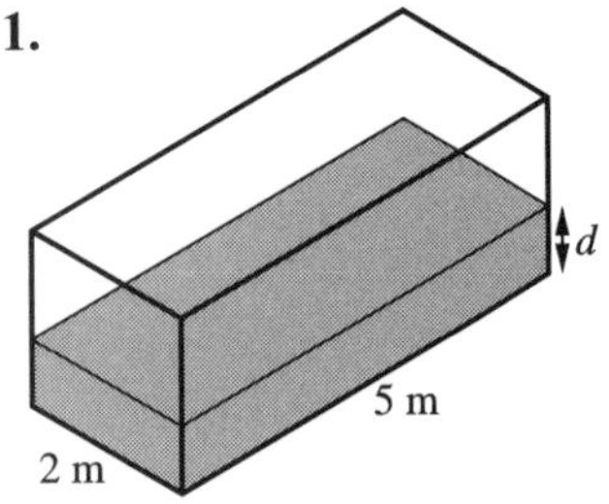

A children's paddling pool has a base 2 m by 5 m. There is $5\,m^3$ of water in the pool.
Calculate the depth of water d in the pool, stating the units clearly.

Prisms

The volume of the object shown can be found by dividing the object into layers, indicated by the thick lines. Each layer contains 6 cubes and there are 4 layers. The volume of the object is $24\,cm^3$.

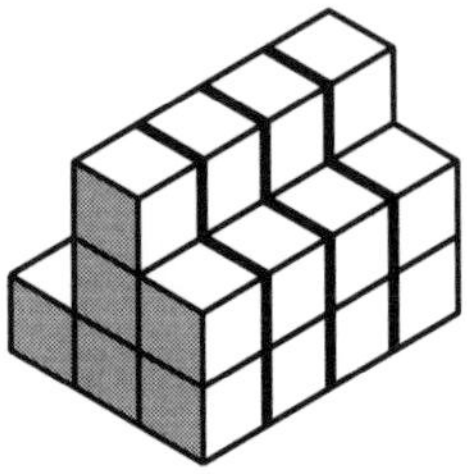

An object which can be cut into identical layers like this is called a *prism*.

A prism has the same cross section throughout its length.

Volume of a prism = (Area of cross section) × (length)

Any cuboid is a prism since it has the same cross section throughout its length.

Find the volume of the prism shown.
All the angles are right angles and the dimensions are in cm.

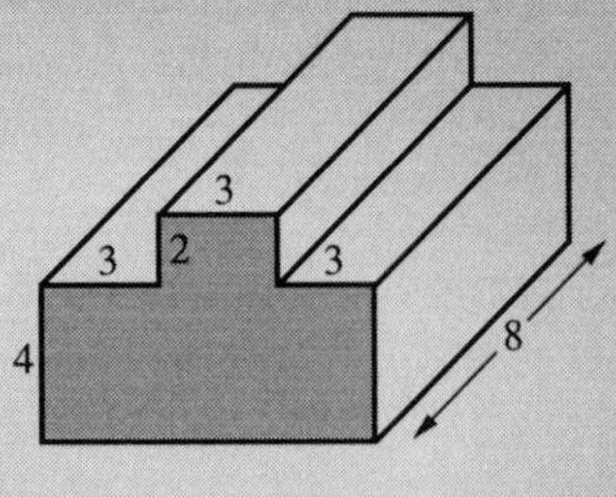

$$\text{Area of cross section} = 4 \times (3 + 3 + 3) + (3 \times 2) = 42\,cm^2.$$

$$\text{Volume of prism} = 42 \times 8 = 336\,cm^3$$

Liquids

The volume of a liquid is usually given in litres or millilitres (ml)

$1000\,\text{ml} = 1$ litre

and 1 ml is the same as $1\,\text{cm}^3$.

The diagram shows a cubic metre of water.

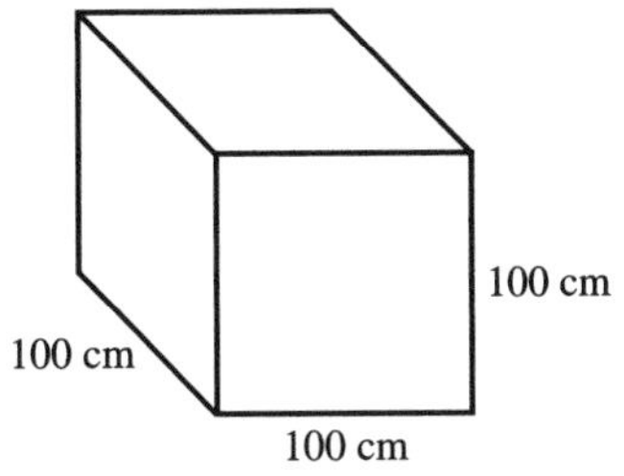

$$
\begin{aligned}
1\,\text{m}^3 &= 100 \times 100 \times 100\,\text{cm}^3 \\
&= 1\,000\,000\,\text{cm}^3 \\
\text{So } 1\,\text{m}^3 &= 1\,000\,000\,\text{ml} \\
&= 1000 \text{ litres}
\end{aligned}
$$

Exercise 2

Find the volume of each prism.

1. 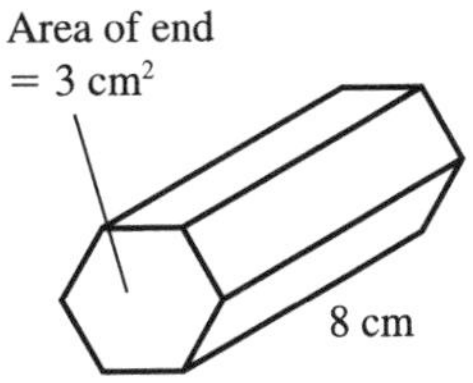

2. 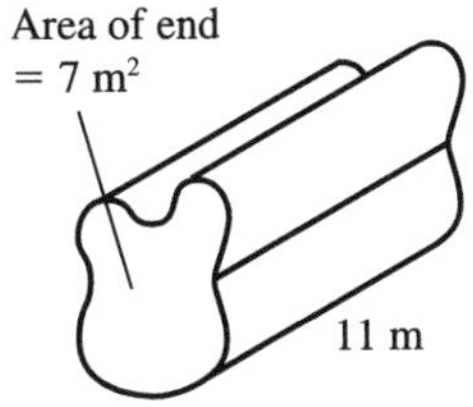

3. 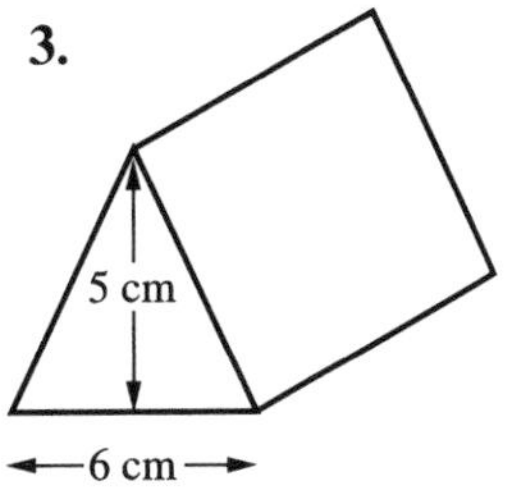

4. 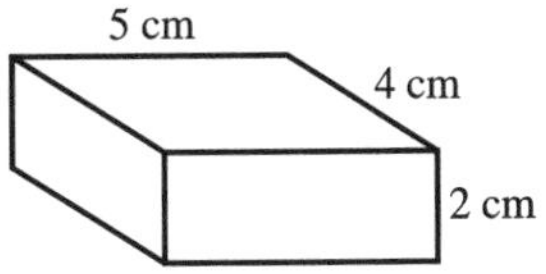

5. 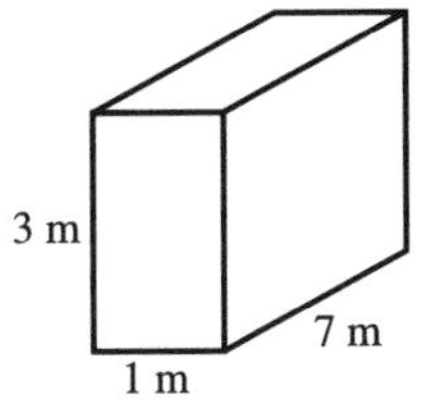

6. 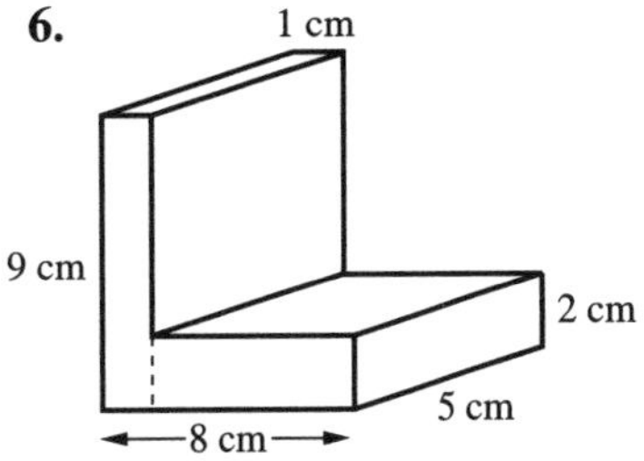

In Questions **7** to **9** find the volume of each prism. All the angles are right angles and the dimensions are in centimetres.

7. 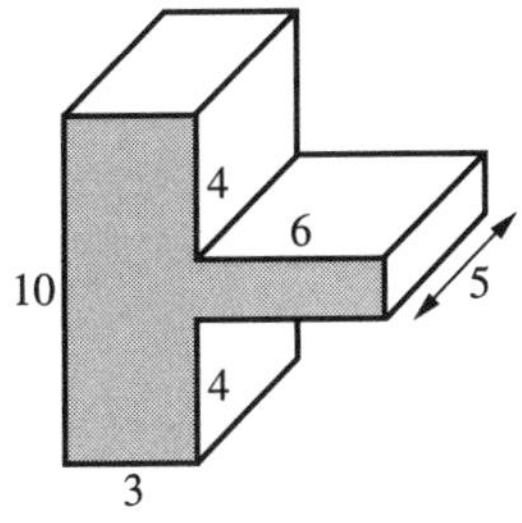

8. 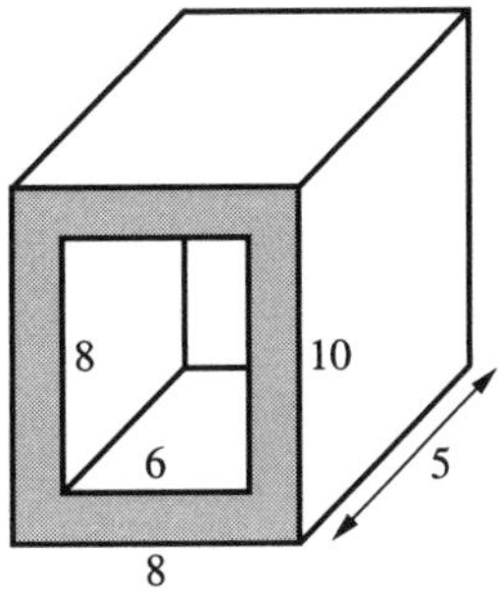

9. 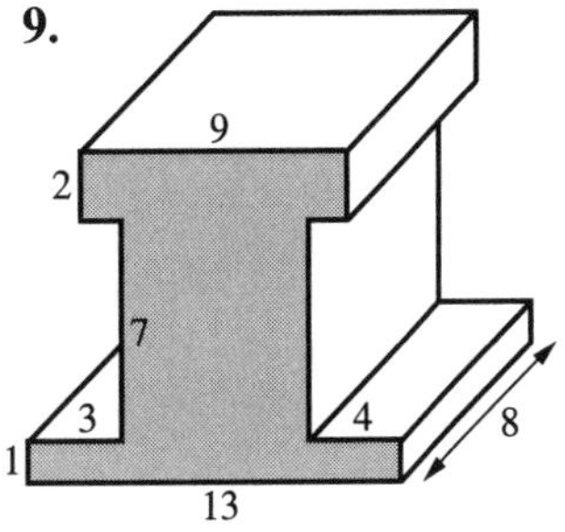

Exercise 3

1. A uniform metal rod of length 5 m has a volume of $3750\,cm^3$. Find the area of the cross-section of the rod.

2. A vertical tower of height 32 m has a square cross-section. Find the length of a side of the square if the volume of the tower is $4608\,m^3$.

3. Find the volume, in litres, of the water trough shown.

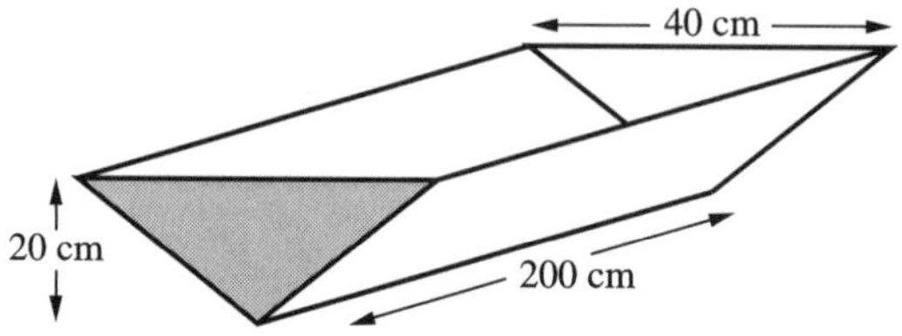

4. Find the capacity, in litres, of a rectangular tank with internal dimensions 60 cm by 20 cm by 1 m. [1 litre = $1000\,cm^3$]

5. Some steps are to be made in concrete.
   (a) Calculate, in cubic metres, the volume of concrete needed.
   (b) The concrete is mixed, by volume, from cement, sand and stones, in the ratio 2 : 3 : 6.
   What volume of sand is required for the steps?

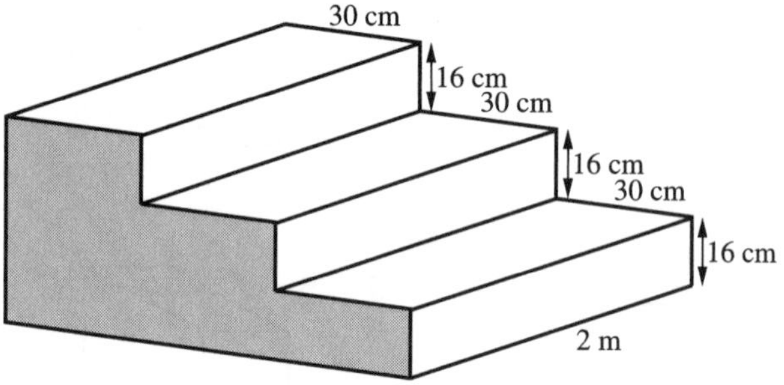

6. The cross section of a plaster moulding for ceilings is a quarter circle cut from a square.
   $1\,cm^3$ of the plaster weighs 1·2 g.
   Calculate the weight of a 4 m length of this moulding.

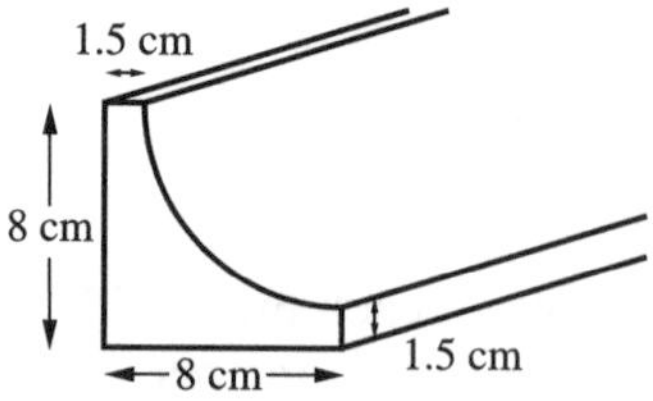

7. The diagram shows the cross section of a swimming pool.
   Water is pumped into the pool at a rate of 20 litres/sec.
   How long, in hours and minutes, will it take to fill the pool?

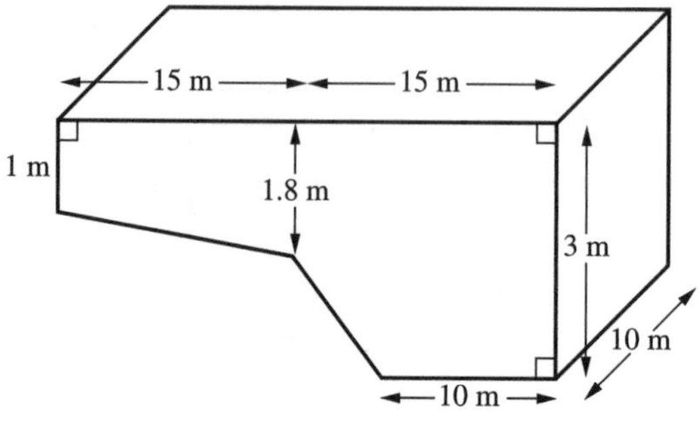

Cylinders

A cylinder is a prism because it has the same cross section throughout its length.

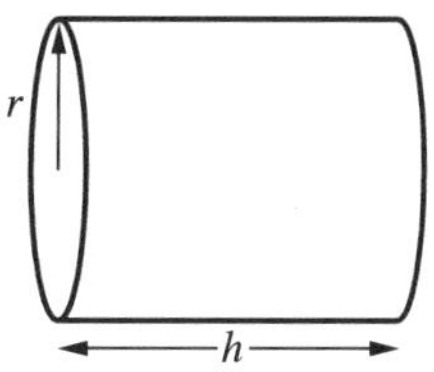

Volume = (area of cross section) × (length)

Volume = $\pi r^2 h$

(a) A cylinder has radius 3 cm and length 10 cm.
Find the volume of the cylinder.

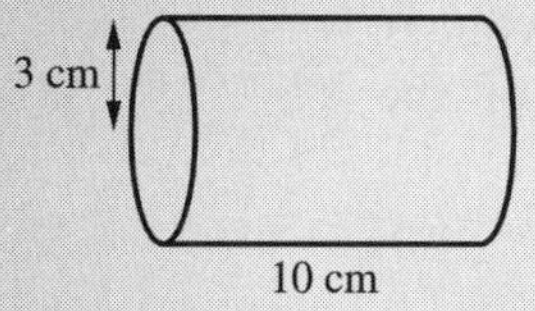

$V = \pi r^2 h$
$V = \pi \times 3^2 \times 10$
$V = 283\,\text{cm}^3$ (to 3 s.f.)

(b) Find the capacity, in litres, of the oil drum shown

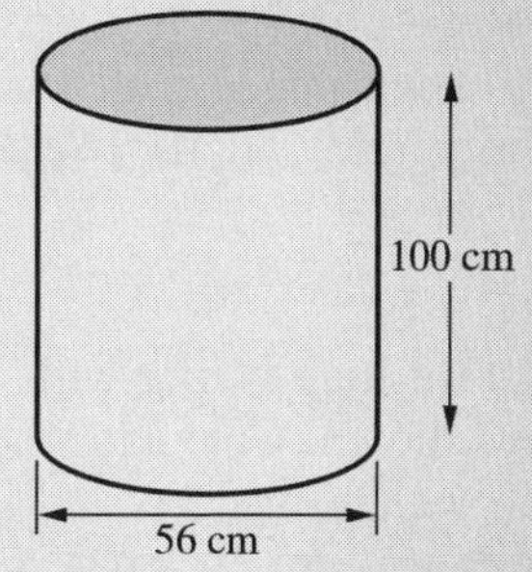

The oil drum is a cylinder.
Volume of oil drum = $\pi \times 28^2 \times 100$
= $246\,000\,\text{cm}^3$ (to 3 s.f.)
Capacity of oil drum = 246 litres (to 3 s.f.)

Exercise 4

Give answers correct to 3 significant figures, where necessary.

1. Find the volume of each cylinder.

(a)
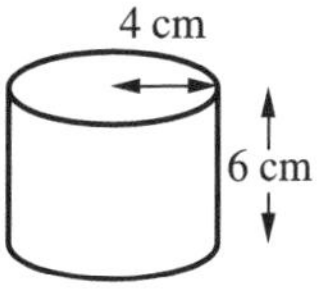

(b)
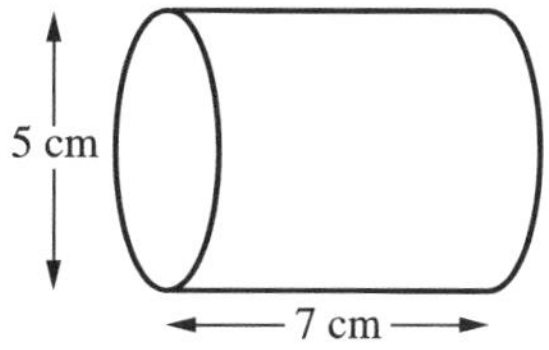

(c)
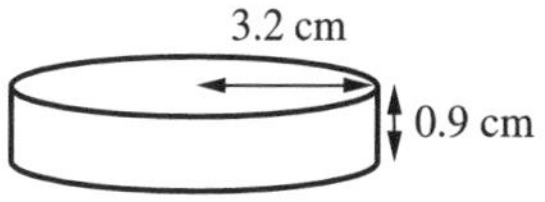

(d)
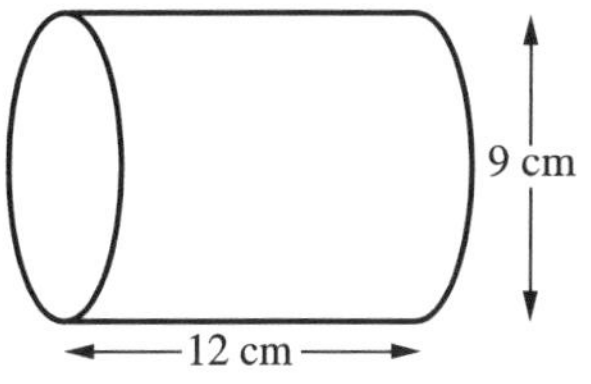

(e)
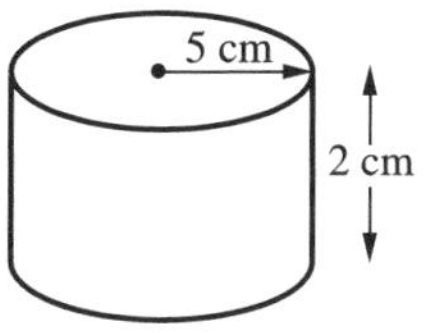

(f)
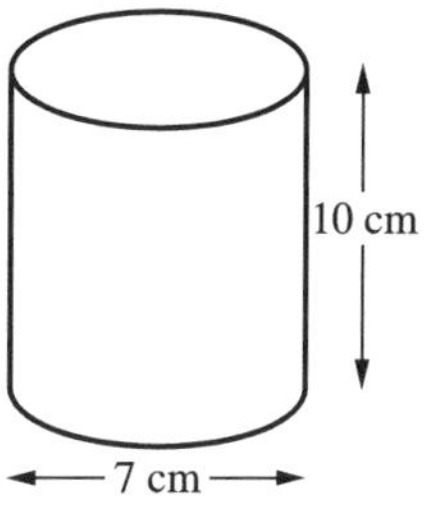

2. Cylinders are cut along the axis of symmetry. Find the volume of each object.

(a)

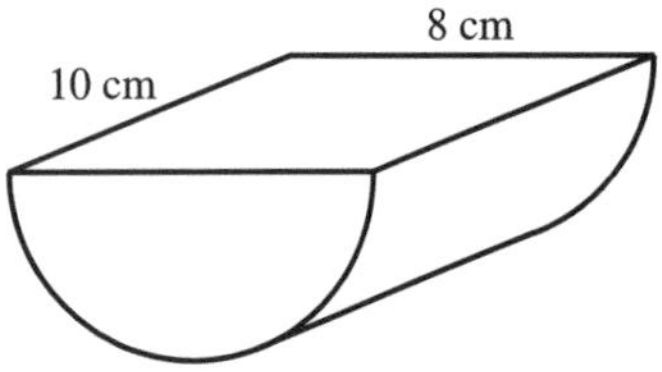

(b)

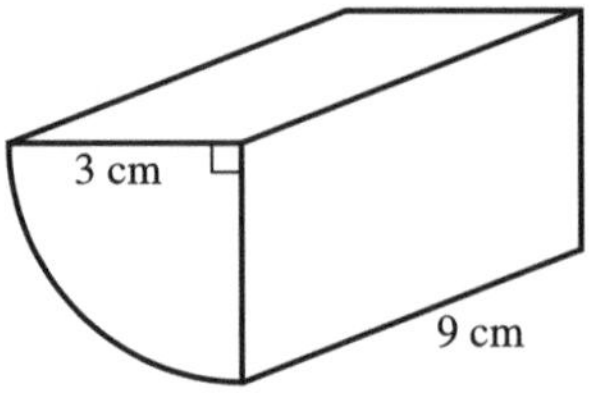

3. Find the volume in litres of a cylindrical tank of radius 40 cm and height 35 cm.

4. The lead in an unsharpened pencil is in the shape of a cylinder of diameter 2 mm and length 16 cm. Find the volume of the lead in cm^3.

5. A mine shaft 200 m long is dug with the cross-section shown. Calculate the volume of earth which must be removed to make way for the shaft.

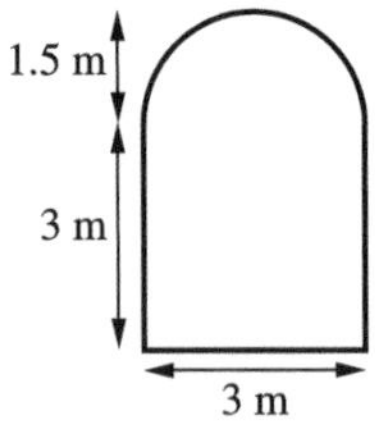

6. Water is poured from the full cylinder A into the empty tank B. Will all the water go in?

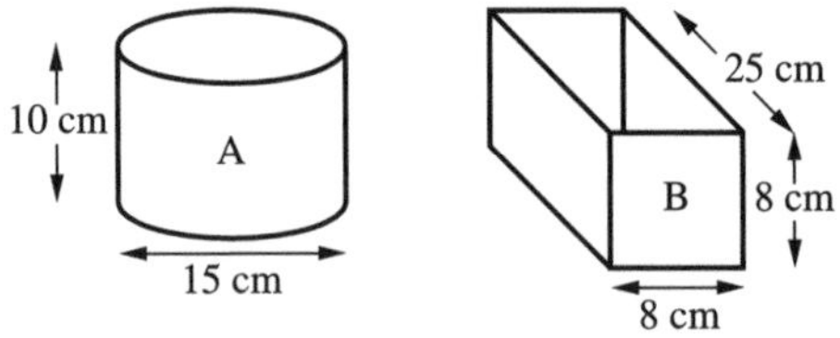

7. An empty cylindrical tank of height 70 cm and diameter 1 metre is to be filled from a tap which delivers water at the rate of 150 ml per second. How long will it take to fill the tank? Give your answer to the nearest minute.

8. How many times can the cylindrical glass be filled from the large drum which is full of milk?

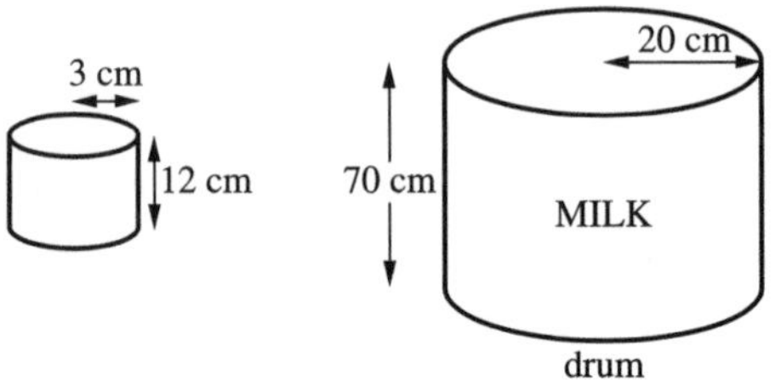

9. A solid sculpture weighing 5·7 kg is made of metal and 1 cm³ of the metal weighs 7·8 grams. The sculpture is to be melted down into solid cylinders of diameter and height 4 cm. How many complete cylinders can be made?

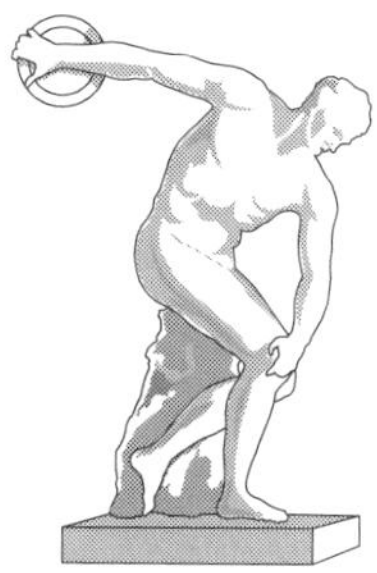

10. The cross-section of a metal pipe is shown below. Calculate the volume of metal used to make a pipe of length 10 m.

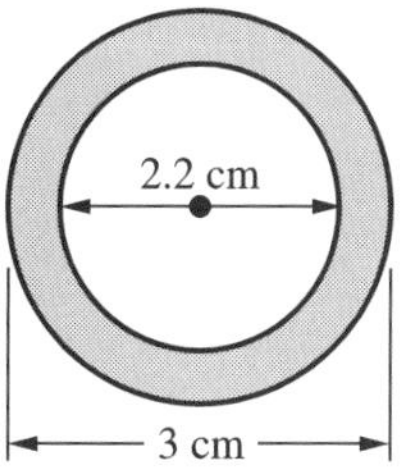

11. 'Vache qui rit' cheese portions are packed in circular boxes. Each portion is 1·4 cm thick and has a top surface which is a sector of a circle of radius 5 cm.

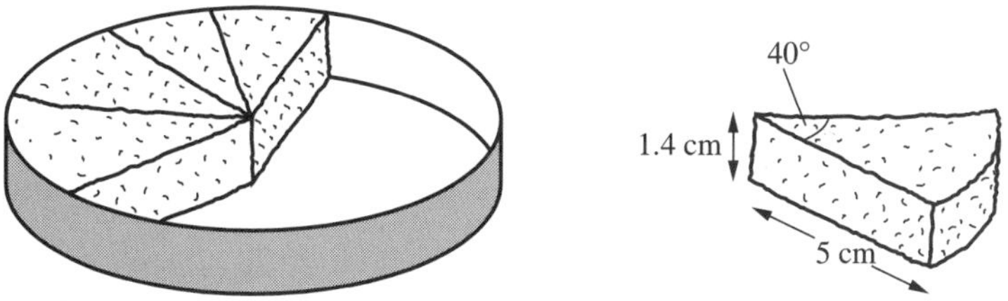

(a) Calculate the volume of the cheese in a full box and hence the volume of one portion.

(b) 100 cm³ of 'Vache qui rit' weighs 113 grams. Find the weight of one portion of cheese.

12. A solid rectangular block has dimensions 35 cm × 28 cm × 18 cm. Calculate the volume of the largest cylinder which can be cut from this block.

13. A cylindrical can of internal radius 20 cm stands upright. It contains water to a depth of 30 cm. Calculate the rise in the level of the water when a brick of volume 1800 cm³ is immersed in the water.

6.7 Mathematical games

Round the class: a game for the whole class

- Fifty cards like those above are handed out around the class.
- One person has a START card. He/she reads the number in the ring at the top of the card (11) and then reads the statement 'You're next if you have this +8'.
- Someone in the class will have the card shown in the middle. That person says '19' and then reads 'You're next if you have this −10'.

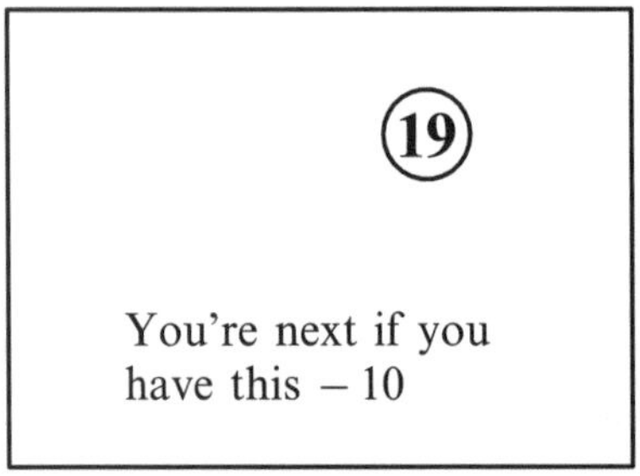

- This process continues around the room until card 50 with the word 'END' is reached. The object of the game is to complete the 50 cards as quickly as possible.
- The class can be split into two teams. Each team completes the 50 cards against the stopwatch and the winner is the team with the quicker time.
- Teacher's note: The cards appear in the Answer Book from which they can be photocopied preferably on card and cut up. A master sheet is also printed for the teacher to keep track of what is going on.

Cross numbers without clues

Here are cross number puzzles with a difference. There are no clues, only answers, and you have to find where the answers go.

(a) Copy out the cross number pattern.

(b) Fit all the given numbers into the correct spaces. Work logically and tick off the numbers from lists as you write them in the squares.

1.

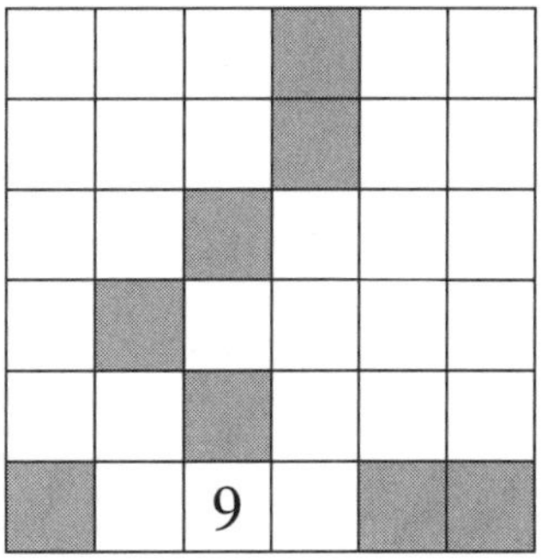

2 digits	*3 digits*	*4 digits*	*5 digits*
23	146	2708	25404
26	235	2715	25814
42	245		37586
57	337		
59	539		
87	695		

2.

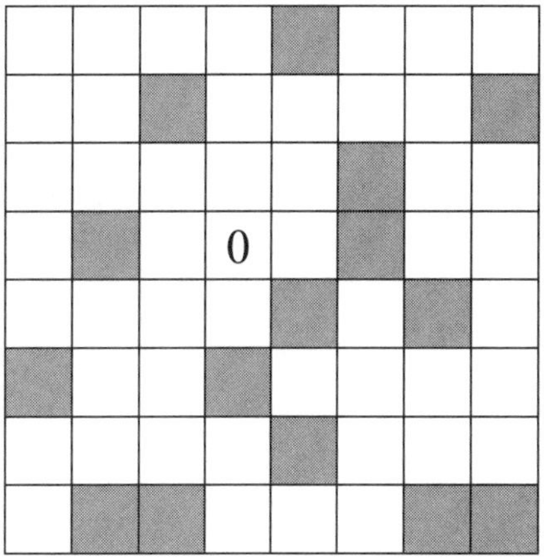

2 digits	*3 digits*	*4 digits*	*5 digits*
18	244	2163	36918
21	247	4133	46514
31	248	4213	54374
33	332	4215	54704
47	333	4283	87234
63	334	4317	
64	608	4394	
77			

3.

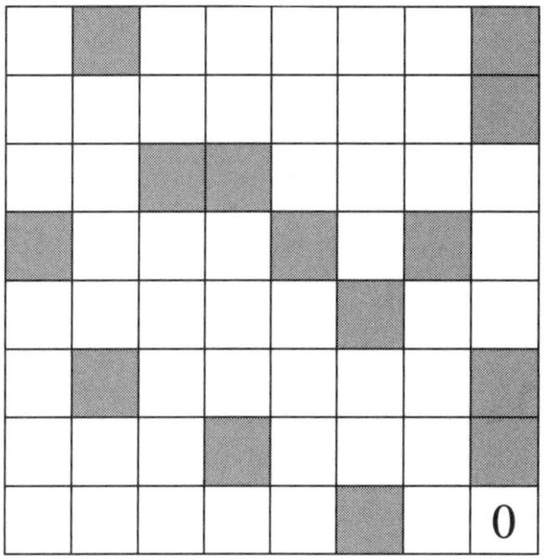

2 digits	*3 digits*	*4 digits*	*5 digits*	*7 digits*
36	145	2286	16145	4235824
52	185	5235	66145	
56	245	5248	66152	
63	246	5249	66272	
65	374	5452	91671	
77	437	6241		
90	646			
	896			

4.

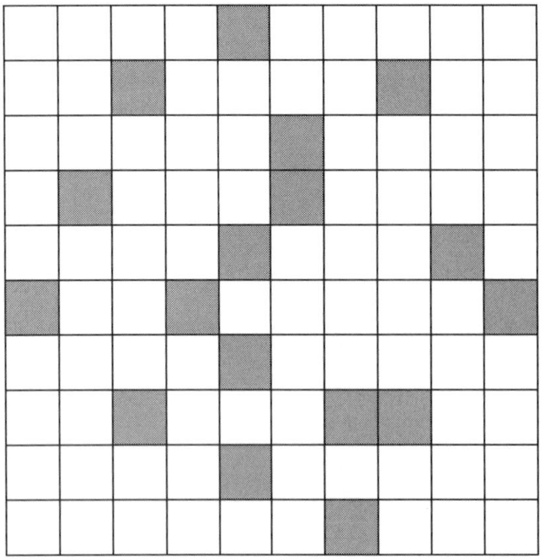

2 digits	*3 digits*	*4 digits*	*5 digits*
14	123	1325	14251
22	231	1478	29163
26	341	1687	29613
43	439	1976	29872
65	531	2523	34182
70	670	4798	54875
81		5601	63712
82		5611	67358
		5621	82146
		6109	84359
		8171	97273

6 digits	*7 digits*
145026	9354234
740136	
983514	

5. This one is more difficult.

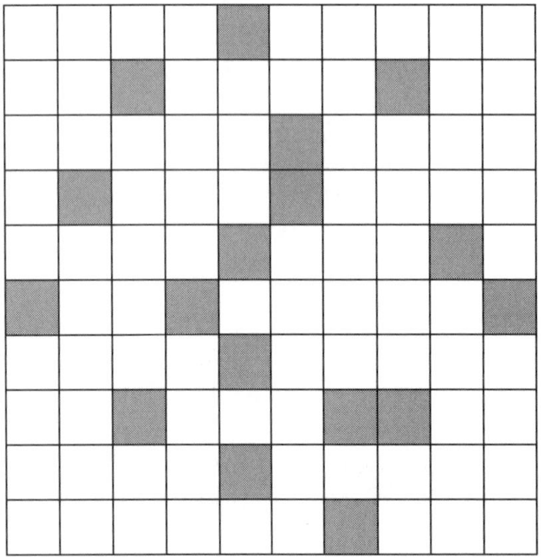

2 digits	*3 digits*	*4 digits*	*5 digits*
15	137	2513	29666
19	206	3048	31873
21	276	3214	40657
22	546	3244	43104
28	592	3437	43158
31	783	3514	54732
77		3517	60783
90		3544	62114
		4122	80751
		4127	82614
		6934	93654

6 digits	*7 digits*
235785	9733764
235815	
452705	

Fraction, Decimal or Percentage pairs

This is a game for 2, 3 or 4 players using the Fraction, Decimal and Percentage cards.

How to play:

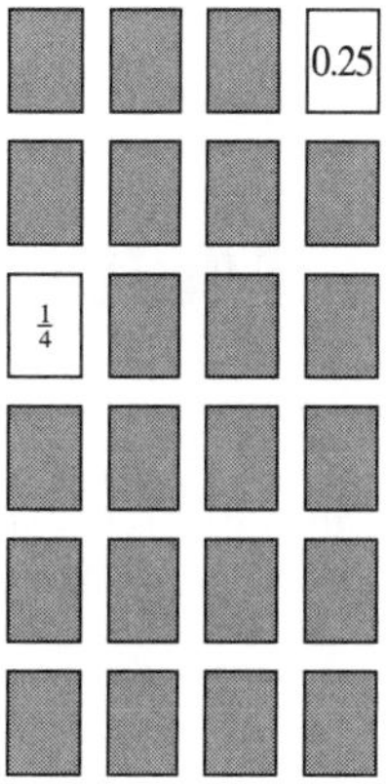

- Shuffle the cards, place them face down in a 6 rows by 4 columns pattern.
- Decide who will go first.
- Each turn requires a player to turn over a pair of cards.
- If the pair are equivalent such as 0·5 and 50% the player keeps the pair. If not turn the cards face down again.
- Try to remember which cards are where!
- If you find a pair you get another go, the player with the most pairs when no cards are left is the winner.
- You can increase the degree of difficulty in the game by including more fraction, decimal and percentage equivalents.
- Teacher's note. The cards may be photocopied from the answer book. Some teachers prefer to have the cards made by the pupils as a preparation.

Printing a book

When a book is made giant sheets of paper containing several pages of the book are printed. These large sheets are then folded to make either 16 or 32 page 'signatures'. The signatures are then bound together to make the whole book and then the edges of the pages are trimmed.

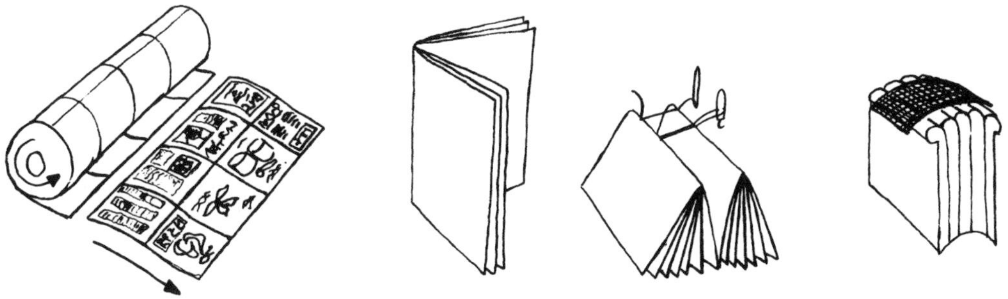

The printed pages are spread all over the large sheet and are upside down in many cases.
Take a sheet of A3 paper (twice the size of A4, 'normal' school paper) and fold it to make a 16 page signature. Work out where pages 1 to 16 would be and also which way up they should be printed.
Now either make drawings, stick in pictures or write a short story on *both* sides of your A3 sheet and number the pages. Finally fold and cut your booklet and fix the pages together with staples.

Part 7

7.1 Multiple choice tests

Test 1

1. Simplify the expression $3(2x - 1) - 2(x + 1)$

A $4x + 2$
B $5x - 5$
C $4x - 5$
D $4x - 1$

2. The area, in cm^2, of a circle of diameter 10 cm is

A 25π
B 20π
C 10π
D 100π

3. Find the median of the numbers:
5, −2, 10, 4, −3, 0, 1,

A $2\frac{1}{7}$
B 1
C $\frac{1}{2}$
D 4

4. A room has a floor which measures 12 m × 14 m. How many square tiles of side 20 cm are needed to cover the floor?

A 168
B 420
C 4200
D 16 800

5. What is the next number in the sequence 1, 1, 2, 3, 5, 8?

A 11
B 12
C 13
D 14

6. Find the actual length of a lake which appears 5·2 cm long on a map of scale 1 : 200 000

A 10·4 km
B 1·04 km
C 104 km
D None of the above

7. Without using a calculator, work out $\sqrt{0{\cdot}0036}$

A 0·6
B 0·06
C 0·006
D 0·018

8. Calculate the perimeter of a semi-circle of radius 3 units

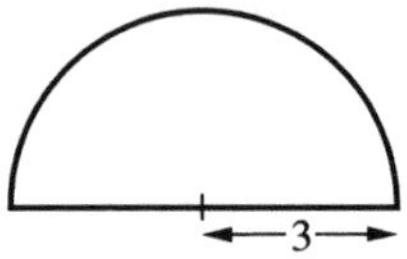

A $3\pi + 3$
B $6\pi + 6$
C $3\pi + 6$
D 9π

9. Calculate the length of the line from (0, 0) to (4, 3).

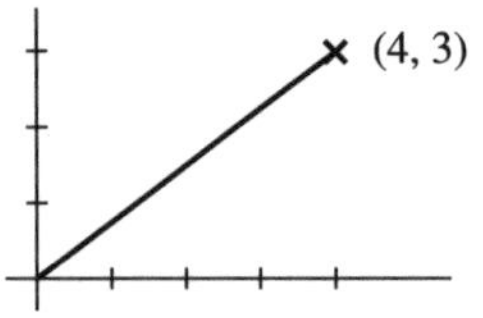

A 4 units
B 5 units
C 6 units
D 7 units

10. Sally worked 3 h 40 min on Friday, 6 h 25 min on Saturday and 2 h 10 min on Sunday. She is paid £2·60 per hour. How much did she earn?

A £29·25
B £30·55
C £38·35
D £31·85

11. $16 - 5 \times 4 =$

A −4
B 4
C 44
D −44

12. Evaluate, correct to 2 d.p.

$$11{\cdot}21 - \left(\frac{8}{1{\cdot}2^2 + 1{\cdot}6^2}\right)$$

A 9·21
B 8·05
C 7·82
D 7·58

13. If $a = 7$, $b = -3$ and $c = -4$, then $ab - c =$

A 17
B −17
C 7
D −25

14. How many lines of symmetry does a regular hexagon have?

A 2
B 6
C 5
D 12

15.

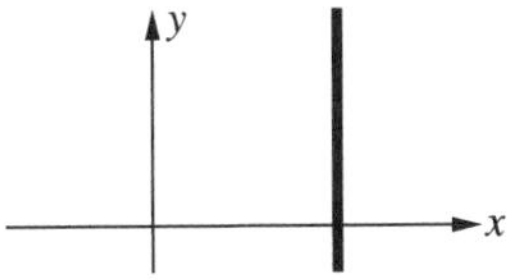

The equation of this line could be:

A $y = x$
B $y = 3$
C $x = 3$
D $x = y$

16. Joshua starts at A and walks 2 km due East to B. He then walks 2 km due South to C. What is the bearing of C from A?

A 0458
B 1358
C 1808
D 2258

17. If $\frac{4}{7} = \frac{28}{n}$, then $n =$

A 4
B 56
C 14
D 49

18. A recipe calls for $1\frac{1}{4}$ kg of apples. How many grams would you need to make $\frac{3}{5}$ of the recipe?

A 750
B 0·75
C 600
D 1·05

19. Meera invests £50 at 13% interest per year. How much will she have after one year?

A £63
B £65
C £6·50
D £56·50

20. Do not use a calculator. Use estimation to decide how many of these calculations are approximately correct:
1. $41{\cdot}7 \times 3{\cdot}9 \approx 160$
2. $\sqrt{50{\cdot}1} \times 0{\cdot}98 \approx 70$
3. $8911 \div 88 \approx 10$

A 0
B 1
C 2
D 3

21. Calculate the length x

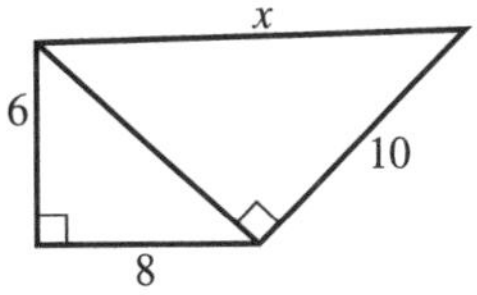

A 20
B 14
C $\sqrt{150}$
D $\sqrt{200}$

22. $r + s = 1$
$rs = -12$
The two numbers r and s are:

A 3, 4
B −3, 4
C 3, −4
D −3, −4

For questions **23**, **24**, **25**, use the diagram below

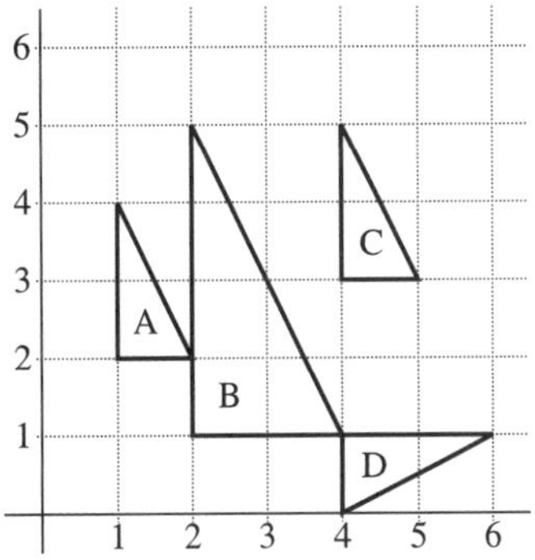

23. The enlargement which maps △A onto △B has centre:

A (0, 0)
B (6, 6)
C (0, 3)
D (3, 0)

24. The rotation which maps △C onto △D has centre:

A (0, 0)
B (5, 2)
C (4, 2)
D (3, 2)

25. The enlargement which maps △C onto △B has centre:

A (6, 6)
B (0, 0)
C (6, 5)
D none of the above

Test 2

1. A train travels half a mile in half a minute. What is its speed?

A 30 mph
B 45 mph
C 60 mph
D 120 mph

2. The bearing of A from B is 1208. What is the bearing of B from A?

A 0608
B 1208
C 2408
D 3008

3. Find the length x.

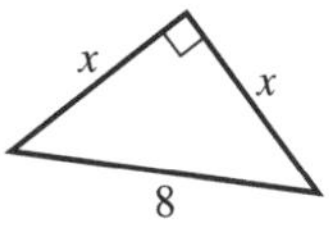

A 4
B $\sqrt{24}$
C $\sqrt{32}$
D 16

4. Which point does *not* lie on the line $y = 3x - 1$?

A $(0, -1)$
B $(3, 8)$
C $(-1, -4)$
D $(1, -2)$

5. Find the next number in the sequence 0, 3, 12, 33, 72.

A 108
B 135
C 144
D 160

6. Solve the equation $3(2x - 1) = 2(x + 5)$

A $1\frac{1}{2}$
B $1\frac{3}{4}$
C 3
D $3\frac{1}{4}$

7. Find the total area in cm^2

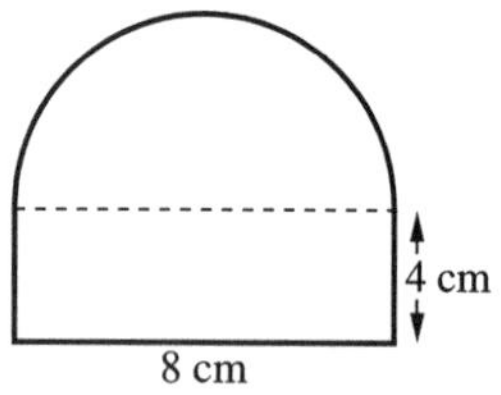

A $4\pi + 32$
B $8\pi + 32$
C $12\pi + 32$
D $16\pi + 32$

8. If $a = 3$, $b = -2$ work out $a^2 - b^2$.

A 2
B 5
C 8
D 13

9. A painting is bought for £80 and later sold for £100. The profit, as a percentage of the cost price, is

A 15%
B 20%
C 25%
D 30%

10. Which of the following are true?
1. $(-6)^2 = 12$
2. $8 - (-3) = 11$
3. $-12 \div (-2) = -6$

A 1 only
B 2 only
C 3 only
D 2 and 3

11. The probability of an event occuring is 0·7. Find the probability of the event *not* occuring.

A $\dfrac{1}{0{\cdot}7}$
B $\frac{7}{10}$
C 0·3
D Impossible to say

12. The first four numbers in a sequence are
6 11 16 21.
What is the 50th term in the sequence?

A 51
B 56
C 251
D 256

For Questions **13**, **14**, **15**, use the diagram below.

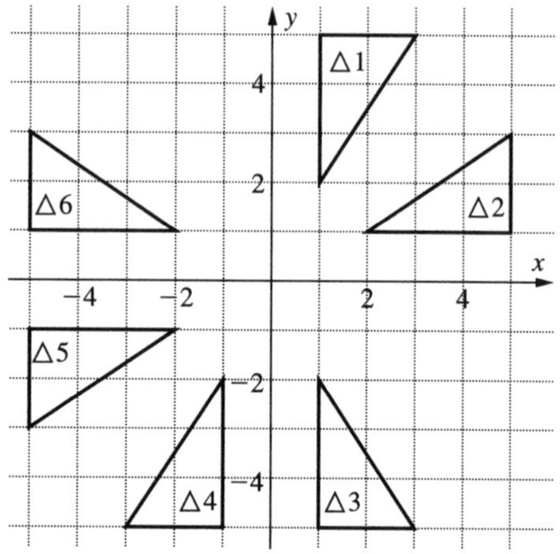

13. △1 is the image of △2 after:

A a reflection
B a rotation
C 2 rotations
D 2 reflections

14. △5 is the image of △2 after:

A rotation about (0, 0)
B rotation about (1, −1)
C reflection in $y = x$
D reflection in $y = -x$

15. △3 is the image of △6 after:

A rotation 1808 about (0, 0)
B two reflections
C reflection in $y = x$
D reflection in $y = -x$

16. Which of the following statements are true?
1. All squares have 4 lines of symmetry
2. The angle sum of a quadrilateral is 3608
3. All parallelograms have 2 lines of symmetry

A 1 and 2
B 1 and 3
C 2 and 3
D 1, 2, 3

17. Find the shaded area.

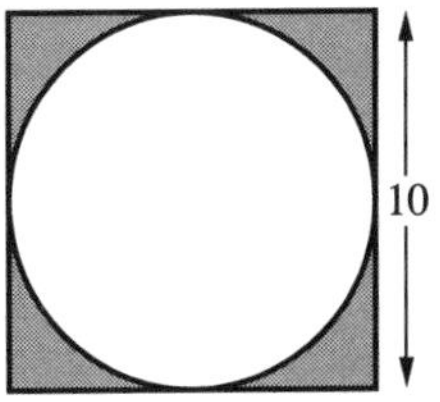

A $100 - 25\pi$
B $100-(\pi\times5)^2$
C $100 - 10\pi$
D $100\pi - 100$

18. Two dice are rolled and the scores are added to give a total. How many different totals can you get?

A 6
B 11
C 12
D 36

19. Which of the following are true?
1. $33\% = \frac{1}{3}$
2. $0{\cdot}8 = 80\%$
3. $1{\cdot}5\% = 0{\cdot}015$

A 1 only
B 2 only
C 3 only
D None of the above

20. The scatter graph shows

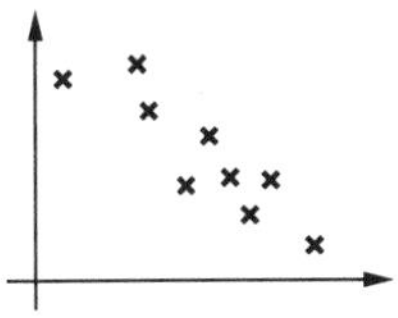

A positive correlation
B negative correlation
C no correlation
D both positive and negative correlation

21. Use a calculator to work out. $\dfrac{8{\cdot}42}{1{\cdot}2^2} - \dfrac{3{\cdot}6}{1{\cdot}57}$

A 3·55
B 7·82
C 46·9
D None of the above

22. The circumference of a circle is 30 cm. Find the radius in cm.

A $\dfrac{30}{\pi}$
B $\dfrac{15}{\pi}$
C $\sqrt{\dfrac{30}{\pi}}$
D 60π

23. The lines $y = x + 2$ and $y = 2x$ cut at the point

A (1, 3)
B (0, 0)
C (2, 4)
D (−2, −4)

24. Do not use a calculator. Use estimation to decide how many of these calculations are approximately correct.
1. $59{\cdot}7 \times 57{\cdot}23 \approx 3600$
2. $897{\cdot}1 \div 9{\cdot}117 \approx 10$
3. $\sqrt{103{\cdot}4} + \sqrt{3{\cdot}98} \approx 12$

A 0
B 1
C 2
D 3

25. Find the length x, correct to 2 d.p.

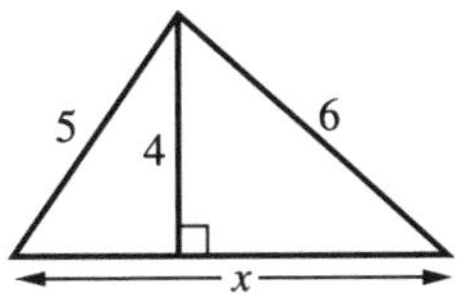

A 7·47
B 7·81
C 8·03
D None of the above

7.2 Numeracy check-up

Do not use a calculator.

A Whole numbers

1. $27 + 118$
2. $71 + 91 + 11$
3. $472 - 29$
4. 17×6
5. $348 \div 3$
6. $196 \div 7$
7. 214×5
8. $2174 - 326$

B Decimals

1. $3{\cdot}2 + 11{\cdot}9$ **2.** $5{\cdot}6 + 13$ **3.** $9 - 3{\cdot}3$ **4.** $23 \times 0{\cdot}3$

5. $213 \times 0{\cdot}5$ **6.** $13{\cdot}2 \div 5$ **7.** $0{\cdot}7 \times 0{\cdot}3$ **8.** $8{\cdot}6 \div 0{\cdot}2$

C Fractions

1. $\frac{2}{3}$ of 36 **2.** $\frac{4}{5}$ of 60 **3.** $\frac{1}{2} \times \frac{3}{5}$ **4.** $\frac{3}{4} \times \frac{3}{4}$

5. $\frac{3}{4} - \frac{1}{2}$ **6.** $\frac{5}{6} - \frac{1}{3}$ **7.** $\frac{5}{8} + \frac{1}{4}$ **8.** $1\frac{2}{3} \times \frac{2}{5}$

D Percentages

1. 20% of £30 **2.** 8% of £50 **3.** Increase £300 by 5%

4. Decrease £40 by 10% **5.** 15% of 40 kg **6.** Write $\frac{9}{20}$ as a percentage

E Negative numbers

1. $-7 + 10$ **2.** $-2 - 6$ **3.** $(-3) \times 4$ **4.** $3 - (-3)$

5. $(-4) \times (-5)$ **6.** $-5 + 5$ **7.** $12 \div (-2)$ **8.** $8 - 11$

F Estimation. Estimate the answer.

1. $98{\cdot}3 \times 2{\cdot}04$ **2.** $0{\cdot}987 \times 21{\cdot}45$ **3.** $9815 \times 31{\cdot}4$ **4.** $5913 \div 29{\cdot}1$

G Miscellaneous

1. How many of these statements are true?

$0{\cdot}3 = 30\%$; $\frac{3}{4} = 0{\cdot}75$; $0{\cdot}1 \times 0{\cdot}2 = 0{\cdot}2$; $17 \div 0{\cdot}5 = 34$

2. 8 boys are 25% of the children in a class.
How many children are there altogether in the class?

Operator squares

Each square contains either a number or an operation (+, −, ×, ÷). Copy each square and fill in the missing details. The arrows act as equals signs.

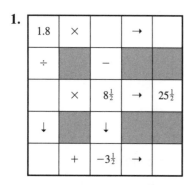

1.

1.8	×		→	
÷		−		
	×	$8\frac{1}{2}$	→	$25\frac{1}{2}$
↓		↓		
	+	$-3\frac{1}{2}$	→	

2.

100	÷		→	
×		−		
	+	368	→	
↓		↓		
775	−		→	143

3.

	−	−16	→	14
+		×		
	÷	3	→	$1\frac{1}{2}$
↓		↓		
	+		→	

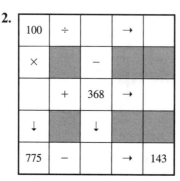

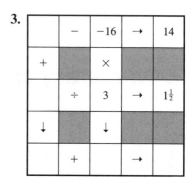

4.

	÷	7	→	7
		×		
	−	2	→	0
↓		↓		
98			→	84

5.

	×	0.5	→	−2.5
		÷		
6	×		→	
↓		↓		
−30		2	→	−28

6.

−7	−	−4	→	
8		−2	→	−16
↓		↓		
1	−		→	−7

7.

$\frac{1}{8}$		−2	→	−0.25
÷		×		
	+		→	5.5
↓		↓		
		−10	→	−9.75

8.

	×	3	→	
×		÷		
$\frac{1}{2}$	×		→	
↓		↓		
	+	−1.5	→	−1.5

9.

0.6		2.4	→	0.25
+		×		
7.2	+		→	−2.3
↓		↓		
	−		→	

10.

	×	5	→	46.5
÷		+		
	−		→	
↓		↓		
4.65		−5	→	−0.35

11.

58	÷		→	$6.\dot{4}$
−		×		
	+		→	72.2
↓		↓		
−12.8	×		→	

12.

$\frac{1}{2}$	+		→	$66\frac{1}{4}$
−		+		
	÷		→	
↓		↓		
$-55\frac{1}{2}$	+	66	→	

The last three are more difficult.

13.

		−3	→	21
+		+		
	÷		→	7
↓		↓		
$-10\frac{1}{2}$	÷	$-3\frac{1}{2}$	→	

14.

	÷	9	→	$0.\dot{5}$
÷		×		
	+		→	
↓		↓		
−0.1		−13.5	→	1.35

15.

			→	$\frac{2}{3}$
×		+		
4	÷		→	$0.\dot{3}\dot{6}$
↓		↓		
$2.\dot{2}$	+	$11.\dot{1}$	→	

7.3 Revision exercises

Revision exercise 1

1. Work out

(a) $-5-6$ (b) $8\times(-2)$ (c) $(-2)\times(-2)$ (d) $6+(-7)$
(e) $3-(-2)$ (f) $8\div(-1)$ (g) -6×0 (h) $-7-(-7)$

2. The diagram shows the lengths of the sides of a rectangle in cm.
(a) Form an equation involving x.
(b) Solve your equation and hence find the *area* of the rectangle.

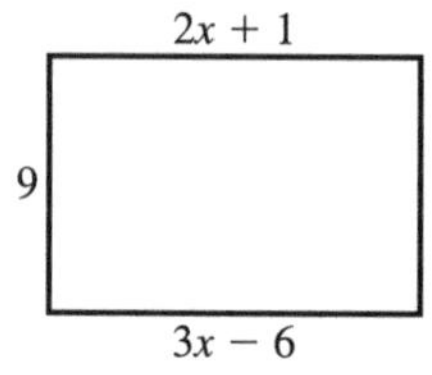

3. Work out, correct to 1 decimal place.

(a) $3{\cdot}2\%$ of $\dfrac{112}{2{\cdot}3}$ (b) $\dfrac{8{\cdot}9}{7{\cdot}1}-\dfrac{1{\cdot}5}{9}$ (c) $15{\cdot}6-1{\cdot}8^2$

(d) $(8{\cdot}2+1{\cdot}4^2)^2$ (e) $\dfrac{\dfrac{4}{11{\cdot}2}+\dfrac{3}{7{\cdot}5}}{2{\cdot}72}$ (f) $\dfrac{5{\cdot}1}{17}+\dfrac{4{\cdot}3}{9}+\dfrac{8{\cdot}9}{13}$

4. The radius of the outer circle is 6 cm. Calculate the shaded area.

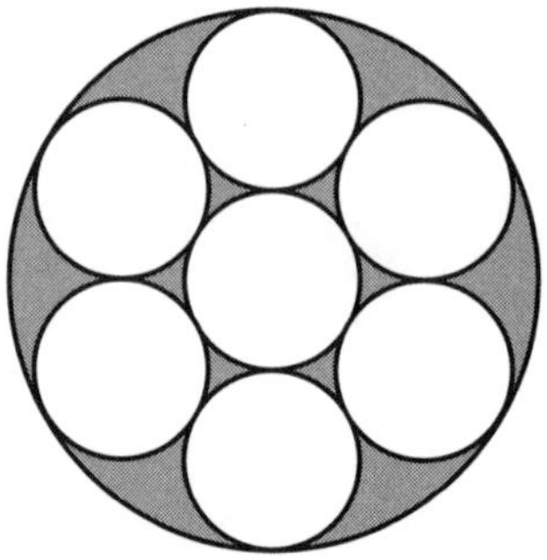

5. Draw the graph of $y=3x-1$, taking values of x from -3 to $+3$.

6. Draw the graph of $y=x^2-3$, taking values of x from -3 to $+3$.

7. Copy each calculation and decide by estimation which is the correct answer from the list given. To obtain any marks you must show the working you used to obtain your estimate.

(a) $3{\cdot}9\times 5{\cdot}2$ (b) $10{\cdot}3\times 9{\cdot}8$ (c) $36{\cdot}96\div 4$
(d) $3{\cdot}62\div 18{\cdot}1$ (e) $20{\cdot}2\div 0{\cdot}101$ (f) $1{\cdot}1\times 2{\cdot}7$

Answers (not in order): 2·97, 0·2, 100·94, 20·28, 200, 9·24

8. The cylinder and the cuboid shown have the same volume. Calculate the height h of the box.

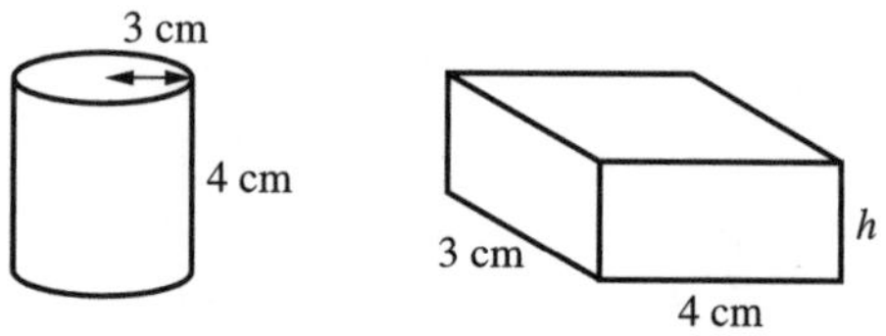

9. Solve the equations

(a) $3x - 3 = 2x + 5$ (b) $5(x - 1) = 2(3 - x)$

10. The length of the rectangle is three times its width. The perimeter of the rectangle is 60 cm.
Form an equation and solve it to find the width of the rectangle.

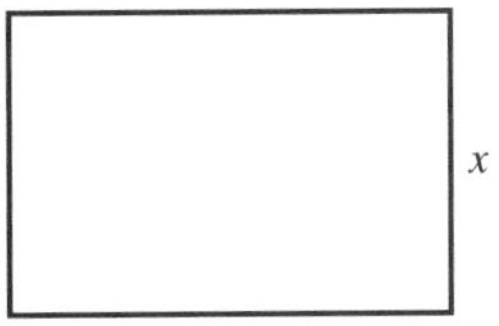

11. Conrad is thinking of a number. When he doubles the number and then adds 7 he gets the same answer as when he adds 10 to the number. What number is he thinking of?

12. Two of the angles of an isosceles triangle are $x°$ and $(x + 9)°$. Form equations to find the *two* possible values of x.

13. Use a calculator to work out the following. Give your answers to 2 decimal places.

(a) $\dfrac{8{\cdot}7}{1{\cdot}65} + \dfrac{1{\cdot}9}{3{\cdot}2}$ (b) $\dfrac{8{\cdot}7 - 5{\cdot}61}{0{\cdot}924 + 1{\cdot}2}$

(c) $\dfrac{1{\cdot}76 + 3{\cdot}2^2}{\sqrt{11{\cdot}8}}$ (d) $\left(\dfrac{3}{1 + \sqrt{2}}\right)\left(\dfrac{3}{1 + \sqrt{2}}\right)$

(e) (32% of £45·60) + (11% of £78·80) + (8% of £15·90)

Give the answer to part (e) correct to the nearest penny.

14. Follow the instructions below to produce the outline of an egg.

(a) Draw line AB 10 cm long and mark the centre of the line.
(b) Draw a semi-circle of radius 5 cm below AB.
(c) Mark point C, 5 cm above the mid-point of AB.
(d) Draw lines AC and BC and extend them.
(e) Draw arc AD with radius 10 cm and centre B.
(f) Draw arc BE with radius 10 cm and centre A.
(g) Draw arc DE with radius CE and centre C.

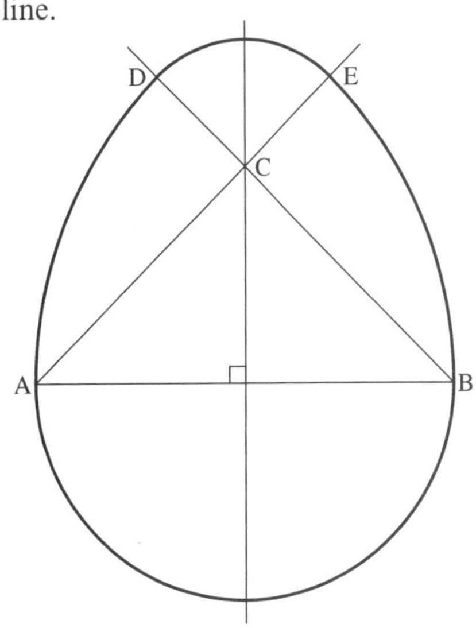

Revision exercise 2

1. *Estimate* the answers to the following. Do not use a calculator.

(a) $47{\cdot}53 \times 102{\cdot}5$ (b) $\dfrac{207{\cdot}4 - 3{\cdot}69}{18{\cdot}2 + 1{\cdot}63}$ (c) $875{\cdot}2 \div 9{\cdot}11$

(d) $\sqrt{38{\cdot}96 \times 11{\cdot}32}$ (e) 9·3% of £198·75

2. Copy the diagram on squared paper.
(a) Measure the bearing of B from A.
(b) Measure the bearing of A from B.
(c) Mark the point C which is on a bearing 225° from B and on a bearing 090° from A.

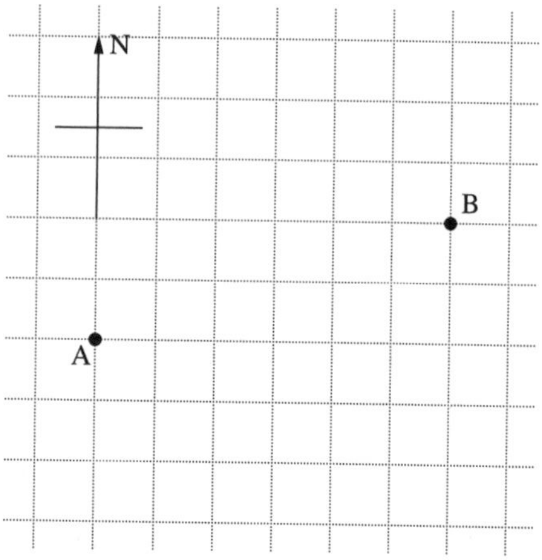

3. (a) Calculate the length of the hypotenuse AC of the triangle ABC.
(b) Calculate the area of the triangle.

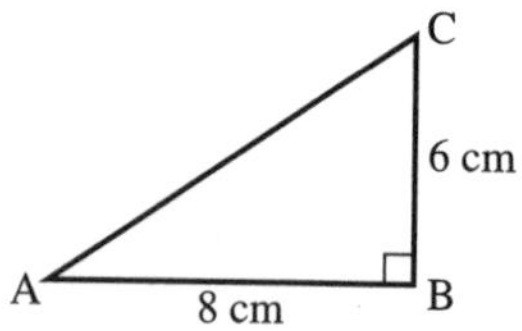

A line BX is drawn perpendicular to AC.
(c) Use the area of the triangle and your value for the length of AC to calculate the length of BX.

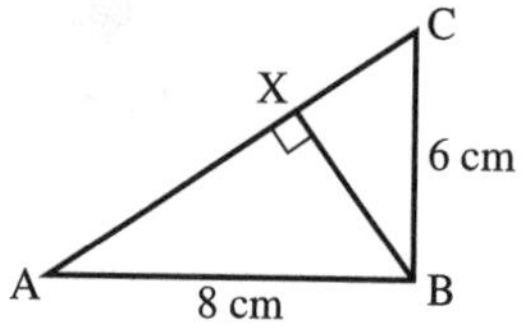

4. Work out the following, giving your answers as decimals.
(a) $\frac{3}{4}$ of 5·2 (b) 35% of 12 (c) $\frac{13}{20}$ of 18.

5. The table shows the marks of pupils in a maths test.

Mark	3	4	5	6	7	8	9
Frequency	5	4	7	10	8	4	2

(a) How many pupils took the test?
(b) Calculate the mean mark for the test.
(c) Find also (i) the median mark (ii) the modal mark.

6. Black and white tiles are used to make 'mini' chess boards of various sizes. As white tiles are more expensive there are never more white tiles than black tiles on any size board.
(a) How many white tiles are there on the 6 × 6 board?
(b) How many black tiles are there on the 7 × 7 board?

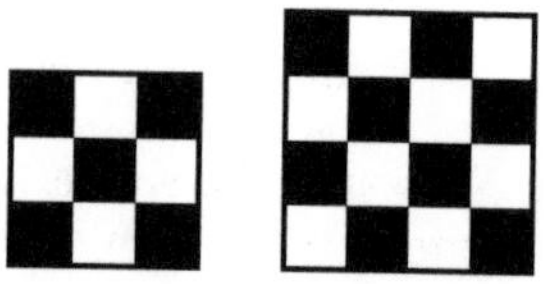

7. In these diagrams a letter 'V' is drawn across each rectangle.

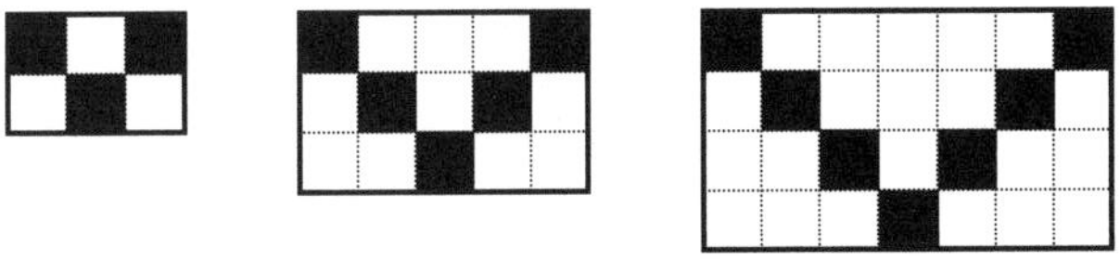

(a) Count the black squares, b, and the white squares, w, in each diagram and write the results in a table.

b	w
3	3

(b) Draw the next diagram in the sequence. Count the black squares and the white squares and add the results to your table.

(c) *Predict* the number of white squares in the next diagram (that is the fifth diagram) in the sequence.

(d) In a later diagram, there are 136 white squares. How many black squares are there in that diagram?

8. The test results of eight pupils are recorded in the table below.

Pupil	A	B	C	D	E	F	G	H	I
Maths	25	10	35	45	20	10	40	15	?
Geography	10	15	15	25	30	35	45	50	38
History	10	15	20	22	27	30	36	40	?

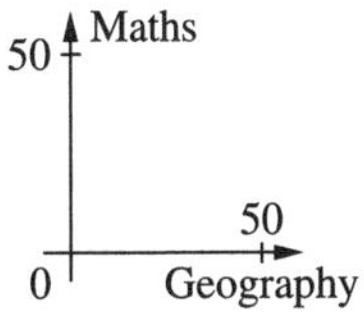

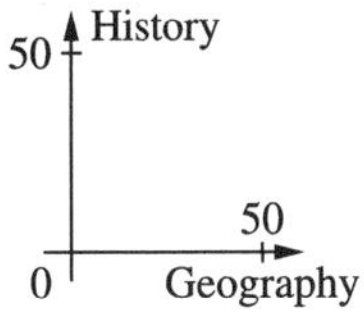

Draw scatter graphs for

(a) the Maths and Geography marks.

(b) the History and Geography marks.

(c) What correlation, if any, is there in the results?

(d) Pupil I got 38 marks in Geography. Estimate, if possible, her marks in Maths and History.

9. A shopkeeper buys a computer for £620 and sells it for £999. Calculate the profit made by the shopkeeper as a percentage of the cost price (£620).

10. A spinner is spun and a dice is rolled at the same time.

(a) List all the possible outcomes on a grid.

(b) Find the probability of obtaining a total score of

(i) 4 (ii) 10

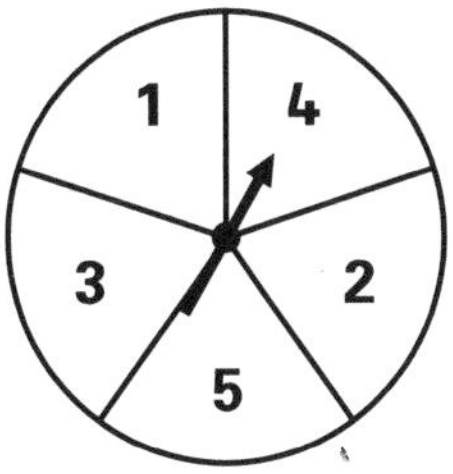

(c) What is the probability of obtaining the same number on the spinner and the dice?

11. Describe the single transformation equivalent to reflection in the line $y = x$ followed by reflection in the line $x = 4$.

Revision exercise 3

1. The graph shows the journeys of Mark and Meera, who drove from their home to an hotel 120 km away.
(a) What was Meera's speed?
(b) What was Mark's speed after his short stop?
(c) How far apart were they at 1030?
(d) What was Mark's *average* speed for the whole journey?

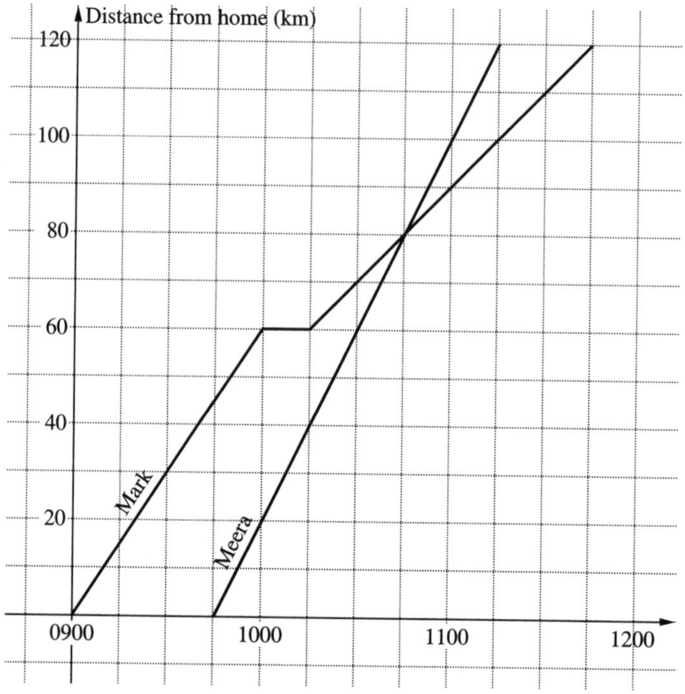

2. Abi is thinking of a number. Three times the number plus 5 gives the same answer as when the number is added to 4 and then the result is doubled. Find the number she is thinking of.

3. Different shapes can be drawn on a grid of nine dots. The vertices of each shape are drawn at any dot.
Here are two examples:
a rectangle and a trapezium.

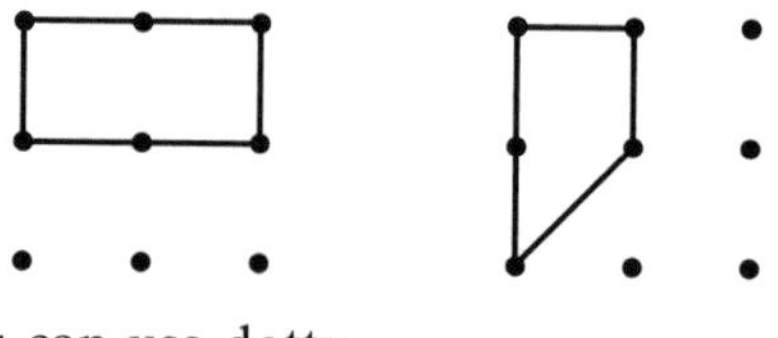

Draw four grids and label them A, B, C, D. [You can use dotty paper but it is not necessary].
(a) On grid A draw any parallelogram.
(b) On grid B draw any isosceles triangle.
(c) On grid C draw another isosceles triangle, different to the one you drew on grid B.
(d) On grid D draw a trapezium, different to the one in the example above.

4. (a) Write each of the following as decimals
(i) 22% (ii) $\frac{5}{8}$ (iii) 7%
(b) Simon got 52 out of 80 in a science test. What was his mark as a percentage?
(c) Write these numbers in order of size, smallest first: 0·11, $\frac{1}{9}$, 10%, 0·01.

5. The trapezium, the square and the circle below all have the same area.

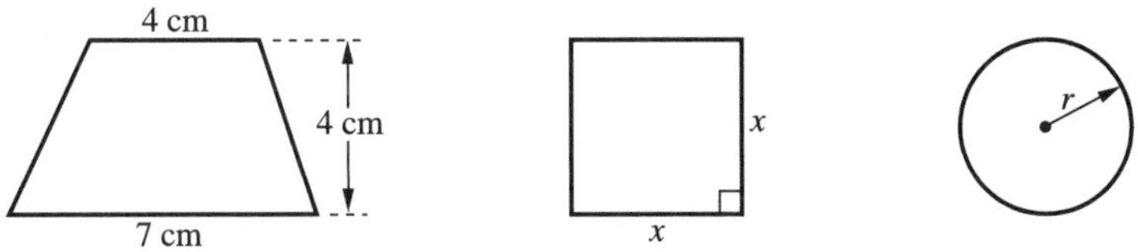

Calculate the values of x and r.

6. A bucket weighs 1·2 kg when it is empty, and 6·6 kg when it is full of water. What will it weigh when it is half full?

7. Use estimation to choose the odd one out.
$315 \times 9{\cdot}7$; $5874 \div 1{\cdot}983$; $152{\cdot}7 \times 2{\cdot}01$; $30\,908 \div 10{\cdot}2$

8. Copy the triangle on squared paper. Find the area of the triangle, giving your answer in square units.

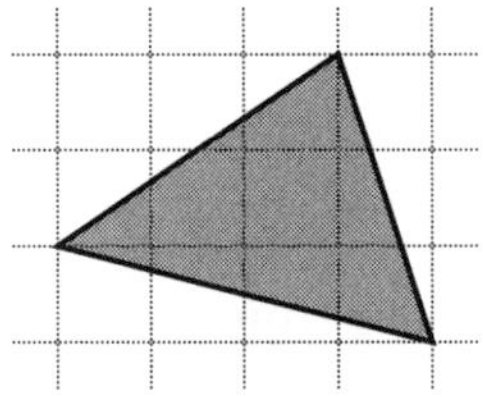

9. Calculate the volume of each of the prisms shown below. All lengths are in cm.

(a)

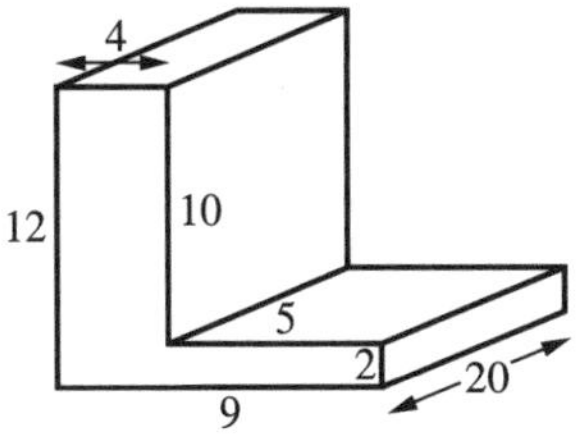

(b)

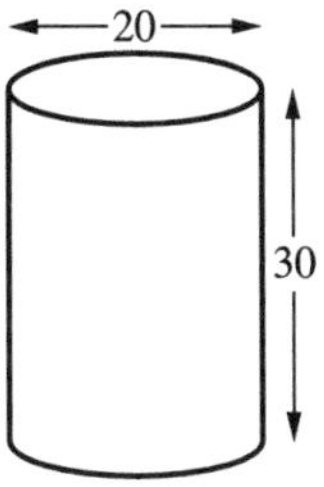

(c)

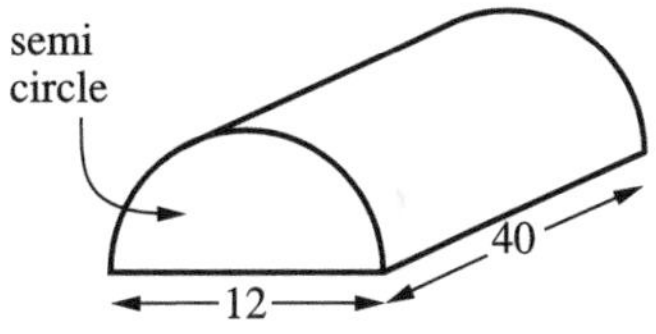

10. Oil from the large drum is used to fill many of the small cans. How many cans may be filled from the drum?

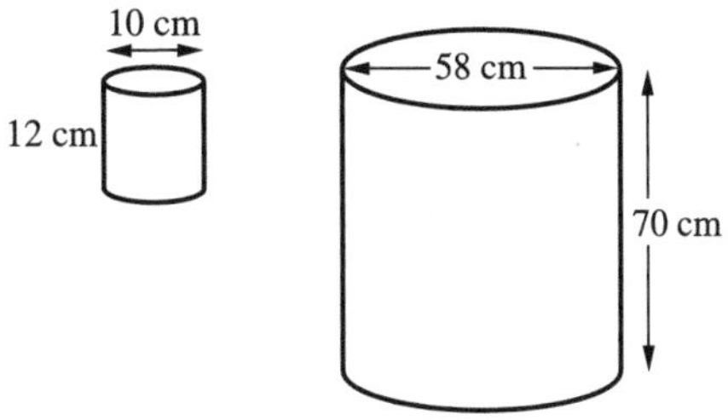

11. The diagram shows an equilateral triangle of side 8 cm with a line of symmetry drawn through A.
(a) Calculate the vertical height of the triangle.
(b) Calculate the area of the triangle.

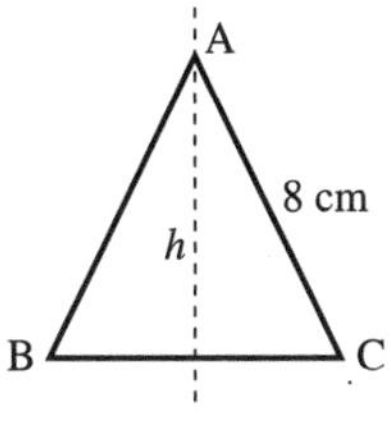

12. Describe fully each of the following transformations.
(a) $\triangle 1 \rightarrow \triangle 2$
(b) $\triangle 1 \rightarrow \triangle 3$
(c) $\triangle 1 \rightarrow \triangle 4$
(d) $\triangle 4 \rightarrow \triangle 5$

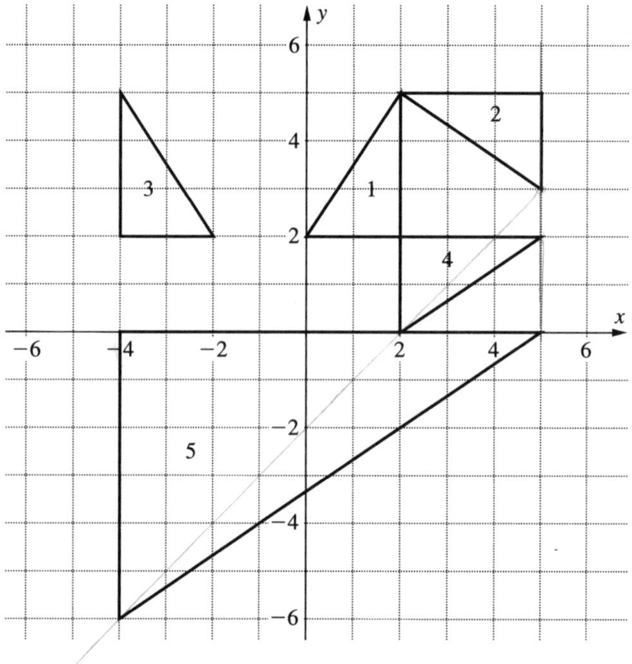

13. Draw x and y axes with values from -8 to $+8$.
Plot and label $\triangle 1$ at $(-4, -3)$, $(-4, -6)$, $(-2, -3)$.
(a) Draw the triangles $\triangle 2$, $\triangle 3$, $\triangle 4$, $\triangle 5$ as follows:
   (i) $\triangle 1 \rightarrow \triangle 2$ rotation, 180°, centre $(0, -3)$
   (ii) $\triangle 2 \rightarrow \triangle 3$ rotation, 180°, centre $(3, 1)$
   (iii) $\triangle 1 \rightarrow \triangle 4$ enlargement scale factor 3, centre $(-5, -7)$
   (iv) $\triangle 1 \rightarrow \triangle 5$ reflection in $y = 1$
(b) Describe fully each of the following transformations:
   (i) $\triangle 1 \rightarrow \triangle 3$
   (ii) $\triangle 3 \rightarrow \triangle 4$.

14. A school teacher thinks there is a connection between her pupils' test results and the average number of hours of television they watch per week. She thinks that those who watch the most television will do least well in the tests.
Here are scatter graphs for her classes in year 8 and year 9.

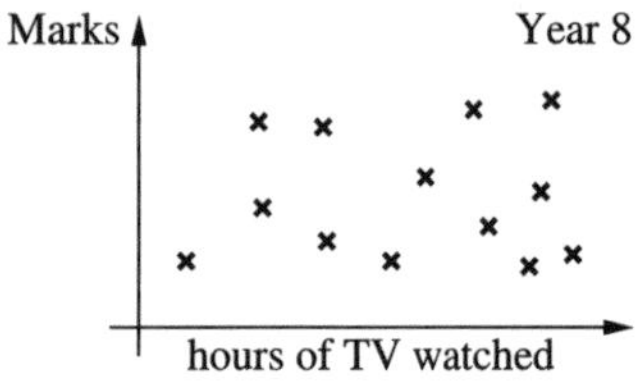

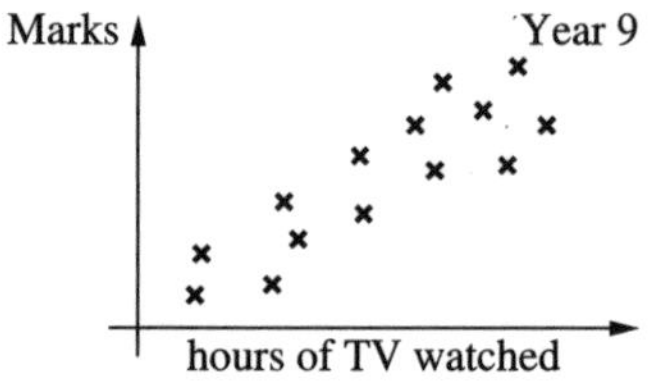

Was the teacher's theory correct for
(a) Year 8 (b) Year 9?
In both cases state briefly what the graphs show.

INDEX